FREE Study Skills Videos/DVD Offer

Dear Customer,

Thank you for your purchase from Mometrix! We consider it an honor and a privilege that you have purchased our product and we want to ensure your satisfaction.

As part of our ongoing effort to meet the needs of test takers, we have developed a set of Study Skills Videos that we would like to give you for FREE. These videos cover our *best practices* for getting ready for your exam, from how to use our study materials to how to best prepare for the day of the test.

All that we ask is that you email us with feedback that would describe your experience so far with our product. Good, bad, or indifferent, we want to know what you think!

To get your FREE Study Skills Videos, you can use the **QR code** below, or send us an **email** at studyvideos@mometrix.com with *FREE VIDEOS* in the subject line and the following information in the body of the email:

- The name of the product you purchased.
- Your product rating on a scale of 1-5, with 5 being the highest rating.
- Your feedback. It can be long, short, or anything in between. We just want to know your impressions and experience so far with our product. (Good feedback might include how our study material met your needs and ways we might be able to make it even better. You could highlight features that you found helpful or features that you think we should add.)

If you have any questions or concerns, please don't hesitate to contact me directly.

Thanks again!

Sincerely,

Jay Willis
Vice President
jay.willis@mometrix.com
1-800-673-8175

CSC

Exam Study Guide 2024-2025

Secrets Review Book and Practice Test Questions for the Cardiac Surgery Certification

2nd Edition

Written and edited by the Mometrix Nursing Certification Test Team

Printed in the United States of America

This paper meets the requirements of ANSI/NISO Z39.48-1992 (Permanence of Paper).

ISBN 13: 978-1-5167-2656-1
ISBN 10: 1-5167-2656-1

DEAR FUTURE EXAM SUCCESS STORY

First of all, **THANK YOU** for purchasing Mometrix study materials!

Second, congratulations! You are one of the few determined test-takers who are committed to doing whatever it takes to excel on your exam. **You have come to the right place.** We developed these study materials with one goal in mind: to deliver you the information you need in a format that's concise and easy to use.

In addition to optimizing your guide for the content of the test, we've outlined our recommended steps for breaking down the preparation process into small, attainable goals so you can make sure you stay on track.

We've also analyzed the entire test-taking process, identifying the most common pitfalls and showing how you can overcome them and be ready for any curveball the test throws you.

Standardized testing is one of the biggest obstacles on your road to success, which only increases the importance of doing well in the high-pressure, high-stakes environment of test day. Your results on this test could have a significant impact on your future, and this guide provides the information and practical advice to help you achieve your full potential on test day.

Your success is our success

We would love to hear from you! If you would like to share the story of your exam success or if you have any questions or comments in regard to our products, please contact us at **800-673-8175** or **support@mometrix.com**.

Thanks again for your business and we wish you continued success!

Sincerely,
The Mometrix Test Preparation Team

TABLE OF CONTENTS

Introduction

Thank you for purchasing this resource! You have made the choice to prepare yourself for a test that could have a huge impact on your future, and this guide is designed to help you be fully ready for test day. Obviously, it's important to have a solid understanding of the test material, but you also need to be prepared for the unique environment and stressors of the test, so that you can perform to the best of your abilities.

For this purpose, the first section that appears in this guide is the **Secret Keys**. We've devoted countless hours to meticulously researching what works and what doesn't, and we've boiled down our findings to the five most impactful steps you can take to improve your performance on the test. We start at the beginning with study planning and move through the preparation process, all the way to the testing strategies that will help you get the most out of what you know when you're finally sitting in front of the test.

We recommend that you start preparing for your test as far in advance as possible. However, if you've bought this guide as a last-minute study resource and only have a few days before your test, we recommend that you skip over the first two Secret Keys since they address a long-term study plan.

If you struggle with **test anxiety**, we strongly encourage you to check out our recommendations for how you can overcome it. Test anxiety is a formidable foe, but it can be beaten, and we want to make sure you have the tools you need to defeat it.

Secret Key #1 – Plan Big, Study Small

There's a lot riding on your performance. If you want to ace this test, you're going to need to keep your skills sharp and the material fresh in your mind. You need a plan that lets you review everything you need to know while still fitting in your schedule. We'll break this strategy down into three categories.

Information Organization

Start with the information you already have: the official test outline. From this, you can make a complete list of all the concepts you need to cover before the test. Organize these concepts into groups that can be studied together, and create a list of any related vocabulary you need to learn so you can brush up on any difficult terms. You'll want to keep this vocabulary list handy once you actually start studying since you may need to add to it along the way.

Time Management

Once you have your set of study concepts, decide how to spread them out over the time you have left before the test. Break your study plan into small, clear goals so you have a manageable task for each day and know exactly what you're doing. Then just focus on one small step at a time. When you manage your time this way, you don't need to spend hours at a time studying. Studying a small block of content for a short period each day helps you retain information better and avoid stressing over how much you have left to do. You can relax knowing that you have a plan to cover everything in time. In order for this strategy to be effective though, you have to start studying early and stick to your schedule. Avoid the exhaustion and futility that comes from last-minute cramming!

Study Environment

The environment you study in has a big impact on your learning. Studying in a coffee shop, while probably more enjoyable, is not likely to be as fruitful as studying in a quiet room. It's important to keep distractions to a minimum. You're only planning to study for a short block of time, so make the most of it. Don't pause to check your phone or get up to find a snack. It's also important to **avoid multitasking**. Research has consistently shown that multitasking will make your studying dramatically less effective. Your study area should also be comfortable and well-lit so you don't have the distraction of straining your eyes or sitting on an uncomfortable chair.

The time of day you study is also important. You want to be rested and alert. Don't wait until just before bedtime. Study when you'll be most likely to comprehend and remember. Even better, if you know what time of day your test will be, set that time aside for study. That way your brain will be used to working on that subject at that specific time and you'll have a better chance of recalling information.

Finally, it can be helpful to team up with others who are studying for the same test. Your actual studying should be done in as isolated an environment as possible, but the work of organizing the information and setting up the study plan can be divided up. In between study sessions, you can discuss with your teammates the concepts that you're all studying and quiz each other on the details. Just be sure that your teammates are as serious about the test as you are. If you find that your study time is being replaced with social time, you might need to find a new team.

Secret Key #2 – Make Your Studying Count

You're devoting a lot of time and effort to preparing for this test, so you want to be absolutely certain it will pay off. This means doing more than just reading the content and hoping you can remember it on test day. It's important to make every minute of study count. There are two main areas you can focus on to make your studying count.

Retention

It doesn't matter how much time you study if you can't remember the material. You need to make sure you are retaining the concepts. To check your retention of the information you're learning, try recalling it at later times with minimal prompting. Try carrying around flashcards and glance at one or two from time to time or ask a friend who's also studying for the test to quiz you.

To enhance your retention, look for ways to put the information into practice so that you can apply it rather than simply recalling it. If you're using the information in practical ways, it will be much easier to remember. Similarly, it helps to solidify a concept in your mind if you're not only reading it to yourself but also explaining it to someone else. Ask a friend to let you teach them about a concept you're a little shaky on (or speak aloud to an imaginary audience if necessary). As you try to summarize, define, give examples, and answer your friend's questions, you'll understand the concepts better and they will stay with you longer. Finally, step back for a big picture view and ask yourself how each piece of information fits with the whole subject. When you link the different concepts together and see them working together as a whole, it's easier to remember the individual components.

Finally, practice showing your work on any multi-step problems, even if you're just studying. Writing out each step you take to solve a problem will help solidify the process in your mind, and you'll be more likely to remember it during the test.

Modality

Modality simply refers to the means or method by which you study. Choosing a study modality that fits your own individual learning style is crucial. No two people learn best in exactly the same way, so it's important to know your strengths and use them to your advantage.

For example, if you learn best by visualization, focus on visualizing a concept in your mind and draw an image or a diagram. Try color-coding your notes, illustrating them, or creating symbols that will trigger your mind to recall a learned concept. If you learn best by hearing or discussing information, find a study partner who learns the same way or read aloud to yourself. Think about how to put the information in your own words. Imagine that you are giving a lecture on the topic and record yourself so you can listen to it later.

For any learning style, flashcards can be helpful. Organize the information so you can take advantage of spare moments to review. Underline key words or phrases. Use different colors for different categories. Mnemonic devices (such as creating a short list in which every item starts with the same letter) can also help with retention. Find what works best for you and use it to store the information in your mind most effectively and easily.

Secret Key #3 – Practice the Right Way

Your success on test day depends not only on how many hours you put into preparing, but also on whether you prepared the right way. It's good to check along the way to see if your studying is paying off. One of the most effective ways to do this is by taking practice tests to evaluate your progress. Practice tests are useful because they show exactly where you need to improve. Every time you take a practice test, pay special attention to these three groups of questions:

- The questions you got wrong
- The questions you had to guess on, even if you guessed right
- The questions you found difficult or slow to work through

This will show you exactly what your weak areas are, and where you need to devote more study time. Ask yourself why each of these questions gave you trouble. Was it because you didn't understand the material? Was it because you didn't remember the vocabulary? Do you need more repetitions on this type of question to build speed and confidence? Dig into those questions and figure out how you can strengthen your weak areas as you go back to review the material.

Additionally, many practice tests have a section explaining the answer choices. It can be tempting to read the explanation and think that you now have a good understanding of the concept. However, an explanation likely only covers part of the question's broader context. Even if the explanation makes perfect sense, **go back and investigate** every concept related to the question until you're positive you have a thorough understanding.

As you go along, keep in mind that the practice test is just that: practice. Memorizing these questions and answers will not be very helpful on the actual test because it is unlikely to have any of the same exact questions. If you only know the right answers to the sample questions, you won't be prepared for the real thing. **Study the concepts** until you understand them fully, and then you'll be able to answer any question that shows up on the test.

It's important to wait on the practice tests until you're ready. If you take a test on your first day of study, you may be overwhelmed by the amount of material covered and how much you need to learn. Work up to it gradually.

On test day, you'll need to be prepared for answering questions, managing your time, and using the test-taking strategies you've learned. It's a lot to balance, like a mental marathon that will have a big impact on your future. Like training for a marathon, you'll need to start slowly and work your way up. When test day arrives, you'll be ready.

Start with the strategies you've read in the first two Secret Keys—plan your course and study in the way that works best for you. If you have time, consider using multiple study resources to get different approaches to the same concepts. It can be helpful to see difficult concepts from more than one angle. Then find a good source for practice tests. Many times, the test website will suggest potential study resources or provide sample tests.

Practice Test Strategy

If you're able to find at least three practice tests, we recommend this strategy:

Untimed and Open-Book Practice

Take the first test with no time constraints and with your notes and study guide handy. Take your time and focus on applying the strategies you've learned.

Timed and Open-Book Practice

Take the second practice test open-book as well, but set a timer and practice pacing yourself to finish in time.

Timed and Closed-Book Practice

Take any other practice tests as if it were test day. Set a timer and put away your study materials. Sit at a table or desk in a quiet room, imagine yourself at the testing center, and answer questions as quickly and accurately as possible.

Keep repeating timed and closed-book tests on a regular basis until you run out of practice tests or it's time for the actual test. Your mind will be ready for the schedule and stress of test day, and you'll be able to focus on recalling the material you've learned.

Secret Key #4 – Pace Yourself

Once you're fully prepared for the material on the test, your biggest challenge on test day will be managing your time. Just knowing that the clock is ticking can make you panic even if you have plenty of time left. Work on pacing yourself so you can build confidence against the time constraints of the exam. Pacing is a difficult skill to master, especially in a high-pressure environment, so **practice is vital**.

Set time expectations for your pace based on how much time is available. For example, if a section has 60 questions and the time limit is 30 minutes, you know you have to average 30 seconds or less per question in order to answer them all. Although 30 seconds is the hard limit, set 25 seconds per question as your goal, so you reserve extra time to spend on harder questions. When you budget extra time for the harder questions, you no longer have any reason to stress when those questions take longer to answer.

Don't let this time expectation distract you from working through the test at a calm, steady pace, but keep it in mind so you don't spend too much time on any one question. Recognize that taking extra time on one question you don't understand may keep you from answering two that you do understand later in the test. If your time limit for a question is up and you're still not sure of the answer, mark it and move on, and come back to it later if the time and the test format allow. If the testing format doesn't allow you to return to earlier questions, just make an educated guess; then put it out of your mind and move on.

On the easier questions, be careful not to rush. It may seem wise to hurry through them so you have more time for the challenging ones, but it's not worth missing one if you know the concept and just didn't take the time to read the question fully. Work efficiently but make sure you understand the question and have looked at all of the answer choices, since more than one may seem right at first.

Even if you're paying attention to the time, you may find yourself a little behind at some point. You should speed up to get back on track, but do so wisely. Don't panic; just take a few seconds less on each question until you're caught up. Don't guess without thinking, but do look through the answer choices and eliminate any you know are wrong. If you can get down to two choices, it is often worthwhile to guess from those. Once you've chosen an answer, move on and don't dwell on any that you skipped or had to hurry through. If a question was taking too long, chances are it was one of the harder ones, so you weren't as likely to get it right anyway.

On the other hand, if you find yourself getting ahead of schedule, it may be beneficial to slow down a little. The more quickly you work, the more likely you are to make a careless mistake that will affect your score. You've budgeted time for each question, so don't be afraid to spend that time. Practice an efficient but careful pace to get the most out of the time you have.

Secret Key #5 – Have a Plan for Guessing

When you're taking the test, you may find yourself stuck on a question. Some of the answer choices seem better than others, but you don't see the one answer choice that is obviously correct. What do you do?

The scenario described above is very common, yet most test takers have not effectively prepared for it. Developing and practicing a plan for guessing may be one of the single most effective uses of your time as you get ready for the exam.

In developing your plan for guessing, there are three questions to address:

- When should you start the guessing process?
- How should you narrow down the choices?
- Which answer should you choose?

When to Start the Guessing Process

Unless your plan for guessing is to select C every time (which, despite its merits, is not what we recommend), you need to leave yourself enough time to apply your answer elimination strategies. Since you have a limited amount of time for each question, that means that if you're going to give yourself the best shot at guessing correctly, you have to decide quickly whether or not you will guess.

Of course, the best-case scenario is that you don't have to guess at all, so first, see if you can answer the question based on your knowledge of the subject and basic reasoning skills. Focus on the key words in the question and try to jog your memory of related topics. Give yourself a chance to bring the knowledge to mind, but once you realize that you don't have (or you can't access) the knowledge you need to answer the question, it's time to start the guessing process.

It's almost always better to start the guessing process too early than too late. It only takes a few seconds to remember something and answer the question from knowledge. Carefully eliminating wrong answer choices takes longer. Plus, going through the process of eliminating answer choices can actually help jog your memory.

Summary: Start the guessing process as soon as you decide that you can't answer the question based on your knowledge.

How to Narrow Down the Choices

The next chapter in this book (**Test-Taking Strategies**) includes a wide range of strategies for how to approach questions and how to look for answer choices to eliminate. You will definitely want to read those carefully, practice them, and figure out which ones work best for you. Here though, we're going to address a mindset rather than a particular strategy.

Your odds of guessing an answer correctly depend on how many options you are choosing from.

Number of options left	5	4	3	2	1
Odds of guessing correctly	20%	25%	33%	50%	100%

You can see from this chart just how valuable it is to be able to eliminate incorrect answers and make an educated guess, but there are two things that many test takers do that cause them to miss out on the benefits of guessing:

- Accidentally eliminating the correct answer
- Selecting an answer based on an impression

We'll look at the first one here, and the second one in the next section.

To avoid accidentally eliminating the correct answer, we recommend a thought exercise called **the $5 challenge**. In this challenge, you only eliminate an answer choice from contention if you are willing to bet $5 on it being wrong. Why $5? Five dollars is a small but not insignificant amount of money. It's an amount you could afford to lose but wouldn't want to throw away. And while losing $5 once might not hurt too much, doing it twenty times will set you back $100. In the same way, each small decision you make—eliminating a choice here, guessing on a question there—won't by itself impact your score very much, but when you put them all together, they can make a big difference. By holding each answer choice elimination decision to a higher standard, you can reduce the risk of accidentally eliminating the correct answer.

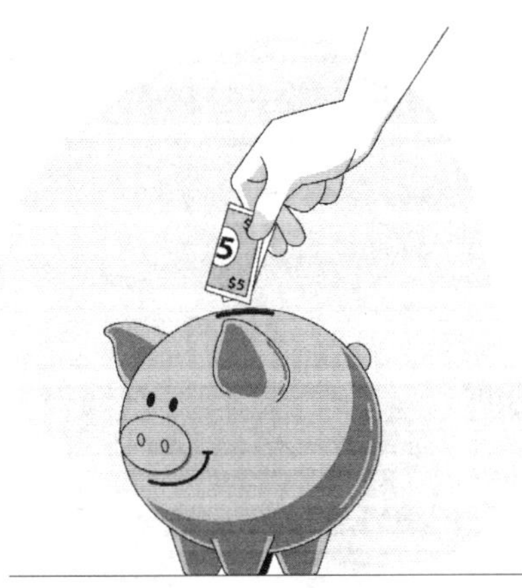

The $5 challenge can also be applied in a positive sense: If you are willing to bet $5 that an answer choice *is* correct, go ahead and mark it as correct.

Summary: Only eliminate an answer choice if you are willing to bet $5 that it is wrong.

Which Answer to Choose

You're taking the test. You've run into a hard question and decided you'll have to guess. You've eliminated all the answer choices you're willing to bet $5 on. Now you have to pick an answer. Why do we even need to talk about this? Why can't you just pick whichever one you feel like when the time comes?

The answer to these questions is that if you don't come into the test with a plan, you'll rely on your impression to select an answer choice, and if you do that, you risk falling into a trap. The test writers know that everyone who takes their test will be guessing on some of the questions, so they intentionally write wrong answer choices to seem plausible. You still have to pick an answer though, and if the wrong answer choices are designed to look right, how can you ever be sure that you're not falling for their trap? The best solution we've found to this dilemma is to take the decision out of your hands entirely. Here is the process we recommend:

Once you've eliminated any choices that you are confident (willing to bet $5) are wrong, select the first remaining choice as your answer.

Whether you choose to select the first remaining choice, the second, or the last, the important thing is that you use some preselected standard. Using this approach guarantees that you will not be enticed into selecting an answer choice that looks right, because you are not basing your decision on how the answer choices look.

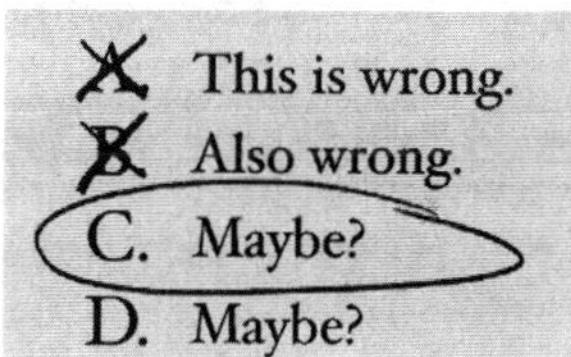

This is not meant to make you question your knowledge. Instead, it is to help you recognize the difference between your knowledge and your impressions. There's a huge difference between thinking an answer is right because of what you know, and thinking an answer is right because it looks or sounds like it should be right.

Summary: To ensure that your selection is appropriately random, make a predetermined selection from among all answer choices you have not eliminated.

Test-Taking Strategies

This section contains a list of test-taking strategies that you may find helpful as you work through the test. By taking what you know and applying logical thought, you can maximize your chances of answering any question correctly!

It is very important to realize that every question is different and every person is different: no single strategy will work on every question, and no single strategy will work for every person. That's why we've included all of them here, so you can try them out and determine which ones work best for different types of questions and which ones work best for you.

Question Strategies

✓ Read Carefully

Read the question and the answer choices carefully. Don't miss the question because you misread the terms. You have plenty of time to read each question thoroughly and make sure you understand what is being asked. Yet a happy medium must be attained, so don't waste too much time. You must read carefully and efficiently.

✓ Contextual Clues

Look for contextual clues. If the question includes a word you are not familiar with, look at the immediate context for some indication of what the word might mean. Contextual clues can often give you all the information you need to decipher the meaning of an unfamiliar word. Even if you can't determine the meaning, you may be able to narrow down the possibilities enough to make a solid guess at the answer to the question.

✓ Prefixes

If you're having trouble with a word in the question or answer choices, try dissecting it. Take advantage of every clue that the word might include. Prefixes can be a huge help. Usually, they allow you to determine a basic meaning. *Pre-* means before, *post-* means after, *pro-* is positive, *de-* is negative. From prefixes, you can get an idea of the general meaning of the word and try to put it into context.

✓ Hedge Words

Watch out for critical hedge words, such as *likely, may, can, sometimes, often, almost, mostly, usually, generally, rarely,* and *sometimes.* Question writers insert these hedge phrases to cover every possibility. Often an answer choice will be wrong simply because it leaves no room for exception. Be on guard for answer choices that have definitive words such as *exactly* and *always.*

✓ Switchback Words

Stay alert for *switchbacks.* These are the words and phrases frequently used to alert you to shifts in thought. The most common switchback words are *but, although,* and *however.* Others include *nevertheless, on the other hand, even though, while, in spite of, despite,* and *regardless of.* Switchback words are important to catch because they can change the direction of the question or an answer choice.

☑ Face Value

When in doubt, use common sense. Accept the situation in the problem at face value. Don't read too much into it. These problems will not require you to make wild assumptions. If you have to go beyond creativity and warp time or space in order to have an answer choice fit the question, then you should move on and consider the other answer choices. These are normal problems rooted in reality. The applicable relationship or explanation may not be readily apparent, but it is there for you to figure out. Use your common sense to interpret anything that isn't clear.

Answer Choice Strategies

☑ Answer Selection

The most thorough way to pick an answer choice is to identify and eliminate wrong answers until only one is left, then confirm it is the correct answer. Sometimes an answer choice may immediately seem right, but be careful. The test writers will usually put more than one reasonable answer choice on each question, so take a second to read all of them and make sure that the other choices are not equally obvious. As long as you have time left, it is better to read every answer choice than to pick the first one that looks right without checking the others.

☑ Answer Choice Families

An answer choice family consists of two (in rare cases, three) answer choices that are very similar in construction and cannot all be true at the same time. If you see two answer choices that are direct opposites or parallels, one of them is usually the correct answer. For instance, if one answer choice says that quantity *x* increases and another either says that quantity *x* decreases (opposite) or says that quantity *y* increases (parallel), then those answer choices would fall into the same family. An answer choice that doesn't match the construction of the answer choice family is more likely to be incorrect. Most questions will not have answer choice families, but when they do appear, you should be prepared to recognize them.

☑ Eliminate Answers

Eliminate answer choices as soon as you realize they are wrong, but make sure you consider all possibilities. If you are eliminating answer choices and realize that the last one you are left with is also wrong, don't panic. Start over and consider each choice again. There may be something you missed the first time that you will realize on the second pass.

☑ Avoid Fact Traps

Don't be distracted by an answer choice that is factually true but doesn't answer the question. You are looking for the choice that answers the question. Stay focused on what the question is asking for so you don't accidentally pick an answer that is true but incorrect. Always go back to the question and make sure the answer choice you've selected actually answers the question and is not merely a true statement.

☑ Extreme Statements

In general, you should avoid answers that put forth extreme actions as standard practice or proclaim controversial ideas as established fact. An answer choice that states the "process should be used in certain situations, if..." is much more likely to be correct than one that states the "process should be discontinued completely." The first is a calm rational statement and doesn't even make a definitive, uncompromising stance, using a hedge word *if* to provide wiggle room, whereas the second choice is far more extreme.

⊘ BENCHMARK

As you read through the answer choices and you come across one that seems to answer the question well, mentally select that answer choice. This is not your final answer, but it's the one that will help you evaluate the other answer choices. The one that you selected is your benchmark or standard for judging each of the other answer choices. Every other answer choice must be compared to your benchmark. That choice is correct until proven otherwise by another answer choice beating it. If you find a better answer, then that one becomes your new benchmark. Once you've decided that no other choice answers the question as well as your benchmark, you have your final answer.

⊘ PREDICT THE ANSWER

Before you even start looking at the answer choices, it is often best to try to predict the answer. When you come up with the answer on your own, it is easier to avoid distractions and traps because you will know exactly what to look for. The right answer choice is unlikely to be word-for-word what you came up with, but it should be a close match. Even if you are confident that you have the right answer, you should still take the time to read each option before moving on.

General Strategies

⊘ TOUGH QUESTIONS

If you are stumped on a problem or it appears too hard or too difficult, don't waste time. Move on! Remember though, if you can quickly check for obviously incorrect answer choices, your chances of guessing correctly are greatly improved. Before you completely give up, at least try to knock out a couple of possible answers. Eliminate what you can and then guess at the remaining answer choices before moving on.

⊘ CHECK YOUR WORK

Since you will probably not know every term listed and the answer to every question, it is important that you get credit for the ones that you do know. Don't miss any questions through careless mistakes. If at all possible, try to take a second to look back over your answer selection and make sure you've selected the correct answer choice and haven't made a costly careless mistake (such as marking an answer choice that you didn't mean to mark). This quick double check should more than pay for itself in caught mistakes for the time it costs.

⊘ PACE YOURSELF

It's easy to be overwhelmed when you're looking at a page full of questions; your mind is confused and full of random thoughts, and the clock is ticking down faster than you would like. Calm down and maintain the pace that you have set for yourself. Especially as you get down to the last few minutes of the test, don't let the small numbers on the clock make you panic. As long as you are on track by monitoring your pace, you are guaranteed to have time for each question.

⊘ DON'T RUSH

It is very easy to make errors when you are in a hurry. Maintaining a fast pace in answering questions is pointless if it makes you miss questions that you would have gotten right otherwise. Test writers like to include distracting information and wrong answers that seem right. Taking a little extra time to avoid careless mistakes can make all the difference in your test score. Find a pace that allows you to be confident in the answers that you select.

⊘ Keep Moving

Panicking will not help you pass the test, so do your best to stay calm and keep moving. Taking deep breaths and going through the answer elimination steps you practiced can help to break through a stress barrier and keep your pace.

Final Notes

The combination of a solid foundation of content knowledge and the confidence that comes from practicing your plan for applying that knowledge is the key to maximizing your performance on test day. As your foundation of content knowledge is built up and strengthened, you'll find that the strategies included in this chapter become more and more effective in helping you quickly sift through the distractions and traps of the test to isolate the correct answer.

Now that you're preparing to move forward into the test content chapters of this book, be sure to keep your goal in mind. As you read, think about how you will be able to apply this information on the test. If you've already seen sample questions for the test and you have an idea of the question format and style, try to come up with questions of your own that you can answer based on what you're reading. This will give you valuable practice applying your knowledge in the same ways you can expect to on test day.

Good luck and good studying!

Procedures

Cardiovascular Surgical Procedures

Considerations for Cardiovascular Surgery

Potential Infection in Cardiac Surgery Patients

The patient and family members or the caregiver should be educated on the signs and symptoms of **infection**, which can be life-threatening in the cardiac surgery patient. An increase in pain at the surgical site can be an early indicator, and pain will continue to increase as the infection worsens. If the infection is present throughout the surgical site, the patient may experience some difficulty breathing or an increase in pain with activity. This can occur if the surrounding soft tissue becomes edematous and increases the pressure within the chest cavity. The signs of infection can include an increase in redness surrounding the surgical incision. The area may also feel very warm. Swelling around the incision may increase, and there may be noticeable purulent discharge from the wound itself. If the drainage is excessive, there may be a foul odor present. Late signs of infection include fevers >100.5 °F and even nausea or vomiting. If an infection becomes systemic, the patient may exhibit signs of mental status changes.

Exposure of Surgical Site During Cardiac Surgery

As with all surgeries, **exposure of the surgical site during cardiac surgery** is very important. Fixed retractors are used to hold back the sternum and ribs and provide better access to the chest. These should be carefully placed to prevent unnecessary rib fracture, especially in those patients who may be at risk for osteoporosis. There is also a risk of intercostal nerve damage from retractors. There are specialized retractors available for different types of cardiac procedures, depending upon the anatomic area that requires exposure. During bypass grafting surgery, the assistant is responsible for actually holding the heart in his or her hand and carefully retracting it to fully expose the coronary artery to the surgeon. This is done very gently to prevent any damage to the artery or cardiac tissue. The hands should be kept very flat to provide a clear view of the artery without obstruction.

Interoperative Care for Cardiac Surgery Patients

The patient will be very closely monitored throughout any cardiac procedures. This may require the use of an internal monitoring line, such as an arterial pressure line or CVP line. Transesophageal echocardiography (TEE) may be performed during surgery to more clearly evaluate valve function during surgery. This is especially useful during valve repair or replacement procedures. It can also be used to assess the dimensions of the existing valve when determining which prosthetic valve should be used for replacement. Most cardiac surgeries require the patient be in a supine position. Care should be taken to prevent over stretching of the upper extremities, which can lead to a brachial plexus or ulnar nerve injury. All bony prominences should be padded. Excessive pressure should be avoided over the vessels and nerves of the extremities to prevent compromised blood flow or permanent nerve damage. All venous or arterial lines should also be kept free to prevent accidental movement of the lines.

Cardiopulmonary Bypass

Initiation

The patient is heparinized about three minutes before **initiating cardiopulmonary bypass (CPB)** and insertion of cannulas. After the heart is accessed through a midsternal incision/sternotomy, one cannula is placed into the right atrium or femoral vein or dual catheters through the right atrium into the superior and inferior vena cava to provide gravity drainage of venous blood, as the pump system creates a vacuum. (If the aortic valve is incompetent, then the left ventricle must be vented to prevent backflow of blood into the left ventricle.) Note, however, that improper placement of the superior vena cava cannula can result in increased central venous pressure and cerebral edema, and improper placement of the inferior vena cava cannula can cause abdominal vascular distention with inadequate venous return to the CPB machine. A return cannula is usually placed in the ascending aorta but may also be placed in the femoral artery. A cross clamp is placed across the aorta (below the return cannula) to divert blood to the CPB machine. (The lungs are not mechanically ventilated during CPB.)

Filtering and Oxygenating the Blood

During cardiopulmonary bypass (CPB), the blood drains from the cannulas into a venous reservoir and then is pumped through a filter that removes air bubbles or clots. After **filtering**, a membrane-gas-interface **oxygenates** the blood to maintain the partial pressure of oxygen with the partial pressure of carbon dioxide at 35–45 mmHg. The blood goes through a heat exchanger to heat or cool the blood, depending on the stage of the operation. Temperature is usually maintained at 18 °C before arrest and 28–32 °C during surgery and then increased to 37 °C before removal from the CPB machine. Cooled blood is more viscous, but it is diluted by crystalloid solutions (commonly 5% dextrose in lactated Ringers). The blood is then pumped back into circulation, bypassing the heart. Cardioplegic potassium-based solution is infused into the aortic root, from which it circulates to the coronary arteries, to ensure cessation of electrical activity, so the heart remains flaccid during CPB. This can result in postoperative hyperkalemia, although excess potassium can be filtered by the CPB machine.

Systemic Hypothermia

During cardiopulmonary bypass (CPB), **systemic hypothermia** (32–34 °C) is used, but the patient should be warmed to no more than 37 °C before leaving the operating room. Because brain temperature may be higher than measurable core temperature, raising the temperature to more than 37 °C may impair neurocognitive functioning. Peripheral vasoconstriction is often used postoperatively after CPB to provide core warming. Vasodilators redistribute core heat and may slow core warming although they increase perfusion. Heated intravenous fluid and humidifiers in the ventilator circuits may treat hypothermia but are usually not effective for increasing core temperatures. A temperature-controlling system or forced air warming devices, such as the Bair Hugger, may help maintain and increase core temperature. Hypothermia increases the risk of atrial and ventricular arrhythmias. Shivering increases oxygen consumption and the production of carbon dioxide and should be controlled with meperidine.

Vasoconstriction/Hypertension During Cooling Stage

Hypothermic vasoconstriction occurs with core temperatures less than 35–36 °C, increasing systemic vascular resistance (SVR) and resulting in **hypertension**. Treatment includes inotropes for a cardiac index less than 2 L/min/m^2 in conjunction with fluid replacement until systolic pressure is 100–120 mmHg and pulmonary artery diastolic pressure or pulmonary capillary wedge pressure is 15–20 mmHg. Warming methods should be used to increase core temperature to 37 °C. Vasodilators used to treat hypothermic vasoconstriction include nicardipine and clevidipine.

Vasodilators reduce afterload, restore preload to adequate levels, and improve peripheral perfusion, reducing SVR and blood pressure. Preload should be maintained 20 mmHg or less but prevented from falling too low as this may precipitate hypovolemia and hypotension. If the cardiac index falls below 2 $L/min/m^2$ with adequate filling pressures but mild hypertension in a patient receiving an inotropic agent, a low-dose vasodilator may be provided. Care should be used when discontinuing an inotropic agent unless cardiac output is adequate because vasoconstriction may be a compensatory mechanism to maintain cardiac function.

Vasodilation/Hypotension During Rewarming Stage

During the **rewarming stage** after **hypothermia**, **vasodilation** occurs, reducing filling pressures and resulting in **hypotension** and decreased cardiac output in patients who are hypovolemic. Volume resuscitation must be adequate to maintain filling pressures, especially in the first 6 postoperative hours, but overloading the patient with fluid (>2 L every 6 hours) may result in hemodilution, requiring blood transfusions and plasma or platelets to increase clotting factors and prevent bleeding. Generally, fluids should be limited to 1500–1750 mL per 24 hr or no more than 20 mL/kg/day. The usual initial bolus of fluid is 500 mL of lactated Ringers or normal saline. Colloids should be avoided with capillary leak syndrome but are indicated for hypotension primarily related to peripheral vasodilation. With marginal hypotension, fluids are provided to increase pulmonary artery diastolic pressure or pulmonary capillary wedge pressure to 18–20 mmHg first with crystalloid and then colloid. If a patient remains hypotensive and the cardiac index (CI) is less than 2.2 $L/min/m^2$, pure alpha agonist phenylephrine is provided. With a CI of 1.8–2.2 $L/min/m^2$, norepinephrine (which is both an alpha- and beta-adrenergic agonist) is provided. If the CI falls to less than 1.8 $L/min/m^2$, an inotrope and norepinephrine are provided as needed.

Discontinuation

To discontinue cardiopulmonary bypass (CPB), the patient must be rewarmed, air evacuated from the system, the aortic cross-clamp opened and removed, and mechanical ventilation restarted. **Guidelines for discontinuation** include the following:

- Core temperature should be 37 °C to prevent metabolic acidosis and decreased myocardial contractility.
- Cardiac status must be stable with sinus rhythm (preferable) without evidence of atrioventricular (AV) block. In some cases, increased potassium levels must be treated with calcium, furosemide, or glucose and insulin. AV pacing may be required. Heart rate should be 80–100 bpm. Bradycardia may be treated with pacing or inotropic agents. Cardioversion may be necessary if supraventricular tachycardia occurs. Perfusion should be adequate.
- Laboratory values must be checked and within normal limits with a hematocrit of 22–25%, potassium less than 5.5 mEq/L, and a pH over 7.20.
- Monitors must be functioning properly.
- Ventilation is resumed with 100% oxygen.
- The patient is weaned slowly from CPB. If pump failure occurs as CPB is discontinued, an intra-aortic balloon pump may be used before another attempt to wean the patient.

Medical Management of Postoperative CPB Patients

The **postoperative care** of cardiopulmonary bypass surgery patients requires careful **medical management**:

- Cardiovascular support to maintain adequate cardiac output may require adjustment in heart rate, preload, afterload, and contractility.
- Regulation of temperature following hypothermia induced during surgery requires warming, but not above 37 °C.
- Bleeding must be monitored carefully, and autotransfusion devices may be used to replace red blood cells.
- Chest tubes must be monitored for patency. Milking and stripping are no longer encouraged in chest tube management. Rather, ensure that tubes are positioned to promote continuous drainage.

Review Video: Chest Tubes
Visit mometrix.com/academy and enter code: 696975

- Cardiac tamponade may occur if blood accumulates around the heart, requiring surgical intervention.
- Respiratory care includes early extubation (usually within 4–8 hours). Supplemental oxygen is given as needed.
- Neurological monitoring is necessary for post-cardiotomy delirium (e.g., disorientation progressing to agitation, hallucinations, paranoia).
- Wound infections may occur, especially if a persistent fever is present. Diabetics may need insulin infusions to maintain glucose levels between 80–110 mg/dL to lower the risk of infection. Hemoglobinuria can result from hemolysis and damage kidney tubules. Urine flow may be increased with furosemide (Lasix) if it is less than 20–30 mL/hr or if it is bloody.

Pathophysiologic Changes of Postoperative CPB Patients

Cardiopulmonary bypass (CPB) is associated with a number of **pathophysiologic changes** that must be monitored and evaluated.

- **Decreased concentration of plasma proteins** from hemodilution and absorption onto bypass circuit's increased inflammatory response and capillary permeability
- Increased epinephrine/norepinephrine for 24 hours after surgery, **increasing systemic resistance**
- Increased cortisol level for 24 hours, increasing **sodium retention and potassium excretion**
- **Hyperglycemia** from hormonal stress
- Decreased level of **triiodothyronine**
- **Pulmonary dysfunction** (decreased surfactant effects, compliance, and functional residual volume, increasing shunts)
- Progressive **hypothermia** (after drop) from chest remaining open after CPB
- **Coagulopathy** because of disruption of the coagulation system, hemodilution from crystalloids that reduce platelets and clotting factors, and activation of platelets in contact with the extracorporeal circuit

- **Activation of renin-aldosterone system**, increasing sodium retention and potassium excretion
- **Elevation of angiotensin II levels**, increasing sodium retention and renal vasoconstriction,
- Release of vasoactive substances, nitric oxide and prostacyclin, which impairs reabsorption of solutes, and complements, kallikrein, and bradykinin, which **increase an inflammatory response**.

Management of Decreased SVR in Postoperative CPB Patients

Decreased systemic vascular resistance (SVR), also referred to as **vasodilatory shock**, occurs in 5–8% of patients after cardiac surgery with cardiopulmonary bypass (CPB) with normal or increased cardiac output, perhaps associated with an inflammatory response to CPB. Patients exhibit an abrupt and precipitous fall in arterial blood pressure with tachycardia as a response to decreased SVR. Hypoperfusion can lead to vasodilation, which can lead to systemic inflammatory response syndrome and multiorgan dysfunction syndrome. Patients with an ejection fraction of less than 35% are at increased risk as are those requiring ventricular assist devices. Initial treatment includes fluid resuscitation, inotropes to increase contractility, and norepinephrine to increase blood pressure through vasoconstriction. If this is ineffective, vasopressin may be administered. Methylene blue may be administered if vasopressin is ineffective.

Increased Levels of Amylase and Pancreatitis in Postoperative Patients

A transient period of **increased amylase levels** (hyperamylasemia) occurs in up to 65% of patients after cardiopulmonary bypass (CPB), but only 3% or less develop pancreatitis. Transient hyperamylasemia can occur with both on-pump and off-pump procedures and may result from decreased excretion through the kidneys. If levels are elevated to 1000 IU/L or more in the early postoperative period, the risk of developing pancreatitis increases, so patients need careful observation. Indications include nausea, lack of appetite, and ileus. Treatment is supportive.

Pancreatitis usually results from ischemia that causes necrosis, often associated with prolonged CPB and persistent low-cardiac output. Patients with a history of alcoholism are at increased risk. Pancreatitis may cause fever, elevated white blood cell count, abdominal distention, abdominal pain, nausea, vomiting, and paralytic ileus. Pancreatitis may be present without marked increase in amylase levels. Treatment includes insertion of a nasogastric tube and antibiotics. Surgical debridement may be necessary in severe cases.

Monitoring of Jugular Venous Pressure in Postoperative CPB Patients

Jugular (neck vein) venous pressure is used to assess the cardiac output and pressure in the right heart as the pulsations relate to changes in pressure in the right atrium. This procedure is usually not accurate if the pulse rate is 100 bpm or more. This is a noninvasive estimation of central venous pressure and waveform. Measurement should be done with the internal jugular if possible; if not, the external jugular may be used.

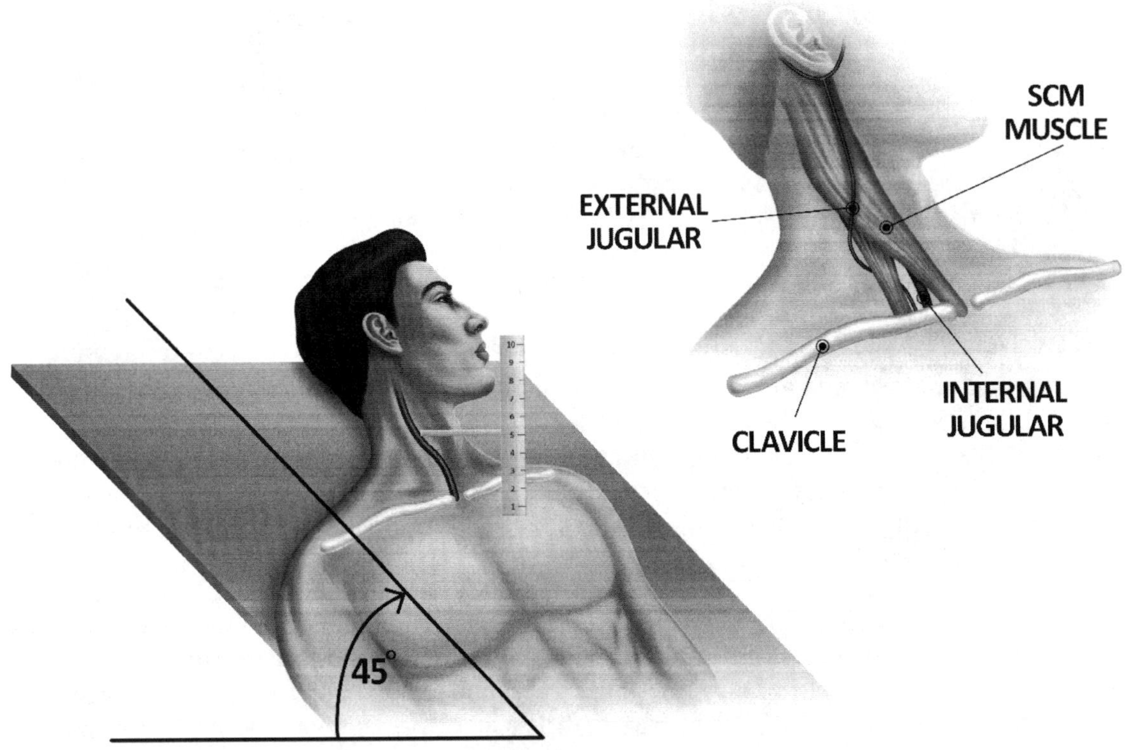

- Elevate the patient's head of bed to 45° (or to 90° if necessary) with the patient's head turned to the opposite side of the examination.
- Position a light at an angle to illuminate veins and shadows.
- Measure the height of the jugular vein pulsation above the sternal joint, using a ruler.
- Normal height is 4 cm or less above the sternal angle.
- Increased pressure (>4 cm) indicates increased pressure in the right atrium and right heart failure. It may also indicate pericarditis or tricuspid stenosis. Laughing or coughing may trigger or increase the Valsalva response.

Coronary Artery Bypass Graft

Indications and Procedure

Coronary artery bypass graft (CABG) is a surgical procedure for the treatment of angina that does not respond to medical treatment, unstable angina, a blockage of 60% or more in the left main coronary artery, a blockage of multiple coronary arteries that include the proximal left anterior descending artery, left ventricular dysfunction, or previous unsuccessful percutaneous cardiac interventions. The surgery is performed through a midsternal incision that exposes the heart, which is chilled and placed on cardiopulmonary bypass with blood going from the right atrium to the machine and back to the body while the aorta is clamped to keep the surgical field free of blood. Bypass grafts are sutured into place to bypass areas of occluded coronary arteries. Grafts may be obtained from various sites:

- Gastroepiploic artery (rarely used)
- Internal mammary artery (commonly used and superior to saphenous vein but procedure is more time-consuming)
- Radial artery
- Saphenous vein (commonly used, especially for emergency procedures)

Harvesting of Grafts

A number of vessels are commonly used for coronary artery bypass **grafts**. In emergency situations, the saphenous vein is often harvested because it can be obtained quickly. Both the greater and lesser saphenous veins may be used. However, using veins as grafts may result in edema of the extremity from which the graft is obtained, although this risk diminishes over time. Long-term, saphenous vein grafts may exhibit atherosclerotic changes in 5–10 years. Arterial grafts remain patent for longer periods and develop atherosclerotic changes more slowly. Arteries that are used for grafts include the right and left internal mammary arteries as well as the radial artery, usually from the nondominant side. One problem with the internal mammary arteries is that they may not be long enough for multiple bypasses. Some procedures require a combination of both venous and arterial grafts.

Vein Harvesting

There are a few different approaches to **harvesting veins for bypass grafting**. A continuous long incision can be made up the inside of the leg to access the greater saphenous vein, a series of small incisions can be made along the vein's path, or an endoscopic technique can be performed which involves making 2 or 3 small incisions. Whichever technique is used, the vein is identified, and the proximal end is clamped. The vessel is then carefully dissected away from the surrounding tissues. Small branches off of the vein should also be severed. Once it is free, the vein is removed from the leg and carefully placed in a sterile saline bath to be irrigated. It is also carefully flushed to assess for patency. Excessive force should not be used to flush the vein. If any small leaks are identified, fine suture can be used to carefully close these openings. The incisions used to access the vein are then sutured closed using either continuous or interrupted sutures for closure.

Use of the Radial Artery as an Alternate Arterial Conduit

The **radial artery** has become increasingly popular as an arterial graft because of its long duration of patency; however, the adequacy of collateral vessels and circulation to the hand by the ulnar artery must be assessed preoperatively by the Allen test and Doppler flow measurements. With the Allen test, flushing that takes 6 seconds or more is considered a contraindication for use of the radial artery. Other contraindications include peripheral vascular disease, Raynaud's syndrome, stroke, or traumatic injury on the graft side. After harvesting, surgeons may place a drain, which is usually removed when drainage decreases to less than 20 mL per 8 hr. A compression dressing is usually left in place for 24 hours. The wound should be assessed for drainage, capillary refill time, indications of infection and hematoma, temperature, and ulnar artery pulse, including evaluating the 6 Ps (pain, pulselessness, pallor, paresthesia, paralysis, polar/cold). Weakness and numbness may persist for 6 months or less. Patients receive calcium channel blockers (e.g., diltiazem) during surgery and for 6 months postoperatively. Cellulitis may develop but usually responds to antibiotics.

On-Pump CABG Postoperative Management

Postoperative management for patients having an on-pump coronary artery bypass graft (CABG) is explained below:

- **Inotropic medications** are usually started at the end of cardio-pulmonary bypass surgery and may need to be continued to maintain cardiac output. Epinephrine (1–2 μg/min) is the drug of choice but dobutamine or dopamine may be used. If the response is inadequate, milrinone is given. Inotropes may be indicated for up to 12 hours with perioperative infarction or myocardial stunning.
- If hemodynamic status remains unstable, an **intra-aortic balloon pump (IABP)** may be necessary, and if the condition persists, a **ventricular assist device (VAD)** may be needed.
- **Nitrates** are used to control hypertension, usually beginning with sodium nitroprusside or nitroglycerin if signs of ischemia are present.
- **Antiarrhythmics** with lidocaine are usually given during surgery to prevent ventricular arrhythmias. Amiodarone is effective in reducing the incidence of atrial fibrillation, and β-blockers (usually metoprolol) is administered on the first postoperative day. Ventricular arrhythmias are treated with β-blockers or placement of an implantable cardioverter defibrillator. Electrocardiographic changes may indicate ischemia or myocardial infarction. Vasodilators prevent spasm of a radial graft, and antiplatelet therapy helps maintain patency of venous grafts.

Port Access Coronary Artery Bypass Graft

Port access coronary artery bypass graft is an alternative form of coronary artery bypass graft (CABG) that uses a number of small incisions (ports) along with cardiopulmonary bypass (CPB) and cardioplegia to do a video-assisted surgical repair. Usually three or more incisions are required, including one in the femoral area to allow access to the femoral artery for a multipurpose catheter that is threaded through to the ascending aorta to return blood from the CPB, block the aorta with a balloon, provide cardioplegic solution, and vent air. Another catheter is threaded through the femoral vein to the right atrium to carry blood to the CPB. An incision is also needed for access to the jugular vein for catheters to the pulmonary artery and the coronary sinus. One to three thoracotomy incisions are made for insertion of video imaging equipment and instruments. While the midsternal incision is avoided, multiple incisions pose the potential for possible morbidity.

Robot-Assisted Coronary Artery Bypass

Some medical centers conduct **robot-assisted** coronary artery bypass, using sophisticated robotic systems, such as the da Vinci Surgical System. The surgeon sits at a console and uses hand grips to control manipulators that do the surgical procedure. Robotics can be used for coronary artery bypass as well as mitral valve repair. Procedures on valves and some on coronary arteries are carried out with cardiopulmonary bypass. Because access to the right ventricle is limited, it is difficult to place pacing wires. Two chest tubes are usually placed, one in the pleura and the other in an anterior mediastinal tube. Surgeons require extensive training and may require a longer time to conduct surgery when they are inexperienced. A prolonged bypass increases the risk of compartment syndrome.

Off-Pump Coronary Artery Bypass

Off-pump coronary artery bypass (OPCAB) applies to a bypass graft on the beating heart through a small median sternotomy with incisional length dependent on many factors. Medications (e.g., esmolol, adenosine) slow the heart rate. Special instruments and deep sutures into the pericardium are used to support the heart and place it into position so it can be accessed and stabilized more easily. The amount of manipulation depends on the areas and number of occlusions. The length of surgery varies as well but is shorter than for on-pump coronary artery bypass. OPCAB is usually preferred over minimally invasive direct coronary artery bypass if there are multiple occlusions, as all coronary arteries can be accessed with OPCAB. If marked ventricular dysfunction is present, then a ventricular assist device may be necessary to stabilize hemodynamics.

Postoperative Management with Off-Pump CABG

Postoperative management with off-pump coronary artery bypass graft (CABG) includes the following:

- Patients should be monitored for hypothermia, and temperature should be maintained.
- Hemodynamic status is usually stable, and decreased cardiac output is not common.
- Graft patency must be evaluated frequently as there is an increased risk for problems because of reduced visibility during surgery. Electrocardiographic changes may indicate problems. Angiography should be done with suspicion of problems.
- Patients should have pacing wires with a heart rate of 80 bpm optimal initially.
- β-Blockers and magnesium are usually administered in surgery to reduce the risk of atrial fibrillation.
- Patients may be fluid-overloaded and may require diuresis when they are stable.
- Mediastinal bleeding is uncommon, but coagulopathy may occur; bleeding should be suspected in patients who are hemodynamically unstable.

Postoperative Complications of OPCAB

While off-pump coronary artery bypass (OPCAB) patients may have fewer and less severe **complications** than those receiving cardiopulmonary bypass for cardiopulmonary bypass grafts, side effects and complications are similar; the inflammatory response is lessoned with OPCAB, and patients are less likely to experience thromboembolism or cerebral hyperperfusion. About 5% of patients must be converted to on-pump coronary artery bypass (ONCAB). Patients tend to experience less bleeding, although mediastinal and pleural tubes must be assessed hourly for bleeding. Patients receive less heparin but may develop coagulopathy and protamine reactions. Serum lactate levels are lower than with ONCAB, but levels of 4 mmol/L or more pose a risk of increased morbidity. Hemodynamic status may be affected with increased pulmonary artery pressure and decreased cardiac output. Manipulation of the heart during surgery may result in decreased compliance and contractility. Incidence of stroke, atrial fibrillation, and postoperative infection is lower with OPCAB than ONCAB. Studies show that cognitive decline can occur with OPCAB as well as ONCAB. Graft occlusion can occur, especially with venous grafts.

MIDCAB

Minimally invasive direct coronary artery bypass (MIDCAB) applies to a bypass graft on the beating heart through several 3- to 5-inch intercostal incisions, without using cardiopulmonary bypass. Different approaches include an 8–12 cm thoracotomy incision, a 5–8 cm vertical incision on one side of the sternum, or an 8–10 cm horizontal intercostal incision. Because the incision must be over the bypass area, this procedure is suitable only for bypass of one or two coronary arteries. A small portion of rib is removed to allow access to the heart, and the internal mammary artery is used for grafting. Special instruments, such as a heart stabilizer, are used to limit movement of the heart during suturing. Surgery usually takes 2–3 hours, and recovery time is decreased as patients have less pain. Because anastomosis is difficult on a beating heart, complications, such as ischemia, may occur during surgery so a cardiopulmonary bypass machine must be available. Early studies indicate that MIDCAB may provide longer lasting relief than angioplasty for single vessel occlusion.

Advantages over Standard CABG

Minimally invasive direct coronary artery bypass (MIDCAB) is more technically difficult than the standard coronary artery bypass graft (CABG) procedure because surgery is on a beating heart and access and visibility are limited. Additionally, incomplete revascularization may result in further intervention. There are a number of **advantages**:

- Patients do not suffer the adverse effects associated with cardiopulmonary bypass.
- Recovery time is faster, and patients are discharged earlier.
- The risk of infection is lower.
- Use of the left or right internal mammary artery as grafts results in longer patency of the donor conduit as they are more resistant to atherosclerosis than venous grafts.
- The risk of hemorrhage and excessive blood loss is decreased.
- Since there is no aortic manipulation, patients have less risk of atrial fibrillation.
- Intraoperative complications are decreased.
- The cost is lower.

Postoperative Issues

Postoperative issues for patients having CABG include the following:

- Blood pressure (BP) usually increases within a few hours of surgery, requiring a vasodilator.
- Patients given β-blockers preoperatively may need pacing after cardiopulmonary bypass is discontinued.
- Patients not given β-blockers preoperatively may develop tachycardia, especially younger patients or those severely anxious. Usual treatment is esmolol or metoprolol.
- Patients with a hyperdynamic left ventricle may respond to vasodilators (to control hypertension) with tachycardia. In this case, systolic BP should be allowed to rise to 140 mmHg, and then both BP and tachycardia are treated with a β-blocker.
- Patients return from surgery with atrial and ventricular pacing wires. Junctional rhythm and bradycardia require pacing at 80 bpm. Atrial pacing is preferred to atrioventricular (AV) sequential pacing with normal AV conduction. Bi-ventricular pacing (RA-BiV) is indicated for moderate-to-severe left ventricular dysfunction. Pacing in DVI or DDD modes is indicated for second- or third-degree heart block.

Maze Procedures for Cardiac Rhythm Disorders

The **left-sided Maze procedure (Cox/Maze)** is usually done with mitral valve surgery to treat atrial fibrillation (Afib) by disrupting reentrant pathways needed for Afib through development of scarring, as restoring normal sinus rhythm improves long-term survival after cardiac surgery. The left-sided Maze procedure (cut-and-sew), done with cardiopulmonary bypass, results in ablation lines around and between the right and left pulmonary veins and an additional line from the inferior box lesion by the right or left inferior pulmonary vein to the mitral valve annulus. The left atrial appendage is removed, and an ablation line is placed from the appendage base to the left pulmonary veins with the base of the appendage over-sewn. A variety of modifications have been made (**Cox/Maze I, II, III, and IV**). Cox/Maze III and IV (which uses radiofrequency ablation instead of surgical cuts externally on a beating heart) are most commonly used presently. Cox/Maze III and IV are associated with fewer recurrences of Afib. Postoperatively, patients may exhibit heart block or bradycardia because of surgical manipulation affecting the conduction system.

Postoperative Care

Postoperative care of patients undergoing Maze procedures is similar to those undergoing open-heart surgery. The heart rate and rhythm must be continuously monitored until both stabilize. Amiodarone is usually given at the conclusion of bypass and during the postoperative period for several months with the dosage gradually decreased as the patient establishes a normal sinus rhythm. Recurrence of atrial arrhythmias is usually treated with external cardioversion. If this is not successful, then β-blockers or digoxin may be indicated. Anticoagulation begins with heparin postoperatively when bleeding is resolved and continues with warfarin, usually for at least 3–6 months or longer if atrial arrhythmias recur or continue. The ultimate goal of treatment is to maintain a normal sinus rhythm without medications.

Left Ventricular Aneurysm

A left ventricular aneurysm in the heart wall may occur secondary to a myocardial infarction (10-35% incidence) although some result from congenital defects. The impaired left ventricle causes reduced ejection fraction and resultant dyspnea, weakness, peripheral and abdominal edema, and cardiac palpitations, leading to heart failure and increased risk of embolism. Risk factors include male gender, age >65, and hypertrophic cardiomyopathy. Treatment depends on the severity of the aneurysm. Small aneurysms are treated with lifestyle changes and monitoring. Medications may include anti-coagulants, statins, and/or vasodilators. Surgical repair, which is indicated for large aneurysms and marked symptoms, requires an open-heart procedure with cardiopulmonary bypass. For a relatively small aneurysm, the damaged area is excised, and the opening is closed through a purse-string suture approach. For a large aneurysm, the damaged area is excised, and a synthetic or biological (such as bovine) patch is sutured into place. Mitral valve leak repairs and/or CABG procedures may also be carried out during the surgery.

ASD

An atrial septal defect (ASD) is an abnormal opening in the septum between the right and left atria. Because the left atrium has higher pressure than the right atrium, some of the oxygenated blood returning from the lungs to the left atrium is shunted back to the right atrium where it is again returned to the lungs, displacing deoxygenated blood. Repair is usually done between ages 2 and 4, but some are not diagnosed until adulthood. Diagnostic procedures include echocardiogram and cardiac catheterization to assess PVR and the defect size.

Symptoms

Symptoms may be few, depending upon the degree of the defect but can include:

- Congestive heart failure
- Heart murmur
- Increased risk for dysrhythmias and pulmonary vascular obstructive disease over time
- Increased PVR and PAH

Treatment

Treatment may not be necessary for small defects, but larger defects require closure:

- Open-heart surgical repair may be done for very large defects
- Heart catheterization and placing of closure device (Amplatzer device) across the atrial septal defect following balloon sizing

Ventricular Septal Defect

Ventricular septal defect (VSD) is an abnormal opening in the septum between the right and left ventricles. Non-congenital/acquired VSD may result from ventricular septal rupture after an acute myocardial infarction, especially if treatment is delayed for more than 24 hours in older female adults (>60). VS rupture may occur within 24 hours or be delayed for 3-14 days. Symptoms include hypotension and hemodynamic instability as well as signs of heart failure (primarily right-sided) and heart murmur (loud, harsh-sounding). Diagnosis is per 2-3 dimensional transthoracic or transesophageal echocardiogram (TTE or TEE) and/or cardiac MRI. Treatment options include heart catheterization and placing of a closure device, such as the Amplatzer VSD device or septal occluder device, to close the opening following balloon sizing. Following repair, patients are maintained on anti-platelets and antibiotic prophylaxis for 6 months. In some cases, patients may require surgical repair, but residual shunts are then often treated later with percutaneous insertion of a closure device.

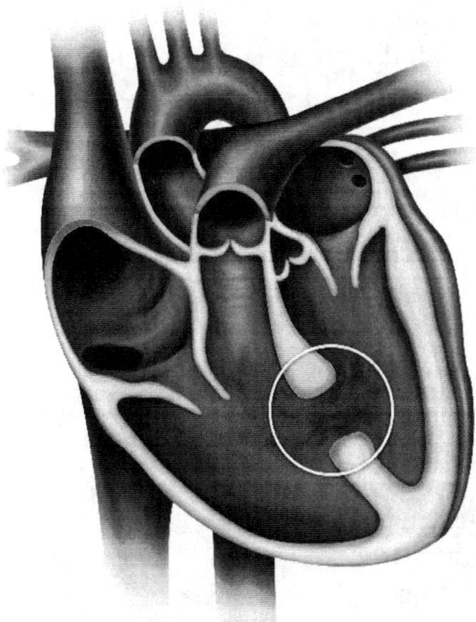

Repair of Cardiac Valves

There are a number of different surgical options for repair of cardiac valves.

- **Valvotomy/valvuloplasty** is usually done through cardiac catheterization. A valvotomy/valvuloplasty may involve releasing valve leaflet adhesions that interfere with functioning of the valve. In balloon valvuloplasty, a catheter with an inflatable balloon is positioned in the stenotic valve and inflated and deflated a number of times to dilate the opening.
- **Closed surgical valvuloplasty** involves a midsternal incision and a small hole into the heart through which the surgeon inserts a finger or dilator to repair the valve without direct visualization.
- **Open commissurotomy** uses cardiopulmonary bypass (CPB) and an incision into the heart for direct visualization of the valve.

- **Annuloplasty** may be done with CPB and an incision into the heart or minimally invasive procedures to repair the valve annulus (junction of valve leaflets and heart wall).
- **Leaflet repair** is usually done with minimally invasive procedures to repair abnormal leaflets.

Cardiac Valve Prostheses

- **Mechanical**: Ball-and-cage or disk mechanical valves pose less risk of infection and are more durable than biologic grafts, but they have an increased risk of thromboembolism; thus, they require long-term anticoagulant therapy. These valves are commonly used for patients with renal failure, hypercalcemia, endocarditis, or sepsis.
- **Xenografts/heterografts**: These biologic valves are derived from pigs (porcine), cows (ovine), or horses (equine). While they do not cause thrombus formation, they are viable for only 7–10 years. They are used for women of childbearing age because of the need to avoid anticoagulation and for patients over 70 years of age, patients with a history of peptic ulcer disease, and patients who cannot tolerate long-term anticoagulation.
- **Homografts/allografts**: Human cadaverous valves are used to replace aortic and pulmonic valves. These grafts are expensive and difficult to obtain, and viability is 10–15 years. Because they are not thrombogenic, they do not require long-term anticoagulation and are resistant to subacute bacterial endocarditis.
- **Autografts/autologous valves**: The pulmonic valve and part of the pulmonic artery are excised to replace an aortic valve. Because this is the patient's own tissue, long-term anticoagulation is not necessary. A homograft may be done to replace the pulmonic valve, or the patient may be left without a pulmonic valve if pulmonic vascular pressures are normal. Autografts are used for children because they grow as the child grows and are also used for women of childbearing age, patients with history of peptic ulcer disease, and patients who cannot tolerate anticoagulation. Viability is 20 years or more.

Bicuspid Aortic Valve Disease

Bicuspid aortic valve disease results in a two-leaflet valve instead of three. Although this is a congenital disorder associated with a connective disease, patients may be asymptomatic until adulthood. Symptoms include increasing dyspnea, chest pain, exercise intolerance, dizziness, and heart failure because of valvular stenosis from calcium deposits. These issues prevent the valve from closing completely and allowing regurgitation, which causes left ventricular dilation. Up to 20% of patients also develop an aortic aneurysm. Diagnosis is per TEE, CT, MRI, ECG, and/or coronary angiography. **Treatment options** include:

- **Aortic valve repair**: A valvotomy/valvuloplasty may involve releasing valve leaflet adhesions interfering with functioning of the valve. In balloon valvuloplasty, a catheter with an inflatable balloon is positioned in the stenotic valve and inflated and deflated a number of times to dilate the opening. A replacement biological valve is then inserted.
- **Aortic valve replacement**: Indicated for severe symptomatic stenosis. This is an open-heart procedure with cardiopulmonary bypass or a transcatheter procedure in which the defective valve is replaced with mechanical (metal, plastic, or pyrolytic carbon) graft, biological (porcine or bovine xenografts) graft, or aortic homograph (donor's aorta with the aortic valve attached to replace the recipient's faulty aortic valve and part of the ascending aorta).

Aortic Valve Replacement

Aortic valve replacement is an open-heart procedure with cardiopulmonary bypass. Aortic valves are tricuspid (three leaflets), and repair is usually not possible, so defective valves must be replaced with either mechanical (i.e., metal, plastic, pyrolytic carbon) or biological (i.e., porcine, bovine xenografts). A newer procedure involves percutaneous aortic valve replacement with the bioprosthesis delivered arterially (femoral vein or artery) by a guidewire and under fluoroscopy.

- **Aortic homograft** uses part of a donor's aorta with the aortic valve attached to replace the recipient's faulty aortic valve and part of the ascending aorta.
- **Ross procedure** uses the patient's pulmonary artery with the pulmonary valve to replace the aortic valve and part of the aorta and then uses a donor graft to replace the pulmonary artery.

TAVR

Transcatheter aortic valve replacement (TAVR) is usually reserved for patients with advanced symptomatic stenosis of the aortic valve and who are unable to tolerate open-heart surgery or are at high risk with the procedure. Symptoms of aortic stenosis include chest pain, peripheral edema, dyspnea, fainting, weakness, and heart failure. With TAVR, patients generally receive a general anesthesia, and a catheter is inserted (most commonly transfemoral but alternatively transaortic or transapical). Two types of replacement valves are available in the US: a balloon expandable valve (Sapien XT) or a self-expanding valve (CoreValve). Once the catheter with a balloon device and the replacement valve attached are in place in the aortic valve, the balloon is inflated to secure the replacement valve, then the balloon is deflated, and the catheter is removed. With the self-expanding valve, the valve is attached to the catheter and expanded when it is in place in the stenotic valve and the catheter is removed.

Postoperative Management

Postoperative complications after aortic valve replacement include heart block and aortic regurgitation, which must be diligently managed.

Heart block	Manipulation and surgery near the conduction system may result in heart block, especially in patients with a history of conduction disorders or aortic regurgitation. Epicardial pacing is usually used for several days after surgery. If complete heart block does not abate after a few days, then a permanent dual chamber (DDD) pacemaker may be implanted.
Aortic regurgitation	Supraventricular rhythm should be maintained. Fluid may not improve filling pressures because of an enlarged left ventricle, but cardiac output should improve. Most patients require an α agent, such as phenylephrine (an α-adrenergic agonist) or norepinephrine, to maintain blood pressure, as patients usually remain vasodilated after surgery.

Mitral Valve Prolapse

Mitral valve prolapse is more common in women than men and is often asymptomatic; however, in rare cases it can deteriorate rapidly and result in sudden death. The cause is usually genetic, with enlargement of one or both leaflets, often with a dilated annulus and elongated chordae tendineae and papillary muscles. During systole, part of one or both leaflets balloons into the atrium. If the valve becomes stretched to the point it does not close during systole, blood regurgitates from the left ventricle back into the left atrium. Symptoms can include lightheadedness, fatigue, dyspnea, anxiety, dizziness, chest pain (unrelated to activity), and palpitations. Medical management includes eliminating smoking, caffeine, and alcohol. Antidysrhythmic medications, nitrates, calcium channel blockers, or β-blockers may be indicated, depending on the patient's symptoms. With advanced disease mitral valvuloplasty or replacement may be indicated.

Mitral Stenosis

Mitral stenosis is caused by an autoimmune response to rheumatic fever, leading to vegetative growths on the mitral valve. It can also be caused by infective endocarditis or lupus erythematosus. Over time, the leaflets thicken and calcify, and the commissures (junctions) fuse, decreasing the size of the valve opening. Mitral stenosis reduces the flow of blood from the left atrium to the left ventricle. Pressure in the left atrium increases to overcome resistance, resulting in enlargement of the left atrium and increased pressure in the pulmonary veins and capillaries of the lung. Symptoms of exertional dyspnea usually occur when the valve is 50% occluded. There are three mechanisms by which mitral stenosis causes pulmonary hypertension:

- Increased left atrial pressure, causing a backward increase in pressure of pulmonary veins
- Hypertrophy and pulmonary artery constriction, resulting from reactive left atrial and pulmonary venous hypertension
- Thrombotic/embolic damage to pulmonary vasculature

Treatment includes drugs to control arrhythmias and hypertension, balloon valvuloplasty, percutaneous mitral balloon valvotomy (commissurotomy), and mitral valve replacement.

Mitral Valve Regurgitation

Mitral valve regurgitation may occur with mitral stenosis or independently. It can result from damage caused by rheumatic fever, myxomatous degeneration caused by a genetic defect in the valvular collagen, infective endocarditis, collagen vascular disease (Marfan's syndrome), or cardiomyopathy. Hypertrophy and dilation of the left ventricle may cause displacement of the leaflets and dilation of the valve. Regurgitation occurs when the mitral valve fails to close completely, causing backflow into the left atrium from the left ventricle during systole, decreasing cardiac output. There are three phases:

- The **acute phase** may occur with rupture of a chordae tendineae or papillary muscle, causing sudden left ventricular flooding and overload.
- The **chronic compensated phase** results in enlargement of the left atrium to decrease filling pressure and hypertrophy of the left ventricle to maintain stroke volume and cardiac output.
- The **chronic decompensated phase** occurs when the left ventricle fails to compensate for the volume overload so that stroke volume and cardiac output decrease.

Postoperative Management of Mitral Valve Surgery

Patients with a history of pulmonary hypertension often develop right ventricular (RV) dysfunction, which is treated initially with fluid administration to improve preload; however, if central venous pressure of more than 20 mmHg does not improve, then further fluids should be avoided as this may lead to increasing dysfunction as well as left ventricular (LV) dysfunction, because the septum may shift. Inotropes are indicated to support both RV and LV function (e.g., milrinone, low-dose epinephrine, dobutamine). Nesiritide may be given to decrease pulmonary arterial pressure, and pulmonary vasodilators (e.g., inhaled nitric oxide, epoprostenol, iloprost) for severe RV dysfunction. LV outflow tract obstruction may occur in some patients with small left ventricles or septal hyperplasia and may require a return to surgery; however, some patients may respond to avoiding hypovolemia, increasing afterload, and treatment with catecholamines and β-blockers. Maintenance of sinus rhythm may require atrial or atrioventricular pacing for up to several days although long-term maintenance is unlikely with longstanding atrial fibrillation. Excess bloody drainage in a chest tube may indicate left ventricular rupture.

Mitral Stenosis Postoperative Management

Patients are at risk for low-cardiac output syndrome because of a small left ventricle, so filling pressure must be maintained. Pulmonary artery pressure usually falls after surgery, especially with vasodilators used during mechanical ventilation. Right ventricular dysfunction usually requires hemodynamic support more than left ventricular dysfunction. Ventilator failure is common because of pulmonary hypertension, fluid overload, and general poor condition. Diuresis, a plan for weaning, and nutritional support are necessary. Most patients are dependent on diuretics and may need them for several months to prevent edema.

Mitral Regurgitation Postoperative Management

Afterload mismatch may occur with underlying left ventricular dysfunction becoming evident because of the need for more stress on the ventricular wall to eject blood. This can lead to left ventricular failure. Reducing volume overload may alleviate symptoms. Inotropic and vasodilatory agents may be necessary. Large volumes of fluid are often required because of enlargement of the left atrium and ventricle.

Aortic Stenosis

Aortic stenosis is a stricture (narrowing) of the aortic valve that controls the flow of blood from the left ventricle, causing the left ventricular wall to thicken as it increases pressure to overcome the valvular resistance, increasing afterload and increasing the need for blood supply from the coronary arteries. This condition may result from a birth defect or childhood rheumatic fever and tends to worsen over the years as the heart grows.

Symptoms

The following are symptoms of aortic stenosis:

- Chest pain on exertion and intolerance of exercise
- Heart murmur
- Hypotension on exertion that may be associated with sudden fainting
- Sudden death
- Tachycardia with faint pulse
- Poor appetite
- Increased risk for bacterial endocarditis and coronary insufficiency
- Increases mitral regurgitation and secondary pulmonary hypertension

Treatment

The following are treatments of aortic stenosis:

- Balloon valvuloplasty to dilate valve non-surgically
- Surgical repair of valve or replacement of valve, depending on the extent of stricture
- Percutaneous aortic valve replacement (tri-leaflet bioprosthesis derived from equine pericardium)

Postoperative Management for Aortic Stenosis Surgery

Postoperative management of aortic stenosis is explained below:

- Hemodynamic status must be monitored carefully as it may deteriorate within 24 hours of surgery, requiring cardioversion for atrial fibrillation. If sinus rhythm is not present, atrioventricular pacing is indicated to maintain a heart rate of 90–100 bpm with left ventricular hypertrophy.

- Preload should be maintained (pulmonary capillary wedge pressure >20 mmHg) so that the left ventricle fills adequately.
- Hypertension is common within a few hours, but vasodilators may cause tachycardia with hyperdynamic cardiac status; a β-blocker (e.g., esmolol) may be effective.
- With hypertrophy and a hyperdynamic left ventricle, filling pressure may increase along with decreased stroke volume and cardiac output. This is usually treated with volume infusions, but inotropes should be avoided, although milrinone or nesiritide may be used.

Aortic Regurgitation

Aortic regurgitation occurs when the aortic valve fails to close properly or remain closed, resulting in reflux of blood from the aorta into the left ventricle during diastole. Causes include infective or rheumatic endocarditis, syphilis, dissecting aneurysm, congenital abnormalities, or blunt trauma. To compensate, reflex vasodilation occurs with reduced systemic vascular resistance and diastolic blood pressure. Patients exhibit low cardiac output and increased heart rate with widened pulse pressure (a characteristic sign). Patients may remain asymptomatic initially or complain of a forceful heartbeat, noted in the head or neck, with arterial pulsation palpable in the carotid or temporal arteries. Over time patients develop signs of left ventricular heart failure, including orthopnea and paroxysmal nocturnal dyspnea. Patients are treated initially with a vasodilator, such as calcium channel blockers and angiotensin-converting enzyme inhibitors, but the treatment of choice is valvuloplasty or valve replacement. Postoperatively, patients may require vasodilators and inotropic agents (e.g., milrinone, dobutamine). The intra-aortic balloon pump may also be used postoperatively to maintain adequate hemodynamic status.

Pulmonic Stenosis

Pulmonic stenosis is a stricture of the pulmonic valve that controls the flow of blood from the right ventricle to the lungs, resulting in right ventricular hypertrophy as the pressure increases in the right ventricle and decreased pulmonary blood flow. The condition may be asymptomatic, or symptoms may not be evident until adulthood, depending on the severity of the defect. Pulmonic stenosis may be associated with a number of other heart defects.

Symptoms

The following are symptoms of pulmonic stenosis:

- Loud heart murmur
- Congestive heart murmur
- Mild cyanosis
- Cardiomegaly
- Angina
- Dyspnea
- Fainting
- Increased risk of bacterial endocarditis

Treatment

The following are treatments of pulmonic stenosis:

- Balloon valvuloplasty to separate the cusps of the valve for children.
- Surgical repair, including the cardiopulmonary bypass pulmonary valvotomy for older children and adults

Tricuspid Valve Regurgitation and Stenosis

The tricuspid valve separates the right atrium and right ventricle and maintains the forward flow of blood to the right ventricle:

- **Regurgitation** may result from congenital abnormalities, infective diseases (e.g., rheumatic fever, endocarditis), toxic reactions, and trauma. It also may occur secondary to pulmonary hypertension, mitral valve disease (most common), aortic valve disease, or left heart failure. Symptoms include weakness, fatigue, peripheral edema, abnormal venous pulsations, and atrial fibrillation.
- **Stenosis** may result from rheumatic heart disease, tumors, or endocarditis. Symptoms include peripheral venous distention, low cardiac output, fatigue, and general malaise.

Surgical repair (e.g., annuloplasty, replacement) for regurgitation is usually done in conjunction with mitral valve repair. For stenosis, procedures can include open or closed commissurotomy and open valvuloplasty. However, regurgitation often develops after surgical repair.

Anticoagulation Therapy with Heart Valve Repair or Replacement

Anticoagulation therapy is indicated indefinitely for patients undergoing valve repair or replacement. Warfarin is given for the following time periods, usually with aspirin given indefinitely:

Procedure	Duration	INR Goal	Additional Medications
Aortic valve replacement (tissue)	3 months	2-3	If risk factors present or aspirin, 75–100 mg, alone if no risk factors
Aortic valve replacement (mechanical)	Indefinitely	2-3	Along with aspirin, 75–100 mg
Mitral valve repair	3 months	2-3	OR aspirin, 75–100 mg
Mitral valve replacement (tissue)	3 months	2-3	Followed by aspirin, 85–100 mg, or indefinitely with aspirin if risk factors present; with no risk factors, may be treated with aspirin alone
Mitral valve replacement (mechanical)	Indefinitely	2.5-3.5	With aspirin, 75–100 mg
Aortic and mitral valve replacements (tissue)	3months	2-3	Followed by aspirin, 325 mg
Aortic and mitral valve replacements (mechanical)	Indefinitely	2.5-3.5	Along with aspirin, 75-100 mg

Heart Transplantation

Heart transplantation is similar to other open-heart procedures in that cardiopulmonary bypass is needed during the procedure. The sternotomy and thymectomy are performed, and then the pericardial sac is opened to expose the heart. If the donor heart is larger than the recipient's, the left pericardium, sparing the phrenic nerve, may be removed.

- In **orthotopic transplantation**, the most commonly used, the posterior portion of the left atrium is left for attachment of the new heart, but the rest of the heart is excised. The donor heart is trimmed and sutured to fit with the remnants of the old heart. If there are a number of structural anomalies, such as transposition of the great vessels, then reconstruction of vessels may be needed during the procedure. Once the new heart is in place, the heart is taken off bypass and is stimulated to begin contractions.
- In **heterotopic transplantation** (rare), the new heart is sutured to the old heart, joining the chambers and creating a double heart.

Postoperative Management

Postoperative management of heart transplant patients is similar to that of other cardiac surgeries. Treatments include the following:

- Mechanical ventilation is used initially, but respiratory care with adequate ventilation must be monitored constantly, especially if the donor heart was larger than the native heart, resulting in compression of the lungs.
- Intravenous fluids and various medications, such as sedation and vasodilators, are administered.
- Antithymocyte globulin, azathioprine, cyclosporine, or tacrolimus may be used for immunosuppression as well as corticosteroids (methylprednisolone). Intravenous immunosuppressive drugs are given after surgery, but these are switched to oral medications as soon as possible. Protocols are established at each institution and may vary. Medication doses are age dependent.

The risk for rejection is the greatest in the first few months and close follow-up is necessary with routine laboratory tests, including echocardiograms, chest x-rays, and blood tests.

Percutaneous Coronary Interventions for Coronary Artery Disease

Percutaneous transluminal coronary angioplasty (PTCA) is an option for patients who are poor surgical candidates, who have an acute myocardial infarction, or who have uncontrolled chest pain. This procedure is usually only done to increase circulation to the myocardium by breaking through an atheroma if there is collateral circulation. Cardiac catheterization is done with a hollow catheter (sheath), usually inserted into the femoral vein or artery and fed through the vessels to the coronary arteries. When the atheroma is verified by fluoroscopy, a balloon-tipped catheter is fed over the sheath, and the balloon is inflated with a contrast agent to a specified pressure to compress the atheroma. The balloon may be inflated a number of times to ensure that residual stenosis is less than 20%. Laser angioplasty using the excimer laser is also used to vaporize plaque. **Stents** may be inserted during the angioplasty to maintain patency. Stents may be flexible plastic or wire mesh and are typically placed over the catheter, which is inflated to expand the stent against the arterial wall.

Complications of Cardiac Catheterization and PTCA

Cardiac catheterization and percutaneous transluminal coronary angioplasty (PTCA) pose the risk of both intraoperative and postoperative complications. During the procedure, there is a risk of damage to both the coronary artery and the heart itself. The artery may dissect, perforate, or constrict with vasospasm. A myocardial infarction may occur when a clot dislodges. Ventricular tachycardia or cardiac arrest may occur. These complications may require immediate surgical repair. Postoperative complications of cardiac catheterization and PTCA include:

- **Hemorrhage or hematoma** at the sheath insertion site may require pressure. The head of the bed should be flat to relieve pressure.
- **Thrombus or embolus** may require further surgery, anticoagulation/thrombolytic treatment, or both.
- **Arteriovenous fistula or pseudoaneurysm** from vessel trauma usually requires compression with ultrasound and surgical repair.
- **Retroperitoneal bleeding** from an arterial tear may cause back or flank pain and may require discontinuation of anticoagulants, intravenous fluids, or blood transfusions.
- **Failure of angioplasty** may require a repeat procedure or other surgical intervention.

Transmyocardial Laser Revascularization

Transmyocardial laser revascularization is used to treat heart disease not responsive to other surgical measures and may be done percutaneously or through a surgical procedure with a midsternal or thoracotomy incision. Percutaneously, a fiberoptic catheter is positioned inside the ventricle and against the ischemic area. Laser bursts are used to cut 20–40 channels into the myocardium but not through it. The laser burns create channels and stimulate an inflammatory response, which causes new blood vessels to form (angiogenesis), improving circulation to the myocardium and reducing ischemia and pain. If the procedure is done surgically, the catheter tip is positioned on the outside of the left ventricle rather than the inside while the heart is beating without bypass. While studies indicate that these do not affect mortality, they do reduce symptoms and increase tolerance to activity, improving the quality of life. Postoperative care for the percutaneous procedure is the same as for percutaneous transluminal coronary angioplasty, while care for the surgical procedure is similar to that of coronary artery bypass graft.

DCA, Rotational Atherectomy, and Transluminal Extraction

Directional coronary atherectomy (DCA) is removal of an atheroma from an occluded coronary artery. This procedure may be more effective than angioplasty because instead of compressing an atheroma, it shaves it away. Sometimes angioplasty is the first step in DCA if the vessel is too narrow for the DCA catheter and the last step if the tissue needs smoothing. The DCA catheter is a large balloon catheter that is usually inserted over a sheath through the femoral artery. The catheter includes an open window on one side of the balloon with a rotational cutting piston that shaves the atheroma with the plaque residue pushed inside the device for removal. The procedure may require 4–20 cuts, depending on the extent of the plaque. A similar procedure is **rotational atherectomy**, which uses a catheter with a diamond-chip drill at the tip, rotating at 130,000–180,000 rpm, pulverizing the atheroma into microparticles. A **transluminal extraction** catheter uses a motorized cutting head with a suction device for residue.

Postoperative Removal of Lines and Tubes

Postoperative removal of lines and tubes are indicated based on patient condition:

- **Swan-Ganz catheter**: When the patient is stabilized to the point of not needing inotropes and vasodilators, the Swan-Ganz catheter is removed.
- **Central lines**: Central lines are removed when they are no longer needed for monitoring.
- **Arterial lines**: Arterial lines are removed after extubation, and a stable arterial blood gas (ABG) is reached. A subsequent ABG after a period on room air must also be obtained. Lines should not be maintained solely for blood sampling.
- **Left atrial line**: The left atrial line is removed before chest tubes are removed in case intrapericardial bleeding occurs when the line is removed.
- **Chest tubes**: Chest tubes are removed when drainage is less than 100 mL per 8 hr. Suction should be turned off before removal of mediastinal tubes. Chest x-ray is done after removal of pleural chest tubes to evaluate for pneumothorax.
- **Pleural drain (lateral chest wall)**: A pleural drain is removed 3–5 days after surgery.
- **Urinary catheter**: When the patient is no longer receiving pronounced diuresis, does not have a risk of urinary retention, and is mobile (usually at the beginning of day 2), the urinary catheter is removed.

Thoracic Surgical Procedures

DeBakey Classification for Dissecting Aortic Aneurysms

A dissecting aortic aneurysm occurs when the wall of the aorta is torn and blood flows between the layers of the wall, dilating and weakening it until it risks rupture (which has a 90% mortality).

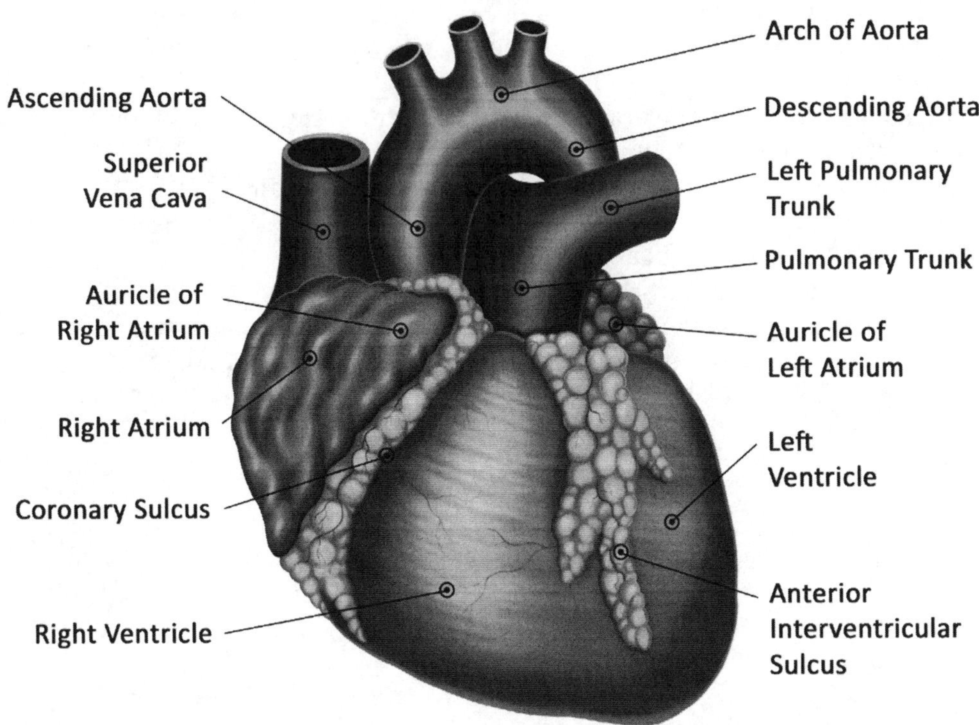

Aortic aneurysms are more than twice as common in men as women, but women have a higher mortality rate, possibly because they are often older. Different classification systems are used to describe the type and degree of dissection. **DeBakey classification** uses anatomic location as the focal point:

- **Type I** begins in the ascending aorta but may spread to include the aortic arch and the descending aorta (60%). This is also considered a proximal lesion or Stanford type A.
- **Type II** is restricted to the ascending aorta (10–15%). This is also considered a proximal lesion or Stanford type A.
- **Type III** is restricted to the descending aorta (25–30%). This is considered a distal lesion or Stanford type B.
- Types I and II are thoracic, and type III is abdominal.

Thoracic Aortic Aneurysms

Thoracic aortic aneurysms are usually related to atherosclerosis but may also result from Marfan syndrome, Ehlers-Danlos disease, and connective tissue disorders. The aneurysms are often asymptomatic but may cause substernal pain, back pain, dyspnea or stridor (from pressure on the trachea), dysphagia, cough, distention of neck veins, and edema of neck and arms. Rupture usually does not allow time for emergent repair, so identifying and correcting before rupture are essential. Diagnosis is often made with x-ray or computed tomography. Cardiac catheterization and echocardiogram may also be needed. Surgery is indicated for aneurysms 6 cm or larger. Endovascular grafting is routinely done for aneurysms of the descending thoracic aorta. There is a 4% occurrence of paraplegia with thoracic aorta aneurysm repair and an increased risk of stroke.

Aneurysms of the Ascending Aorta

Aneurysms of the ascending aorta may result from congenital abnormalities in otherwise healthy individuals or in elderly patients with a history of hypertension, chronic lung disease, and generalized atherosclerosis. Different procedures are used, depending on which part of the ascending aorta or arch is involved. Some are repaired with an aortic cross-clamp in place with cardiopulmonary bypass and mild hypothermia, and others are cannulated for bypass (femoral or axillary artery). If extended periods of deep hypothermic circulatory arrest are required, neuroprotective procedures that increase cerebral blood flow may be used, such as selective antegrade cerebral perfusion or retrograde cerebral perfusion. Postoperative hypertension must be controlled, and neurologic status must be monitored. Prolonged hypothermia may result in an extended period (24 hours) of neurologic recovery. Patients usually require a temperature-controlling device postoperatively as temperature may fall. Coagulopathies and bleeding must be treated aggressively.

Surgical Procedures for Aortic Dissections and Aneurysms

Type A dissection	Resuspension or replacement of the aortic valve, resection of a tear, and insertion of an interposition graft. Elephant trunk Dacron graft is inserted if the dissection occurs across the arch. Surgery utilizes deep hypothermic circulatory arrest (DHCA), but the aortic cross-clamping is not required.
Type B dissection	Classic approach: Resection of the tear and insertion of a graft Newer approach: Insertion of an endovascular stent Measures are required to reduce spinal cord ischemia.
Ascending arch aneurysm repair	Procedures include insertion of supracoronary interposition graft or valved conduit (Bentall procedure). Aortic-valve sparing procedure is indicated for some patients (Marfan syndrome or bicuspid valves). Cardiopulmonary bypass is required. Simple cross-clamping and DHCA (central core temperature to 20-25 °C) is sometimes necessary; retrograde or antegrade cerebral perfusion should be used with DHCA.
Transverse arch aneurysm repair	May include a hemiarch repair with deep hypothermic circulatory arrest (DHCA) with retrograde or antegrade cerebral perfusion, interposition graft, individual trifurcation grafts. The distal arch per left thoracotomy is done without cardiopulmonary bypass (CPB) or with CPB and DHCA.
Descending thoracic aneurysm repair	Graft replacement of the damaged aorta and reimplantation of the intercostal vessels (T8–T12) with large aneurysms per left thoracotomy. Aortic cross-clamping is used for traditional approaches. Cardiopulmonary bypass is required. Methods to prevent spinal cord ischemia and ischemia with aortic cross-clamping include medications, cerebral spinal fluid drainage, shunting, left-heart bypass alone, and femoro-femoral bypass, sometimes with DHCA if aortic clamping not possible. Aortic cross-clamping is not necessary with thoracic endovascular aortic repair.

Postoperative Care of Type A Aortic Dissections

The primary treatment for type A aortic dissections of the ascending aorta is surgical repair, although patients may later develop a distal aneurysm. Postoperatively, incisional bleeding is common, so status must be monitored carefully. Hypertension must be strictly controlled by antihypertensive medications to reduce blood pressure and the force of contractions, including intravenous β-blockers (esmolol, metoprolol, labetalol) with or without nitroprusside. When converted to oral medications, calcium channel blockers or angiotensin-converting enzyme inhibitors may be added. β-blockers reduce the risk of developing further aneurysm. Because deep hypothermic circulatory arrest is required for surgery, patients must be monitored carefully for neurological impairment or stroke. Blood products should be used early if there is excessive bleeding or if coagulopathy is suspected.

Postoperative Care for Descending Thoracic Aortic Aneurysms

Repair of a descending thoracic aortic aneurysm may result in a number of complications. Excessive blood loss often requires multiple transfusions that, in turn, cause coagulopathy that requires multiple blood components and sometimes a return to surgery. Patients experience significant pain, and some require tracheostomy for prolonged mechanical ventilation. A cerebrospinal fluid (CSF) drain is placed during surgery and left in place for about 72 hours to maintain a CSF pressure of 10 mmHg or less. The mean arterial pressure is maintained at 90 mmHg to prevent spinal ischemia and paraplegia even though this may increase bleeding. Paraplegia may occur several days after surgery, usually because of a fall in blood pressure (BP), so treatment includes increasing BP, high-dose steroids, and replacing the CSF drain if it was removed. About 10–15% of patients may experience renal failure as a result of impaired renal perfusion with cross-clamping of the aorta, so renal status must be carefully monitored.

Surgical Options for Esophageal Cancer

Surgical options for esophageal cancer include:

- **Esophagectomy (en bloc)**: Abdominal, chest, and neck incisions are made and the esophagus, lymph nodes, and part of the stomach are removed. The remaining stomach is moved upward, and the parts are reconnected.
- **Transthoracic esophagectomy**: The cancerous part of the esophagus and the proximal stomach are removed. A colonic graft may be used to replace the esophagus or the remaining parts reconnected.
- **Transhiatal esophagectomy**: An incision is made from the sternum to the naval and in the left neck. The esophagus is removed, the stomach is moved upward, and the remaining are parts reconnected.
- **Endoscopic mucosal resection (EMR)**: Used primarily for superficial esophageal cancer in the early stages (≤1.5 cm). Involves suctioning the lesion into a cap, snaring, and using electrocautery to remove the lesion. Larger lesions are removed through repetitive snaring.
- **Endoscopic submucosal dissection**: Used for larger superficial lesions. The periphery of the lesion is marked with cautery, and electrocautery is then used to carefully remove the lesion.

Surgical Options for Lung Cancer

Surgical options for lung cancer include open thoracotomy, video-assisted thoracic surgery (VATS) with a thoracoscope (minimally-invasive procedure), and robotic-assisted thoracic surgery (also minimally-invasive). The types of resections that are carried out include:

- **Wedge resection**: A small wedge-shaped area of cancerous tissue is removed. This procedure may be used to remove small tumors, metastatic lesions, or non-malignant lesions. Recurrence rates tend to be higher than with segmentectomy.
- **Segmentectomy**: A segment of a lobe is removed. Lobes have 2-5 segments. This procedure is preferred over lobectomy for patients with limited lung reserves (such as from COPD).
- **Lobectomy**: An entire lobe of a lung is removed. The right lung contains 3 lobes and the left, 2. This is usually primary treatment when a tumor is limited to one lobe.
- **Pneumonectomy**: An entire lung is removed, usually with more extensive cancerous lesions or if a lesion is located medially and difficult to otherwise access and remove.

Complications

Cardiovascular

Cardiogenic Shock

Cardiogenic shock in adults is most often secondary to myocardial infarction damage that reduces the contractility of the ventricles, interfering with the pumping mechanism of the heart and decreasing oxygen perfusion. Cardiogenic shock may occur as a postoperative complication. Cardiogenic shock has three characteristics: **increased preload**, **increased afterload**, and **decreased contractility**. Together these result in decreased cardiac output and an increase in systemic vascular resistance to compensate and protect vital organs. This results in an increase of afterload in the left ventricle with an increased need for oxygen. As the cardiac output continues to decrease, tissue perfusion decreases, coronary artery perfusion decreases, fluid backs up, and the left ventricle fails to pump the blood adequately, resulting in pulmonary edema and right ventricular failure.

Symptoms and Treatment

The following are **symptoms** of cardiogenic shock:

- Hypotension with systolic blood pressure less than 90 mmHg
- Tachycardia over 100 bpm with a weak thready pulse and dysrhythmias
- Decreased heart sounds
- Chest pain
- Tachypnea and basilar rales
- Cool, moist skin, and pallor

The following are **treatments** of cardiogenic shock:

- Intravenous fluids
- Inotropic agents
- Antidysrhythmic medications
- Intra-aortic balloon pump or left ventricular assist device

Postoperative Diuresis/Hypotension in the Cardiopulmonary Bypass Patient

Diuresis in the cardiac postoperative period may result in the production of copious quantities of urine, causing lowered filling pressures, decreased cardiac output, and hypotension. Cardiopulmonary bypass often results in relative diuresis of 200–400 mL/hr because of hemodilution and drugs that affect osmosis, so urinary output is not a good indication of perfusion in the first few hours after surgery. Identifying the cause of diuresis is important to provide compensatory treatment when needed. Causes and interventions may include:

- If caused by vasoactive drugs, such as nesiritide, fenoldopam, or dopamine (provided during surgery to promote renal function), it may be necessary to change medications to low-dose epinephrine, milrinone, or dobutamine.
- If caused by furosemide, which is provided during surgery, increased fluids may be required.

- If caused by mannitol, which is provided during surgery, increased fluids may be required.
- If caused by hyperglycemia, blood glucose should be maintained at less than 180 mg/dL.
- If it is a response to hemodilution and increased interstitial fluid or crystalloid and colloid administration, care must be taken to avoid excess colloid, which can produce hemodilution.

Post-Cardiovascular Surgery Hypertension

Hypertension in the post-cardiovascular surgery patient may result from anxiety and pain, intolerance of the ETT, inadequate sedation, or hypercarbia. Some medications, such as vasopressors, may cause hypertension, especially if the dosage is too high. Patients who are post aortic valve repair or replacement for aortic stenosis are at increased risk of postoperative hypertension because of the sudden improvement in blood flow combined with the hypertrophy of the left ventricle that usually results from aortic stenosis. Those who are post coronary bypass surgery are also at increased risk. Complications associated with hypertension include myocardial ischemia, cardiac arrhythmias, aortic dissection, stroke, hypertensive crises, dislodgement of the graft, and bleeding. Patients who develop hypertension are at increased risk of prolonged hospitalization and mortality. Treatment will vary depending on the patient's general condition and the type of surgery but may include increasing the dosage of pre-surgical antihypertensives, administration of an ARB (such as irbesartan), an ace inhibitor (such as lisinopril), a calcium channel blocker (such as clevidipine or nicardipine), a beta-blocker (such as labetalol), or nitroglycerine.

Postoperative Angina and Myocardial Infarctions

Angina

Impairment of blood flow through the coronary arteries leads to ischemia of the cardiac muscle and **angina pectoris**, pain that may occur in the sternum, chest, neck, arms (especially the left), or back. Crushing substernal pain frequently occurs, radiating down the left arm or both arms, although this type of pain is more common in men than women, whose symptoms may appear less acute and include nausea, shortness of breath, and fatigue. Elderly or diabetic patients may also have pain in the arms, no pain at all (silent ischemia), or weakness and numbness in the arms.

Stable Angina

Stable angina episodes usually last for less than 5 minutes and are fairly predictable exercise-induced episodes caused by atherosclerotic lesions blocking 75% or more of the lumen of the affected coronary artery. Precipitating events include exercise, decrease in environmental temperature, heavy eating, strong emotions (e.g., fright, anger), or exertion, including coitus. **Stable angina** episodes usually resolve in less than 5 minutes by decreasing activity level and administering sublingual nitroglycerin.

Unstable and Variant Angina

Unstable angina (also known as preinfarction or crescendo angina) is a progression of coronary artery disease and occurs when there is a change in the pattern of stable angina. The pain may increase, may not respond to a single nitroglycerin, and may persist for 5 minutes or more. Usually pain is more frequent, lasts longer, and may occur at rest. Unstable angina may indicate rupture of an atherosclerotic plaque and the beginning of thrombus formation so it should always be treated as a medical emergency as it may indicate a myocardial infarction.

Variant angina (also known as Prinzmetal's angina) results from spasms of the coronary arteries, can be associated with or without atherosclerotic plaques, and is often related to smoking, alcohol, or illicit stimulants. Elevation of ST segments usually occurs with variant angina. Variant angina frequently occurs cyclically at the same time each day and often while the person is at rest. Nitroglycerin or calcium channel blockers are used for treatment.

Myocardial Infarctions

Myocardial infarctions (MIs) are classified according to their location and the extent of injury. MI most frequently damages the left ventricle and the septum, but the right ventricle may be damaged, depending upon the damaged area:

- **Anterior wall infarction** occurs with occlusion in the proximal left anterior descending artery and may damage the left ventricle.
- **Left lateral wall infarction** occurs with occlusion of the circumflex coronary artery, often causing damage to anterior wall as well.
- **Inferior wall infarction** occurs with occlusion of the right coronary artery and causes conduction malfunctions.
- **Right ventricular infarction** occurs with occlusion of the proximal section of the right coronary artery and damages the right ventricle and the inferior wall.
- **Posterior wall infarction** occurs with occlusion in the right coronary artery or circumflex artery and may be difficult to diagnose.

Review Video: Myocardial Infarctions
Visit mometrix.com/academy and enter code: 148923

Non–ST-Segment Elevation Myocardial Infarction (NSTEMI)

ST elevation on the electrocardiogram (ECG) occurs in response to myocardial damage resulting from infarction or severe ischemia. The absence of ST elevation may be diagnosed as unstable angina or NSTEMI, but cardiac enzyme levels increase with NSTEMI, indicating partial blockage of coronary arteries with some damage. Symptoms are consistent with unstable angina, with chest pain or tightness, pain radiating to the neck or arm, dyspnea, anxiety, weakness, dizziness, nausea, vomiting, and feelings of heartburn. Initial treatment may include nitroglycerin, β-blockers, antiplatelet agents, or antithrombotic agents. Ongoing treatment may include β-blockers, aspirin, statins, angiotensin-converting enzyme inhibitors, angiotensin-receptor blockers, and clopidogrel. Percutaneous coronary intervention is not recommended.

ST-Segment Elevation MI (STEMI)

This more severe type of MI involves complete blockage of one or more coronary arteries with myocardial damage, resulting in ST elevation. Symptoms are those of acute MI. As necrosis occurs, Q waves often develop, indicating irreversible myocardial damage, which may result in death, so treatment involves immediate reperfusion before necrosis can occur.

Q-Wave and Non–Q-Wave MIs

Myocardial infarctions (MIs), formerly classified as transmural or nontransmural, are currently classified as Q-wave or non–Q-wave or ST-segment elevation MI (STEMI) or non–ST-segment elevation MI (NSTEMI).

Q-wave (STEMI)	Non–Q-wave (NSTEMI)
• Q-wave MI is characterized by a series of abnormal Q waves (wider and deeper) on electrocardiogram (ECG), especially in the early morning, related to adrenergic activity and ST-segment elevation. • Infarction is usually prolonged and results in necrosis. • Coronary occlusion is complete in 80–90%. • Q-wave MI is often, but not always, transmural. • Peak creatine kinase (CK) levels occur in about 27 hours. • Mortality rates are about 10%.	• Non–Q-wave MI is characterized by changes in the ST-T wave with ST depression (usually reversible). • Usually reperfusion occurs spontaneously, so infarct size is smaller. Contraction necrosis related to reperfusion is common. • Non–Q-wave MI is usually nontransmural. • Coronary occlusion is complete in only 20–30%. • Peak CK levels occur in 12–13 hours. • Mortality rates are about 2–3%. • Reinfarction is common, so 2-year survival rates are similar to Q-wave MI.

Clinical Manifestations of MI

Clinical manifestations of myocardial infarction (MI) may vary considerably, with men presenting with the "classic" symptom of sudden onset of crushing chest pain and women and those under 55 presenting with atypical symptoms. Diabetic patients may have a reduced sensation of pain because of neuropathy and may complain primarily of weakness. Elderly patients may also have neuropathic changes that reduce the sensation of pain. More than half of all patients present with acute MIs with no prior symptoms of cardiovascular disease. **Symptoms** may include the following:

- Angina with chest pain that may radiate to neck or arms
- Palpitations
- Hypertension or hypotension
- Changes on the electrocardiogram, such as ST-segment and T-wave changes, tachycardia, bradycardia, and dysrhythmias
- Dyspnea
- Pulmonary edema and dependent edema
- Nausea and vomiting
- Decreased urinary output
- Pallor, cold and clammy skin, and diaphoresis
- Neurological or psychological disturbances, such as anxiety, light-headedness, headache, visual abnormalities, slurred speech, and fear

Abnormal Pulsus Paradoxus

Pulsus paradoxus is a systolic blood pressure that is markedly lower during inhalation than exhalation. Pulsus paradoxus with a 10 mmHg or more difference is considered abnormal and is a common sign of cardiac tamponade. A decrease in blood pressure by 10 mmHg or less during inspiration is a normal finding, but an increased pressure difference may indicate a number of cardiopulmonary complications, including pericardial effusion, pericarditis, pulmonary embolism, cardiogenic shock, chronic obstructive pulmonary disease, asthma, and obstruction of the superior vena cava. Blood pressure should be reevaluated if pulsus paradoxus is found to ensure correct readings. Pulsus paradoxus is evaluated by finding the first systolic reading during exhalation and then decreasing blood pressure cuff readings until the systolic pressure can be heard during both cycles. A difference between the exhalation-only systolic reading and the inhalation–exhalation reading of 10 mmHg or more is positive for pulsus paradoxus.

Myocardial Stunning and Myocardial Hibernation

Myocardial stunning is a period of left ventricular (LV) dysfunction occurring with reperfusion after a period (5–20 minutes) of myocardial ischemia or infarction that is too short to result in necrosis. Stunning may result from cardiopulmonary bypass or cardiac arrest. Myocardial stunning is characterized by decreased contractility, decreased tissue perfusion, and decreased levels of tissue adenine nucleotide, although coronary blood flow is normal. Symptoms usually subside over a few hours or days. The heart does not show permanent changes or adaptation due to the temporary lack of adequate perfusion.

Myocardial hibernation is LV dysfunction, resulting from chronic ischemia, such as with chronic coronary disease, myocardial infarction, and heart failure. The heart adapts to the lack of adequate perfusion over time. Restoration of blood flow reverses the symptoms; however, if revascularization does not occur, permanent fibrotic changes and dysfunction can lead to congestive heart failure.

Caring for an Open Chest Wound from the Operating Room

A cardiac surgery patient may return from the operating room with an **open chest wound** if an infection, such as severe mediastinitis, occurred that required debridement of tissue, leaving the wound open to heal by secondary intention. The wound may contain packing and be covered with a sterile dressing that should be changed at least every 24 hours. An open wound increases the risk of further infection, so the patient is placed on broad-spectrum antibiotics and monitored carefully. In most cases, patients are kept intubated and sedated to prevent movement until the wound can be covered with a muscle flap. Vacuum-assisted closure (negative pressure) may be used. Episodes of ischemia during surgery may cause myocardia or pulmonary edema that prevents closure of the chest wound because compression may cause cardiac tamponade. The sternum is left open until the edema subsides. A protective rubber dam is placed over the sternal opening and sutured to the skin. The dam is covered with gauze saturated in povidone-iodine and a sterile bandage.

Postoperative Dysrhythmias

Cardiac Dysrhythmias

Cardiac dysrhythmias, abnormal heart beats, in adults are frequently the result of damage to the conduction system during major cardiac surgery or as the result of a myocardial infarction:

- **Bradydysrhythmias** are pulse rates that are abnormally slow.
  - Complete atrioventricular block may be congenital or a response to surgical trauma.
  - Sinus bradycardia may be caused by the autonomic nervous system or a response to hypotension and a decrease in oxygenation.
  - Junctional/nodal rhythms often occur in postsurgical patients when the absence of the P wave is noted, but heart rate and output usually remain stable; unless there is compromise, no treatment is necessary.
- **Tachydysrhythmias** are pulse rates that are abnormally fast.
  - Sinus tachycardia is often caused by illness, such as fever or infection.
  - Supraventricular tachycardia (200–300 bpm) may have a sudden onset and result in congestive heart failure.
- **Conduction irregularities** are irregular pulses that often occur postoperatively and are usually not significant.
  - Premature contractions may arise from the atria or ventricles.

Sinus Bradycardia

Sinus bradycardia (SB) is caused by a decreased rate of impulse from the sinus node. The pulse and electrocardiogram usually appear normal except for a slower rate.

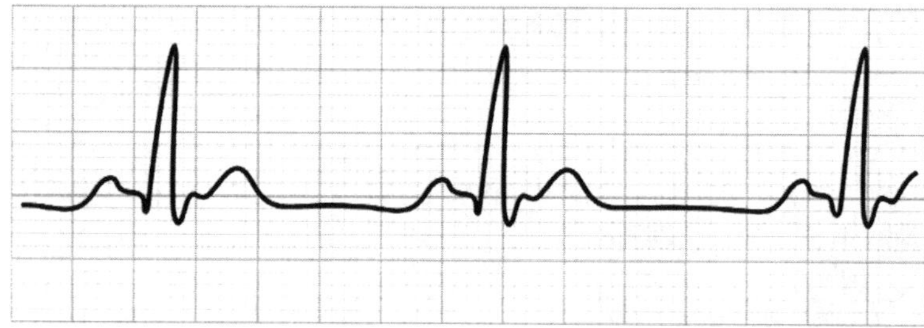

SB is characterized by a regular pulse less than 50–60 bpm with P waves in front of each QRS, which are usually normal in shape and duration. The PR interval is 0.12–0.20 seconds, the QRS interval is 0.04–0.11 seconds, and the P:QRS ratio is 1:1.

A number of factors may cause SB:

- Conditions that lower the body's metabolic needs, such as hypothermia or sleep
- Hypotension and a decrease in oxygenation
- Medications, such as calcium channel blockers and β-blockers
- Vagal stimulation that may result from vomiting, suctioning, or defecating
- Increased intracranial pressure
- Myocardial infarction

Treatment involves eliminating the cause, if possible, such as changing medications. Atropine, 0.5–1.0 mg, may be given intravenously to block vagal stimulation. Postoperatively, a pacemaker is inserted for atrial or atrioventricular pacing as well as catecholamine infusion.

Sinus Tachycardia

Sinus tachycardia (ST) occurs when the sinus node impulse increases in frequency. ST is characterized by a regular pulse over 100 bpm with P waves before each QRS but sometimes part of the preceding T wave. QRS is usually of normal shape and duration (0.04–0.11 seconds) but may have consistent irregularity. The PR interval is 0.12–0.20 seconds, and the P:QRS ratio is 1:1. The rapid pulse decreases diastolic filling time and causes reduced cardiac output with resultant hypotension. Acute pulmonary edema may result from the decreased ventricular filling if untreated.

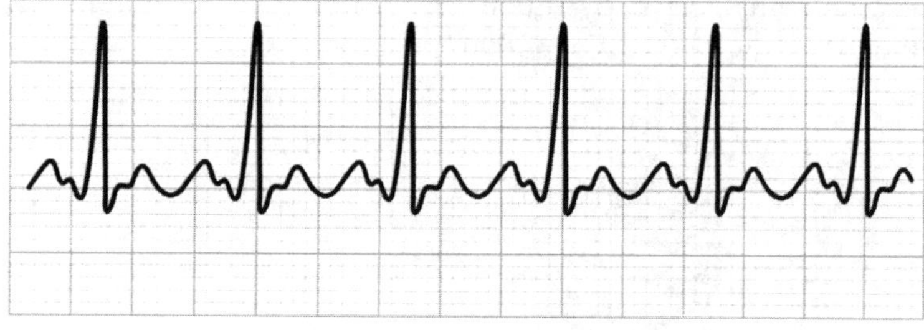

ST may be caused by a number of factors:

- Acute blood loss, shock, hypovolemia, and anemia
- Sinus arrhythmia and hypovolemic heart failure
- Hypermetabolic conditions, fever, and infection
- Exertion, exercise, and anxiety
- Medications, such as sympathomimetic drugs

Treatment includes eliminating precipitating factors. With normal left ventricular function, treatment is usually not necessary. Calcium channel blockers and β-blockers may be used to reduce heart rate.

Supraventricular Tachycardia

Supraventricular tachycardia (SVT) (>100 bpm) may have a sudden onset and result in congestive heart failure. Heart rate may increase to 200–300 bpm. SVT originates in the atria rather than the ventricles but is controlled by the tissue in the area of the atrioventricular node rather than the sinoatrial node. Rhythm is usually rapid but regular. The P wave is present but may not be clearly defined, as it may be obscured by the preceding T wave. The QRS complex appears normal. The PR interval is 0.12–0.20 seconds, and the QRS interval is 0.04–0.11 seconds with a P:QRS ratio of 1:1. SVT may be episodic with periods of normal heart rate and rhythm between episodes of SVT, so it is often referred to as paroxysmal SVT.

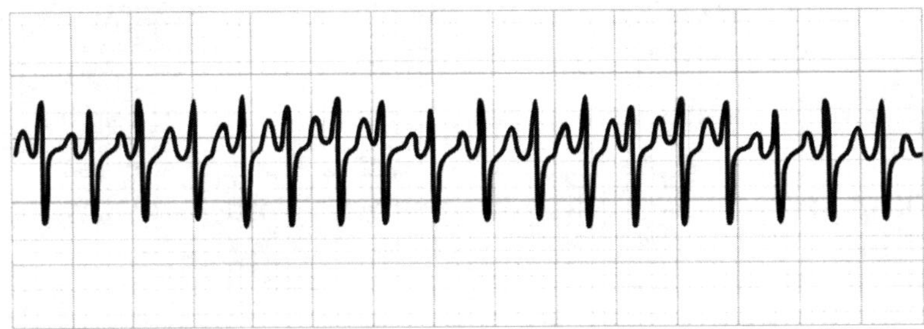

Treatment includes adenosine but may require atrial overdrive pacing or cardioversion. Vagal maneuvers may be attempted prior to more invasive interventions if the patient is stable. Other medications include verapamil/diltiazem, β-blockers, and digoxin.

Sinus Arrhythmia

Sinus arrhythmia (SA) results from irregular impulses from the sinus node, often paradoxical (increasing with inspiration and decreasing with expiration) because of stimulation of the vagal nerve during inspiration; it rarely causes a negative hemodynamic effect.

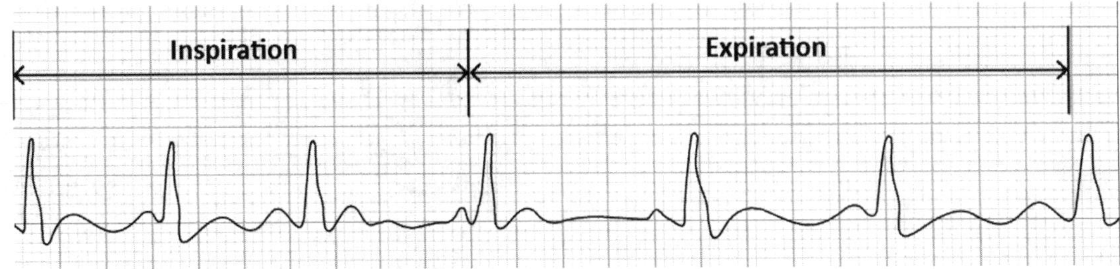

These cyclic changes in the pulse during respiration are quite common in both children and young adults; they often lessen with age but may persist in some adults. Sinus arrhythmia can, in some cases, relate to heart or valvular disease and may be increased with vagal stimulation for suctioning, vomiting, or defecating. Characteristics of SA include a regular pulse of 50–100 bpm with possible variation in the P-P interval, P waves in front of QRS with a duration of 0.4–0.11 seconds, and a normal shape of QRS, a PR interval of 0.12–0.20 seconds, and a P:QRS ratio of 1:1. Treatment is not necessary unless SA is associated with bradycardia.

Premature Atrial Contractions

There are three primary types of **atrial dysrhythmias**, including premature atrial contractions (PACs), atrial flutter, and atrial fibrillation. PACs are essentially extra beats precipitated by an electrical impulse to the atrium before the sinus node impulse. The extra beat may be caused by alcohol, caffeine, nicotine, hypervolemia, hypokalemia, hypermetabolic conditions, atrial ischemia, or infarction. PACs increase the risk of atrial tachyarrhythmias. Characteristics include an irregular pulse because of extra P waves, usually a normal shape and duration of QRS (0.04–0.11 seconds) but QRS may also be abnormal, a PR interval between 0.12–0.20 seconds, and a P:QRS ratio of 1:1. Rhythm is irregular with varying P-P and R-R intervals. PACs can occur in an essentially healthy heart and are not usually cause for concern unless they occur for more than 6 hours and cause severe palpitations. In that case, atrial fibrillation should be suspected. Postsurgical treatment may include atrial pacing, magnesium sulfate, β-blockers, calcium channel blockers, and amiodarone.

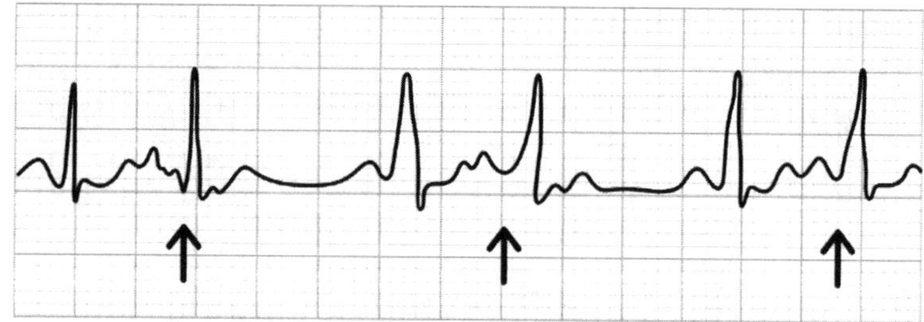

Atrial Flutter

Atrial flutter (AF) occurs when the atrial rate is faster, usually 250–400 bpm, than the atrioventricular (AV) node conduction rate, so not all of the beats are conducted into the ventricles. Some are effectively blocked at the AV node, preventing ventricular fibrillation although some extra ventricular impulses may go through. AF is caused by the same conditions that cause atrial fibrillation: coronary artery disease, valvular disease, pulmonary disease, heavy alcohol ingestion, and cardiac surgery. AF is characterized by atrial rates of 250–400 bpm with ventricular rates of 75–150 bpm, with a regular ventricular rate. P waves are saw-toothed (referred to as F waves), the shape and duration (0.4–0.11 seconds) of QRS are usually normal, the PR interval may be hard to calculate because of F waves, and the P:QRS ratio is between 2:1 and 4:1.

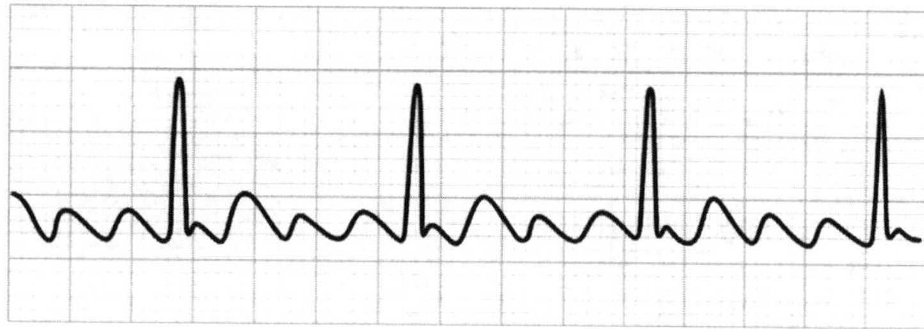

Symptoms include chest pain, dyspnea, and hypotension. Treatment includes the following:

- Rapid atrial pacing, cardioversion if the condition is unstable
- Medications to slow ventricular rate and conduction through the AV node, such as Cardizem (Diltiazem) and verapamil (Calan)
- Medications to convert to sinus rhythm, such as ibutilide (Corvert), quinidine (Cardioquin), disopyramide (Norpace), and amiodarone (Cordarone)

ATRIAL FIBRILLATION

Atrial fibrillation (Afib) describes rapid, disorganized atrial beats that are ineffective in emptying the atria so that blood pools, which can lead to thrombus formation and emboli. The ventricular rate increases with a decreased stroke volume, and cardiac output decreases with increased myocardial ischemia, resulting in palpitations and fatigue. Afib is caused by coronary artery disease, valvular disease, pulmonary disease, heavy alcohol ingestion, and cardiac surgery. Afib is characterized by a very irregular pulse with an atrial rate of 300–600 bpm, a ventricular rate of 120–200 bpm, and a normal shape and duration (0.4–0.11 seconds) of QRS. Fibrillatory (F) waves are seen instead of P waves. The PR interval cannot be measured, and the P:QRS ratio is highly variable. Afib during sleep is characterized by an irregular ventricular rhythm and varying rapid oscillations replacing P waves. Treatment may include the following:

- Cardioversion (50–100 joules)
- Ventricular pacing
- Amiodarone, propafenone/ibutilide, or electrical cardioversion to convert to sinus rhythm
- β-blockers, diltiazem, amiodarone, or digoxin to control heart rate
- Anticoagulant therapy if Afib persists for more than 24 hours

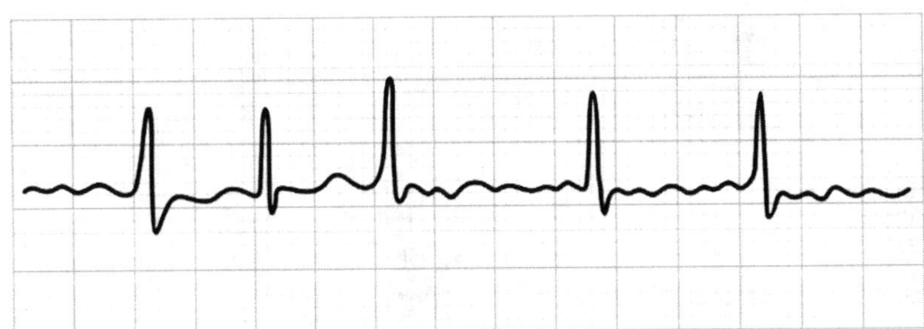

Review Video: Atrial Fibrillation and Atrial Flutter
Visit mometrix.com/academy and enter code: 263842

PROPHYLAXIS TO PREVENT POSTSURGICAL AFIB OR AF

The most common postsurgical arrhythmias are atrial fibrillation (Afib) and atrial flutter (AF). With Afib, the heart rate may be more than 380 bpm but is less than 380 bpm with AF, occurring in up to 30% of patients, even with prophylaxis. Afib and AF occur most often on day 2 or 3 postoperatively. **Prophylaxis** reduces the incidence by half. Low-dose β-blockers are administered 12–24 hours after surgery and reduce incidence by 65%:

- Metoprolol, 25–50 mg may be given PO twice daily (increase as needed to a max of 200 mg/day), or atenolol, 25 mg PO daily.
- Carvedilol, 3.125–25 mg may be given PO twice daily.
- Sotalol, 80 mg may be given PO twice daily.
- Dual-site atrial pacing may be used.

- Amiodarone may be given by itself or with a β-blocker. Various dosages have been used, including administration of 10 mg/kg daily for 6 preoperative days, continuing postsurgically with 200 mg/day for a total of 13 days of treatment. Other protocols include administering 200 mg three times daily for 5 preoperative days and 400 mg twice daily for 4–6 postoperative days.

Postoperative Management of Atrial Fibrillation

Atrial fibrillation (Afib) in the postsurgical patient requires assessment of hemodynamic status and underlying causes, as it can decrease cardiac output by 25–50%. Treatment aims to control rate (of primary concern) and rhythm. Medications used to control rate include β-blockers, calcium channel blockers, and digoxin (although it is less effective than β-blockers). The β-blocker of choice in most cases is metoprolol, while the calcium channel blocker of choice is usually diltiazem. Calcium channel blockers are usually reserved for patients who do not respond to β-blockers. Medications used to convert from Afib include metoprolol, diltiazem, ibutilide, and amiodarone. Ibutilide is usually used if cardioversion is unsuccessful, but the patient must be monitored carefully for the development of torsade de pointes, a form of ventricular tachycardia in which the QRS complex varies with each heartbeat.

Premature Junctional Contractions

The area around the AV node is the junction, and dysrhythmias that arise from the junction are called junctional dysrhythmias. Premature junctional contractions (PJCs) occur when a premature impulse starts at the AV node before the next normal sinus impulse reaches the AV node. PJCs are similar to premature atrial contractions (PACs) and generally require no treatment although they may be an indication of digoxin toxicity. The ECG may appear basically normal with an early QRS complex that is normal in shape and duration (0.04-0.11 seconds). The P wave may be absent, precede, be part of, or follow the QRS with a PR interval of <0.12 seconds. The P:QRS ratio may vary from <1:1 to 1:1 (with inverted P wave). Rhythm is usually regular at a heart rate of 40-60. Significant symptoms related to premature junctional contractions are rare.

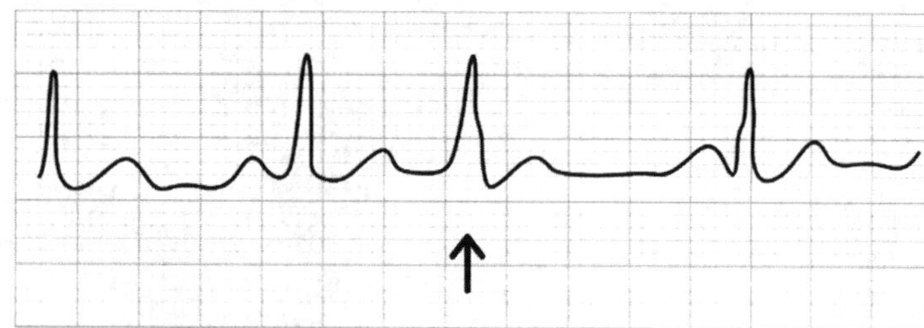

Junctional Escape Beats/Rhythms

Junctional escape beats are delayed heartbeats that occur as a protective mechanism when SA rate of depolarization is slower than the AV node. The junctional escape beats usually arise from the Bundle of His, when atrial impulses are blocked by the AV node. The sinus beat slows intermittently. Junctional beats occur irregularly but may be regular if a junctional escape rhythm develops.

Junctional escape rhythms are usually regular with R-R rhythm consistent and a heart rate of 40-60 per minute, reflecting the underlying rate of the AV node. Usually, P waves are missing or inverted, but this depends on the site where the junctional beat originates. When P waves occur, the duration is 0.12–0.20 seconds. The QRS segment is <0.12 seconds.

Junctional Rhythms

Junctional rhythms occur when the atrioventricular (AV) node becomes the pacemaker of the heart because the sinus node is depressed from increased vagal tone or block at the AV node, preventing sinus node impulses from being transmitted. While the sinus node normally sends impulses 60–100 bpm, the AV node junction usually sends impulses at 40–60 bpm. The QRS complex is of usual shape and duration (0.4–0.11 seconds). The P wave may be inverted or may be absent, hidden, or after the QRS. If the P wave precedes QRS, the PR interval is less than 0.12 seconds. The P:QRS ratio is less than 1:1 or 1:1. The junctional escape rhythm is a protective mechanism preventing asystole with failure of the sinus node. Slow junctional rhythm is treated with atrial to AV to ventricular pacing.

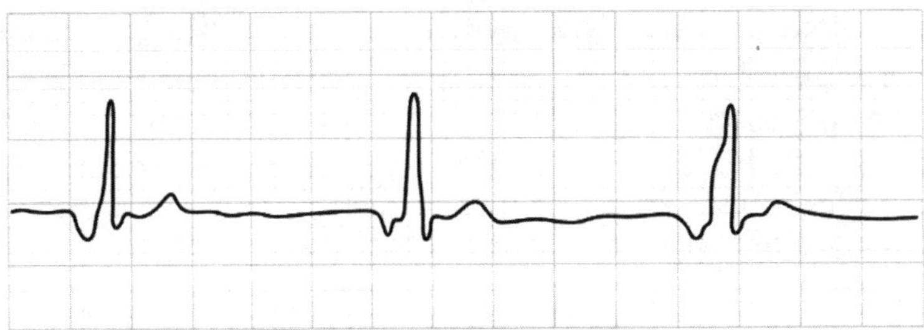

Accelerated Junctional Rhythm and Nonparoxysmal AV Junctional Tachycardia

Accelerated junctional rhythm is similar to slow junctional rhythm except that with accelerated junctional rhythm the heart rate is 60–100 bpm. Junctional tachycardia, which is rare, occurs with a heart rate of 100–160 bpm. Junctional tachycardia may be paroxysmal, with abrupt starting and stopping, or nonparoxysmal. **Nonparoxysmal atrioventricular (AV) junctional tachycardia** is characterized by a ventricular rate of 70–100 bpm. This is a cardinal sign of digoxin toxicity, but it rarely occurs with adequate monitoring of serum levels. It may also be an indication of damage to the AV junction from an acute myocardial infarction. Nonparoxysmal junctional tachycardia may be chronic. Treatment includes stopping digoxin for those taking it, administering potassium and phenytoin, or beginning digoxin for those not already taking the drug.

AV Nodal Reentry Tachycardia

Atrioventricular (AV) nodal reentry tachycardia occurs when an impulse conducts to an area of the AV node, and the impulse is sent in a rapidly repeating cycle back to the same area and to the ventricles, resulting in a fast ventricular rate. The onset and cessation are usually rapid. AV nodal reentry tachycardia (i.e., paroxysmal atrial tachycardia or supraventricular tachycardia if there are no P waves) is characterized by an atrial rate of 150–250 bpm with a ventricular rate of 75–250 bpm, a P wave that is difficult to see or absent, a QRS complex that is usually normal, and a PR interval >0.12 seconds if a P wave is present. The P:QRS ratio is 1:1 to 2:1. Precipitating factors include nicotine or caffeine ingestion, hypoxemia, anxiety, and underlying coronary artery disease and cardiomyopathy. Cardiac output may be decreased with a rapid heart rate, causing dyspnea, chest pain, and hypotension.

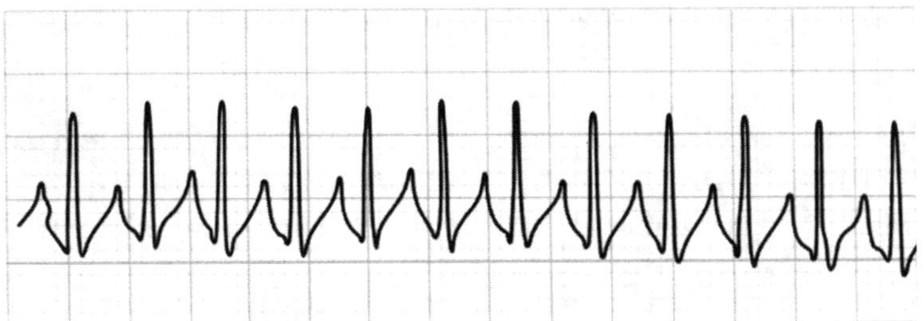

Treatment may include the following:

- Vagal maneuvers (e.g., carotid sinus massage, gag reflex, holding breath)
- Medications (e.g., adenosine, verapamil, diltiazem)
- Cardioversion if other methods unsuccessful

PVCs

Premature ventricular contractions (PVCs) are those in which the impulse begins in the ventricles and conducts through them before the next sinus impulse. The ectopic QRS complexes may vary in shape, depending on whether there is one (unifocal) or more (multifocal) sites that are stimulating the ectopic beats. PVCs usually cause no morbidity unless there is underlying cardiac disease or an acute myocardial infarction. PVCs are characterized by an irregular heartbeat, a QRS that is 0.12 seconds or more and oddly shaped, a P wave that may be absent or may precede or follow the QRS, a PR interval of less than 0.12 seconds if a P wave is present, and a P:QRS ratio of 0–1:1. Postoperative PVCs may result from alterations in magnesium or potassium levels. Because PVCs may occur with any supraventricular dysrhythmia, the underlying rhythm (e.g., atrial fibrillation) must be noted as well as the PVCs. Treatment includes treating potassium and magnesium alterations, lidocaine, amiodarone, and atrial overdrive pacing.

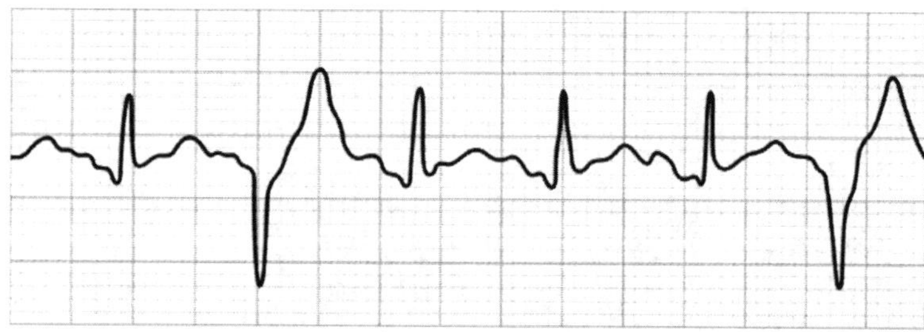

Ventricular Tachycardia

Ventricular tachycardia (VT) is three or more premature ventricular contractions (PVCs) in a row with a ventricular rate of 100–200 bpm. VT may be triggered by the same things that trigger PVCs and is often related to underlying coronary artery disease, but the rapid rate of contractions makes VT dangerous as the ineffective beats may render the person unconscious with no palpable pulse. A detectable rate is usually regular, and the QRS complex is 0.12 seconds or more and is usually abnormally shaped. The P wave may be undetectable with an irregular PR interval if a P wave is present. The P:QRS ratio is often difficult to ascertain because of absence of P waves. Treatment includes defibrillation (if there is no palpable pulse), amiodarone, and lidocaine.

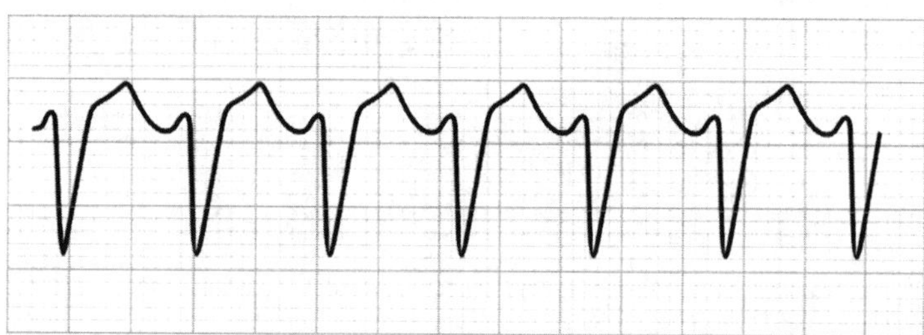

Wide-Complex and Narrow-Complex Tachycardias

Tachycardias are classified as narrow complex or wide complex. Wide and narrow refer to the configuration of the QRS complex.

- **Wide complex tachycardia (WCT)**: About 80% of cases of WCT are caused by ventricular tachycardia. WCT originates at some point below the AV node and may be associated with palpitations, dyspnea, anxiety, diaphoresis, and cardiac arrest. Wide complex tachycardia is diagnosed with more than 3 consecutive beats at a heart rate >100 BPM and QRS duration ≥0.12 seconds.

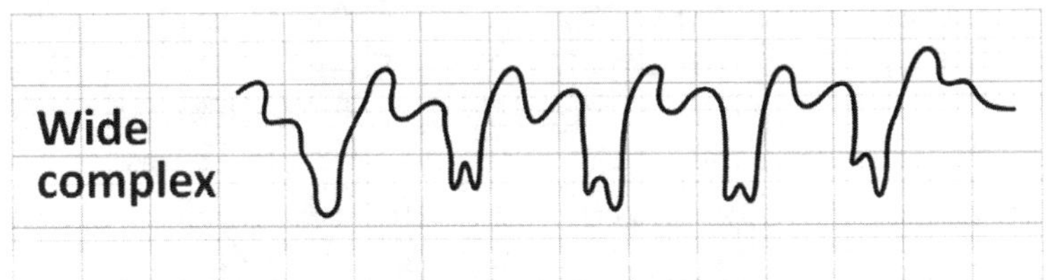

- **Narrow complex tachycardia (NCT)**: NCT is associated with palpitations, dyspnea, and peripheral edema. NCT is generally supraventricular in origin. Narrow complex tachycardia is diagnosed with ≥3 consecutive beats at heart rate of >100 BPM and QRS duration of <0.12 seconds.

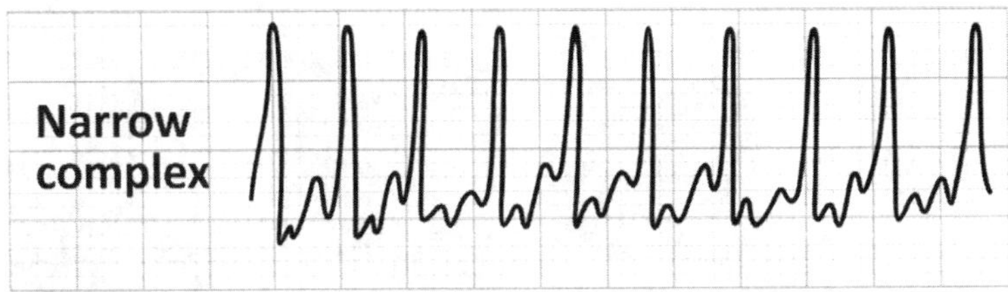

Ventricular Fibrillation

Ventricular fibrillation (VF) is a rapid, very irregular ventricular rate of over 300 bpm with no atrial activity observable on the electrocardiogram (ECG), caused by disorganized electrical activity in the ventricles. The QRS complex is not recognizable as the ECG shows irregular undulations. The causes are the same as for ventricular tachycardia (VT), such as use of alcohol, caffeine, and nicotine or underlying coronary disease, in addition to myocardial infarction, cardiomyopathy, drug toxicity, or systemic organ failure. VF may also result if VT is not treated or as a result from an electrical shock or congenital disorder, such as Brugada syndrome. VF is accompanied by lack of a palpable pulse, audible pulse, or respirations and is immediately life-threatening without defibrillation. After emergency defibrillation, the cause should be identified and limited. Mortality is high if VF occurs as part of a myocardial infarction.

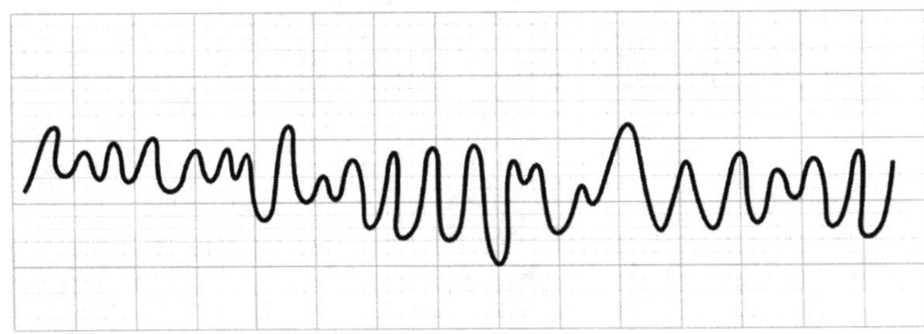

VENTRICULAR ESCAPE RHYTHM

Ventricular escape rhythm (idioventricular) occurs when the Purkinje fibers below the atrioventricular (AV) node create an impulse. This may occur if the sinus node fails to fire or if there is blockage at the AV node so that the impulse does not go through. Idioventricular rhythm is characterized by a regular ventricular rate of 20–40 bpm. Rates over 40 bpm are called accelerated idioventricular rhythms. The P wave is missing, and the QRS complex has a very bizarre and abnormal shape with a duration of 0.12 seconds or more. The low ventricular rate may cause a decrease in cardiac output, often making the patient lose consciousness. In some patients, the idioventricular rhythm is not associated with low cardiac output.

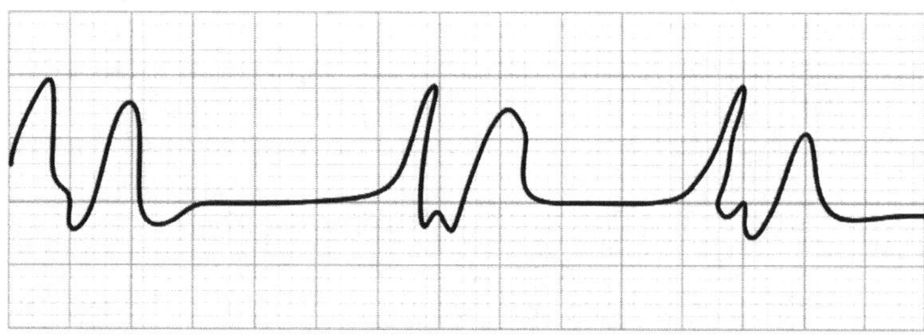

VENTRICULAR ASYSTOLE

Ventricular asystole is the absence of an audible heartbeat, palpable pulse, and respirations, a condition often referred to as "flat lining" or "cardiac arrest." While the electrocardiogram (ECG) may show some P waves initially, the QRS complex is absent although there may be an occasional QRS "escape beat." Cardiopulmonary resuscitation is required with epinephrine (1 mg IV/IM every 3–5 minutes), intubation for ventilation, and establishment of a large bore intravenous line for fluids (if not already established). Without immediate treatment, the patient will suffer from severe hypoxia and brain death within minutes. Identifying the cause is critical for the patient's survival and could include hypoxia, acidosis, electrolyte imbalance, hypothermia, or drug overdose. Even with immediate treatment, the prognosis is poor, and ventricular asystole is often a sign of impending death.

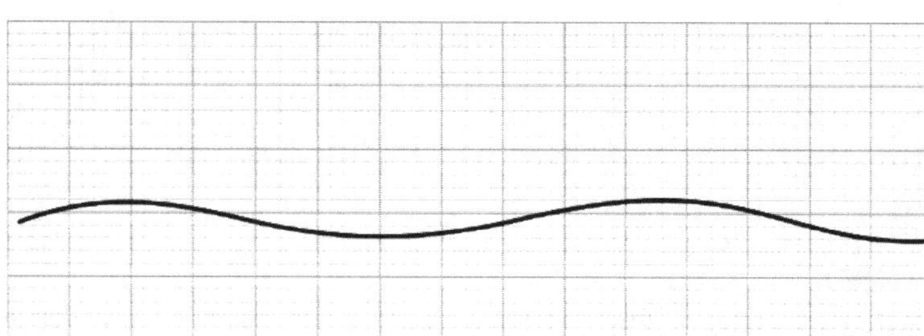

Sinus Pause

Sinus pause occurs when the sinus node fails to function properly to stimulate heart contractions, so there is a pause on the ECG recording that may persist for a few seconds to minutes, depending on the severity of the dysfunction. A prolonged pause may be difficult to differentiate from cardiac arrest. During the sinus pause, the P wave, QRS complex and PR and QRS intervals are all absent. P:QRS ratio is 1:1 and the rhythm is irregular. The pulse rate may vary widely, usually 60–100 BPM. Patients with frequent pauses may complain of dizziness or syncope. The patient may need to undergo an electrophysiology study and medication reconciliation to determine the cause. If measures such as decreasing medication are not effective, a pacemaker is usually indicated (if symptomatic).

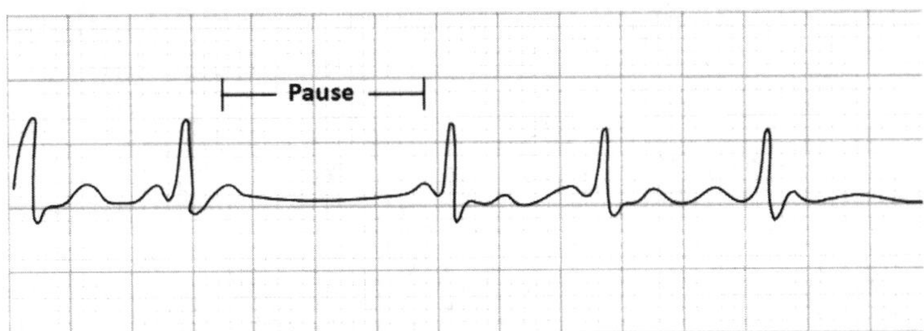

Postoperative Complications of Minimally Invasive Cardiac Surgery

Dysrhythmias	**Atrial fibrillation** is common, decreasing cardiac output. Treatment can include diltiazem or metoprolol to control rate or amiodarone to convert rhythm. **Bradycardia** (often occurring with Maze procedures) may require epicardial pacing, transcutaneous pacing, or transvenous pacing. **Ventricular tachycardia (VT)/ventricular fibrillation (VF)** may occur early in the postoperative period, especially with electrolyte imbalance or acidosis. VT/VF may require emergent reopening of the chest.
Hypothermia	Less common in minimally invasive procedures than those requiring cardiopulmonary bypass, hypothermia may have a number of adverse effects, including coagulopathy, bleeding, hemodynamic instability, increased systemic vascular resistance, hypertension, vasoconstriction, and dysrhythmias. Shivering increases the need for oxygen, so it should be controlled with meperidine. Rewarming must be done carefully to avoid vasodilation. Volume replacement and vasopressors may be needed to prevent hypotension.
Bleeding	Postoperative bleeding is a concern for all surgical procedures, so the patient's incision, vital signs, and hemodynamic status must be monitored.

Postoperative Cardiac Tamponade

Cardiac tamponade occurs with pericardial effusion, causing pressure against the heart. It may be a complication of trauma, pericarditis, cardiac surgery, or heart failure. About 50 mL of fluid normally circulates in the pericardial area to reduce friction, and a sudden increase in this volume can compress the heart, causing a number of cardiac responses:

- Increased end-diastolic pressure in both ventricles
- Decrease in venous return
- Decrease in ventricular filling

Symptoms may include pressure or pain in the chest, dyspnea, and pulsus paradoxus of 10 mmHg or more. Beck's triad (increased central venous pressure, causing distended neck veins; a fall in arterial pressure; distant muffled heart sounds) is common. A sudden decrease in chest tube drainage can occur as fluid and clots accumulate in the pericardial sac, preventing the blood from filling the ventricles and decreasing cardiac output and perfusion of the body, including the kidneys (resulting in decreased urinary output). X-rays may show a change in cardiac silhouette and mediastinal shift (in 20%). Treatment includes pericardiocentesis with a large bore needle or surgical repair to control bleeding and relieve cardiac compression.

Review Video: Cardiac Tamponade
Visit mometrix.com/academy and enter code: 920182

Pericardiocentesis

Pericardiocentesis is done with ultrasound guidance to diagnose pericardial effusion or with an electrocardiogram (ECG) or ultrasound guidance to relieve cardiac tamponade. Pericardiocentesis may be done as treatment for cardiac arrest or with presentation of **pulseless electrical activity** with increased jugular venous pressure. Non-hemorrhagic tamponade may be relieved in 60–90% of cases, but hemorrhagic tamponade requires thoracotomy, as blood will continue to accumulate until the cause of the hemorrhage is corrected. Resuscitation equipment must be available, including a defibrillator and intravenous access, and cardiac monitoring must be instituted:

- The chest is elevated to 45° to bring the heart closer to chest wall.
- Premedication with atropine may prevent vasovagal reactions.
- If abdominal distention is present, a nasogastric tube should be inserted.

After insertion of the needle, the obturator is removed, and a syringe is attached for aspiration. A sterile alligator clamp is attached from the needle to any precordial lead of the ECG for monitoring to ensure that the ventricle is not punctured. A post-procedural chest x-ray should be done to check for a pneumothorax.

Postoperative Edema

Edema is an indication of hypervolemia-associated hyponatremia, so cardiac surgical patients should be monitored for peripheral and dependent edema. Edema is usually checked by pressing the index finger into the tissue on top of each foot, behind the medial malleolus, and over the shin, starting distally and moving proximally to the highest level of edema, comparing both legs.

Edema is rated on a 1-to-4 scale:

- 1+ slight pitting to about 2 mm (persists 10–15 seconds)
- 2+ moderate pitting to about 4 mm (persists 10–15 seconds)
- 3+ moderately severe pitting to about 6 mm (persists >1 minute)
- 4+ severe pitting to 8 mm or more (persists 2–5 minutes)

There are various **types of edema:**

- **Venous edema** is edema from the ankle to the knee and may involve some limitation in ankle movement. Dependent pitting edema occurs but may become nonpitting in chronic disease.
- **Lymphedema** is usually unilateral nonpitting hard edema from the toes to the groin.
- **Lipedema** is symmetrical bilateral soft rubbery tissue from the ankle to the groin and sometimes on the hips with pain on palpation and frequent bruising.

Postoperative Compartment Syndrome

Compartment syndrome occurs when the myofascial compartment size decreases because of constriction or contents of a compartment increase (usually swelling, hemorrhage, or infiltrated intravenous line). However, prolonged cardiopulmonary bypass (CPB) may result in ischemic/reperfusion injury to a lower extremity, especially if retrograde reperfusion is in the femoral artery. The increased compartment pressure reduces capillary perfusion below the level necessary for tissue viability and damages nerves:

- Normal values: 0–8 mmHg
- Compartment syndrome: 30–40 mmHg or higher

Edema of the involved lower extremity is common after surgery, but if ischemia persists for 4–6 hours, then pressures should be measured. Symptoms include the "six Ps": paresthesia, pain (i.e., deep, throbbing, relentless pain, and positive Homan's sign for lower extremities), pressure, pallor, paralysis, and pulselessness in the peripheral pulses (although this may indicate arterial occlusion rather than compartment syndrome). Surgical fasciotomy may be necessary if elevation of the limb is not effective in reducing pressure.

Postoperative DVT

Deep vein thrombosis (DVT) is usually related to poor circulation or damage to vessels and is more common in patients over 40 years of age. DVT is associated with inactivity (e.g., during flying) and surgery and should be differentiated from other injuries when patients complain of calf pain. Homan's sign (i.e., pain in the palpated calf on dorsiflexion of the ankle) occurs in only 10%.

Signs and Symptoms

The following are signs and symptoms of DVT, though in some cases there may not be any overt symptoms:

- Unilateral leg edema
- Pain and tenderness
- Erythema
- Temperature over 38 °C (100.4 °F)
- Edema and cyanosis of the lower extremities (with involvement of the inferior vena cava)
- Increased risk of embolization, including pulmonary embolism

Treatment

The following are **treatments of DVT**:

- Bed rest with elevation of extremity above the heart
- Warm compresses
- Elastic compression stockings (Class II: 30–40 mmHg) when able to ambulate (used for 3–6 months)
- Anticoagulants (e.g., unfractionated heparin, low-molecular-weight heparins, hirudin derivatives, warfarin)
- Surgical intervention (e.g., venous thrombectomy, insertion of vena cava interruption devices)
- Analgesia

Postoperative Acute VTE

Acute venous thromboembolism (VTE) is a condition that includes both deep vein thrombosis (DVT) and pulmonary emboli (PE). VTE may be precipitated by invasive procedures, lack of mobility, and inflammation, so it is a common complication in critical care units. Virchow's triad comprises common risk factors: blood stasis, injury to endothelium, and hypercoagulability. Some patients may be initially asymptomatic, but symptoms may include the following:

- Aching or throbbing pain
- Positive Homan's sign (pain in calf when foot is dorsiflexed)
- Erythema and edema
- Dilation of vessels
- Cyanosis

Diagnosis may be made by ultrasound or the D-dimer test, which tests the serum for cross-linked fibrin derivatives. Computed tomography scan, pulmonary angiogram, and a ventilation–perfusion lung scan may be used to diagnose pulmonary emboli. Prophylaxis is very important, but once diagnosed, treatment involves bed rest, elevation of the affected limb, anticoagulation therapy, and analgesics. Elastic stockings are worn when the patient begins ambulating.

Review Video: DVT Prevention and Treatment
Visit mometrix.com/academy and enter code: 234086

Postoperative Vascular Complications

Pseudoaneurysm

Pseudoaneurysm (AKA false aneurysm) is injury to the inner layers of the arterial wall allowing blood to collect and balloon out between the two outer layers of the arterial wall. This results in a thin-walled cavity that is prone to rupture. If all 3 layers of the artery are disrupted, the blood may be contained by surrounding tissue. A pseudoaneurysm may occur with injury to the arterial wall associated with:

- **PCI procedures**, especially with femoral catheterization: Blood may leak and pool at the insertion site. Contributing factors include periprocedural anticoagulation, inadequate compression of the insertion site after removal of the catheter, hypertension, and arterial calcifications. Treatment includes watching and waiting as small pseudoaneurysms may heal spontaneously, ultrasound-guided compression, ultrasound-guided thrombin injection, or surgical repair.
- **Cardiac surgery**, such as aortic valve repair/replacement or CABG: Most commonly affects the ascending aorta (associated with infection) and less commonly the descending aorta (associated with trauma). Treatment includes surgical resection and grafting.

HEMATOMA

Hematoma may occur at catheter insertion sites (most commonly femoral or radial artery). Risk factors include female gender, hypertension, multiple punctures, prolonged sheath time, and pre-procedure anticoagulation. Patients may complain of local pain and exhibit hypotension, swelling, and purplish discoloration:

- **Femoral**: Occurs at the insertion site, especially if compression is interrupted or inadequate. Manual compression is adequate for activated clotting times less than 150 seconds. For greater ACTs, a vascular closure device (such as Angio-Seal or Perclose) may be indicated. With sheath removal, firm pressure should be applied for 15-20 minutes or longer, checking pedal pulses every 2-3 minutes to ensure the pressure is not compromising peripheral circulation. The site should be observed for 5 minutes for bleeding recurrence. The FemoStop compression device may be used instead of manual compression.
- **Radial**: Occurs at the insertion site if there is inadequate compression, or at a distance (in the case of a perforation). Treatment may include application of TR band, ACE bandage, or sphygmomanometer cuff (inflated to systolic or slightly above systolic pressure with deflation for 15 seconds every 2-3 minutes) and application of ice bag. Surgical repair may be indicated if ischemia of the limb occurs.

PERIPHERAL ISCHEMIA

Postoperative vascular complications can include peripheral ischemia. Causes may include:

- Vasoconstrictive drugs (such as vasopressin), hypothermia, decreased cardiac output, and cardiac embolization may all result in impaired peripheral circulation. In some cases, thrombosis may occur at a bypass graft, sheath insertion site, or limb artery.
- Insertion of an IABP: Risk factors include pre-existing peripheral arterial disease, older age, female gender, and diabetes mellitus. Risk increases with prolonged use of the IABP and when ventricular function is compromised.

Treatment depends on the cause of the peripheral ischemia but may include adjusting medications, vasodilators, and anticoagulants. If related to an IABP, removing the sheath from the femoral artery may improve circulation. If the patient is stable, the IABP may be removed altogether or removed and placed on the opposite side. If associated with hypothermia, rewarming the patient increases blood flow but nitroglycerine may be required for some patients. For thrombosis, emergent thrombolysis or thrombectomy is critical to avoid amputation.

RETROPERITONEAL BLEEDING

Retroperitoneal bleeding may occur as a complication of femoral artery catheterization (such as for PCI procedures) when the artery is perforated or dissected. A large hematoma forms and dissects the artery with bleeding into the retroperitoneum, a life-threatening complication. Factors that increase the risk of perforation include large catheter size, multiple attempts at insertion, long dwell time, inadequate vascular closure, and accidental perforation. Risk of severe hemorrhage is increased with the use of periprocedural anticoagulation and antiplatelet agents. Patents of older age and large size/body weight as well as those with preexisting coagulopathy, hypertension, and renal disease also have increased risk. With bleeding, patients may complain of abdominal, back or groin pain or swelling, and some may exhibit unexplained hypotension and bradycardia or tachycardia. Diagnosis is confirmed by symptoms and CT. Treatment includes transfusions and surgical repair.

Postoperative Papillary Muscle Rupture

The atrioventricular valves separate the atria from the ventricles with the tricuspid valve on the right and the bicuspid (mitral) valve on the left. The papillary muscles are located on the sides of the ventricular walls and connect to the valves with fibrous bands called chordae tendineae. During systole, the papillary muscles contract, tightening the chordae tendineae and closing the valves. One complication of a myocardial infarction (MI) is **papillary muscle rupture**, usually on the left, affecting the mitral valve, with the posteromedial papillary muscle more often affected than the anterolateral. Dysfunction of the papillary muscles occurs in about 40% of those with a posterior septal infarction, but rupture can occur with infarction of the inferior wall or an anterolateral MI. Rupture on the right-side results in tricuspid regurgitation and right ventricular failure while rupture on the left side leads to mitral regurgitation with resultant pulmonary edema and cardiogenic shock. Early identification and surgical repair are critical.

Complications and Monitoring Associated with Heart Valve Repair or Replacement

Patients usually tolerate heart valve repair or replacement well, but postoperative complications can include the following:

- **Cardiovascular**: Thromboembolism (especially if the patient received a mechanical valve), atrial dysrhythmias (most commonly atrial fibrillation), atrioventricular block, heart failure, low cardiac output, and myocardial infarction
- **Renal**: Insufficiency
- **Neurological**: Stroke, transient ischemic attack, and changes in mental status
- **Respiratory**: Insufficiency, dyspnea, and orthopnea
- **Bleeding**: Hemorrhage, sometimes requiring a return to surgery for exploration
- **Infection**: Sternal wound infection as well as infection of the valve itself; antibiotic prophylaxis routinely given preoperatively and for 2 days postoperatively to prevent infection

Routine monitoring includes heart rate and rhythm, hemodynamic status, chest tube drainage, respiratory status, neurological status, serum electrolytes, fluid volume (avoiding reduction in preload), and pain.

Infective Valve Endocarditis

Infective valve endocarditis may occur in native valves and prosthetic valves, generally affecting the mitral, tricuspid, or aortic valve. Indications may include fever, heart murmur, and hemodynamic instability. Signs of heart failure may occur. Vegetations, ulcerations, and abscesses may occur. Indications for surgery vary, according to the degree of involvement, the spread of infection, the infective agent, and the persistence and size of vegetations. During surgery, all infected tissue must be removed:

- **Aortic valve**: Replacement may be with a homograft (preferred if possible), tissue, or mechanical valves.
- **Tricuspid valve**: Repair is preferred, especially for high-risk patients, such as drug abusers. In some cases, valvulectomy (if no pulmonary hypertension) or valve replacement may be indicated.
- **Mitral valve**: Leaflet repair may be sufficient with early intervention, although more severe disease requires valve replacement.

Antibiotics are usually given for 6 weeks perioperatively, but when cultures taken during surgery show organisms, antibiotics are usually continued for 6 weeks postoperatively.

Hyperdynamic State Without Documented Infection

A hyperdynamic state without documented infection may occur after cardiac surgery, especially after prolonged extracorporeal circulation (ECC). Symptoms usually occur within 6 hours of ECC. An immune (cellular and humoral) response occurs from blood contact with the ECC unit. Proinflammatory cytokines are released. The triad of characteristics associated with the hyperdynamic state includes the following:

- Temperature elevation >38 °C (best indicator)
- Increased cardiac index over 3.5 $mL/min/m^2$
- Systemic vascular resistance index less than 1600 $dynes/sec/cm^{-5}$

Patients with coronary artery surgery are at increased risk over those with valve surgery, perhaps because the length of time on cardiopulmonary bypass for valvular surgery is decreased. Typically, patients exhibit vasodilation and increased cardiac output as an inflammatory response, often resulting in hypotension leading to shock. Treatment may include fluid resuscitation and vasopressors. Other causes of the hyperdynamic state can include hyperthyroidism, Paget's disease, and beriberi.

Pulmonary

Respiratory Failure

Symptoms of Acute Respiratory Failure

The symptoms of acute respiratory failure include:

- Tachypnea
- Tachycardia
- Anxiety and restlessness

In cardiac surgery patients, acute respiratory failure may be caused by bilateral phrenic nerve injury and diaphragmatic paralysis. Early signs may include difficulty weaning from the ventilator. After removal from ventilation, signs and symptoms include changes in the depth and pattern of respirations with flaring nares, sternal retractions, expiratory grunting, wheezing, and extended expiration as the body tries to compensate for hypoxemia and increasing levels of carbon dioxide. Cyanosis may be evident. Central nervous depression, with alterations in consciousness, occurs with decreased perfusion to the brain. As the hypoxemia worsens, cardiac arrhythmias, including bradycardia, may occur with either hypotension or hypertension. Dyspnea becomes more pronounced with depressed respirations. Eventually stupor, coma, and death can occur if the condition is not reversed.

Hypoxemic and Hypercapnic Respiratory Failure

Hypoxemic respiratory failure occurs suddenly when gaseous exchange of oxygen for carbon dioxide cannot keep up with the demand for oxygen or the production of carbon dioxide.

- Partial pressure of oxygen (PaO_2) <60 mmHg
- Partial pressure of carbon dioxide ($PaCO_2$) may be normal (35-45 mmHg) or increased
- Arterial pH <7.35

Hypoxemic respiratory failure can be the result of low-inhaled oxygen, as at high elevations or with smoke inhalation. The following ventilatory mechanisms may be involved: Alveolar hypotension, ventilation-perfusion mismatch (the most common cause), intrapulmonary shunts, and/or diffusion impairment.

Hypercapnic respiratory failure results from an increase in $PaCO_2$ (>45–50 mmHg) associated with respiratory acidosis and may include the following:

- Reduction in minute ventilation, total volume of gas ventilated in 1 minute, often related to neurological, muscle or chest-wall disorders, drug overdoses, or obstruction of upper airway
- Increased dead space with wasted ventilation (related to lung disease or disorders of the chest wall, such as scoliosis)
- Increased production of carbon dioxide (usually related to infection, burns, or other causes of hypermetabolism)

Management of Respiratory Failure

Respiratory failure must be treated immediately before severe hypoxemia causes irreversible damage to vital organs. Identifying and treating the underlying cause should be done immediately because emergency medications or surgery may be indicated. Medical treatments vary widely, depending on the cause; for example, cardiopulmonary structural defects may require surgical repair; pulmonary edema may require diuresis; inhaled objects may require surgical removal; and infections may require aggressive antimicrobials.

- **Intravenous lines/central lines** are inserted for testing, fluids, and medications.
- **Oxygen therapy** should be initiated to attempt to reverse hypoxemia; however, if refractory hypoxemia occurs, then oxygen therapy alone will not suffice. Oxygen levels must be titrated carefully.
- **Intubation and mechanical ventilation** are frequently required to maintain adequate ventilation and oxygenation. Positive end expiratory pressure may be necessary with refractory hypoxemia and collapsed alveoli.
- **Respiratory status** must be monitored constantly, including arterial blood gases and vital signs.

ALI AND ARDS

Acute lung injury (ALI) comprises a syndrome of respiratory distress culminating in **acute respiratory distress syndrome (ARDS)**, a rare complication of cardiac surgery. ALI and ARDS usually occur more than 24 hours postoperatively. ARDS is characterized by damage to the vascular endothelium and an increase in the permeability of the alveolar–capillary membrane when damage to the lung results from toxic substances (e.g., gastric fluids, bacteria, chemicals, toxins emitted by neutrophils as part of the inflammatory-mediated response). These substances reduce surfactant and cause pulmonary edema as the alveoli fill with blood and protein-rich fluid and then collapse (atelectasis). This decrease in surfactant also leads to decreased lung compliance (sometimes referred to as stiffening). The fluid in the alveoli becomes a medium for infection. Because there is neither adequate ventilation nor perfusion, the result is increasing hypoxemia and tachypnea as the body tries to compensate to maintain a normal partial pressure of carbon dioxide. Untreated, the condition results in respiratory failure, multiorgan failure, and a mortality rate of 15–70% when it occurs as a complication of cardiac surgery.

ARDS

SYMPTOMS

Patients presenting with acute respiratory distress syndrome (ARDS) may initially present with only mild tachypnea, but more serious symptoms develop as respiratory function becomes more compromised:

- Crackling rales or wheezing may be heard throughout the lungs.
- A decrease in pulmonary compliance (lung volume), referred to as "baby lung," results in increasing tachypnea with expiratory grunting.
- Cyanosis may develop with characteristic blue discoloration of lips and skin mottling.
- Hypotension and tachycardia may occur.
- Respiratory alkalosis is often an early sign but is replaced as the disease progresses with hypercarbia and respiratory acidosis.
- X-ray studies may be normal at first but then show diffuse infiltrates in both lungs, but the heart and vessels still appear normal.

MANAGEMENT

The management of acute respiratory distress syndrome (ARDS) involves providing adequate gas exchange and preventing further damage to the lung from forced ventilation. Treatment includes the following:

- Oxygen therapy by nasal prongs/cannula or mask may be sufficient in mild cases to maintain oxygen saturation (SpO_2) above 95% (with a goal of >88% for patients with COPD). Oxygen should be administered at 100% because of the mismatch between ventilation (V) and perfusion (Q), which can result in hypoxia on position change.
- Endotracheal intubation may be needed if SpO_2 falls or carbon dioxide levels rise.
- Mechanical ventilation with lower tidal volumes (6 mL/kg) or high-frequency oscillatory ventilation to maintain SpO_2 over 90%.
- Inhaled nitric oxide may be prescribed for pulmonary hypertension.
- Prophylactic antibiotics are not indicated.
- Steroids may increase survival rates if given later in treatment if ARDS has not resolved within a week.

AIR LEAK SYNDROME

Air leak syndrome may occur spontaneously or secondary to some type of trauma (e.g., accidental, mechanical, iatrogenic) or disease. As pressure increases inside the alveoli, the alveolar wall pulls away from the perivascular sheath and subsequent alveolar rupture allows air to follow the perivascular planes and flow into adjacent areas. There are various types of air leak syndromes specific to the location of the leak:

- **Pneumothorax**: Air in the pleural space
- **Pneumoperitoneum**: Air in the peritoneal area, including the abdomen
- **Pneumomediastinum**: Air in the mediastinal area between the lungs
- **Pneumopericardium**: Air in the pericardial sac
- **Subcutaneous emphysema**: Air in the subcutaneous tissue planes of the chest wall
- **Pulmonary interstitial emphysema**: Air trapped in the interstitium between the alveoli

Retrosternal and neck pain, dyspnea, and slight neck edema indicate pneumomediastinum. **Hamman's sign**—a precordial rasping sound heard on auscultation during a heartbeat as the heart moves against tissues filled with air—is an indication of both pneumomediastinum and pneumopericardium but is not generally present with pneumothorax or cardiac tamponade.

PNEUMOTHORAX

SYMPTOMS AND DIAGNOSIS

Pneumothorax occurs when there is a leak of air into the pleural space, resulting in complete or partial collapse of a lung, because of direct injury, central venous cannulation, or barotrauma. Pneumothorax usually occurs early after cardiac surgery. Tension pneumothorax often occurs with mechanical ventilation, usually after right pneumothorax caused by an accidental cut into the right pleura.

Symptoms vary widely, depending on the cause and degree of the pneumothorax and whether or not there is underlying disease:

- Acute pleuritic pain (95%), usually on the affected side
- Decreased breath sounds
- **Tension pneumothorax**: Tracheal deviation, distended neck veins, and hemodynamic compromise

Diagnosis consists of the following:

- **Clinical findings**: Deteriorating arterial blood gasses, hemodynamic instability, and an increase in peak inspiratory pressure with ventilation
- **Radiograph**: 6-foot upright posterior–anterior
- **Ultrasound** to attempt to detect traumatic pneumothorax

Treatment

Treatment of a pneumothorax includes:

- Chest-tube thoracostomy with underwater seal drainage (most common treatment)
- **Tension pneumothorax**: Immediate needle decompression and chest tube thoracostomy
- **Small pneumothorax**: Oxygen administration (3–4 L/min) and observation for 3-6 hours

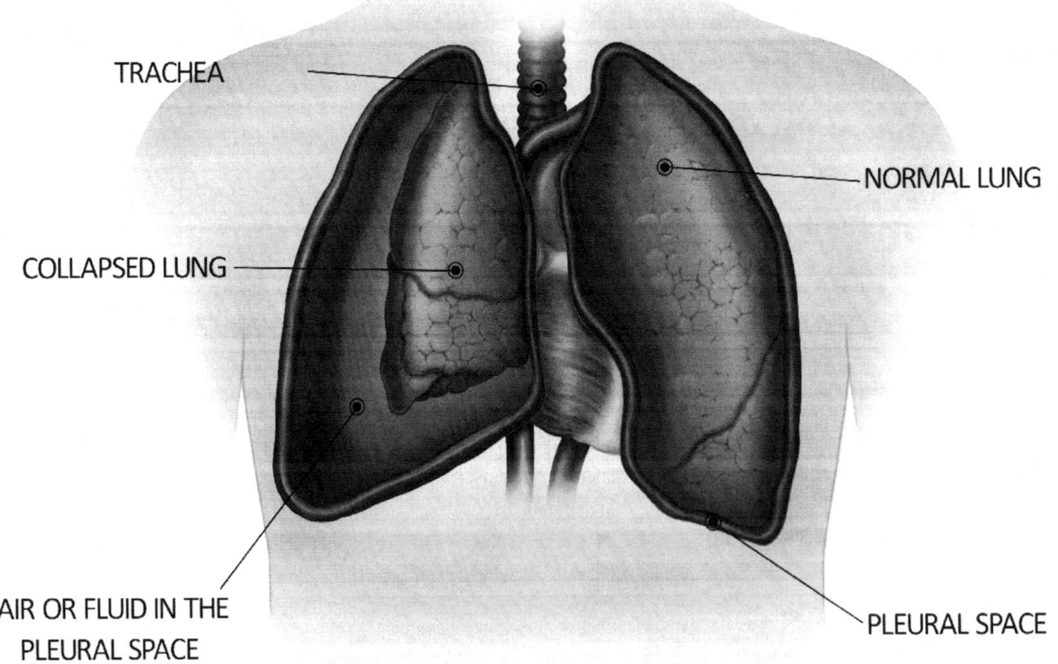

Review Video: Pneumothorax
Visit mometrix.com/academy and enter code: 186841

Postoperative Aspiration

Patients with neurovascular disorders, such as a history of stroke or Alzheimer's, and those with GERD or disorders of esophageal motility are most at risk for **postoperative aspiration**, which can lead to pneumonia and increased mortality. Other risk factors include altered mental status, chronic co-morbidities (such as diabetes), and some medications. Aspiration of gastric acids (which are generally sterile) may cause chemical irritation and pneumonitis, but aspiration of food particles may introduce bacteria into the lungs. Both can result in ARDS. In the postoperative period, patients should have assessment of swallowing prior to beginning oral intake. Diagnosis is based on clinical findings, ABGs showing hypoxemia, infiltrates observed on x-ray, and leukocytosis if infection is present. Symptoms may include cough (often with copious sputum), respiratory distress, cyanosis, tachycardia, and hypotension. Treatment includes:

- Suctioning as needed to clear upper airway
- Supplemental oxygen
- Antibiotic therapy as indicated after 48 hours if symptoms are not resolving
- Symptomatic respiratory support

Left Lower Lobe Atelectasis

Atelectasis, especially of the left lower lobe, occurs postoperatively in up to 70% of patients who have had cardiac surgery. Right-sided atelectasis most commonly occurs with fluid overload. Direct topical hypothermia (cold cardioplegia) to the heart can damage the left phrenic nerve and cause paresis or paralysis of the diaphragm, resulting in increased incidence of left lower lobe atelectasis. Harvesting of the internal thoracic artery is also associated with high rates of pleural effusion and atelectasis. Additionally, single lung ventilation and collapsing of one lung as part of the intraoperative procedure increases risks. Symptoms may be evident in the immediate postoperative period and include splinting, decreased ventilation, decreased oxygen saturation, and increased heart rate. Deep breathing, use of an incentive spirometer, intermittent positive pressure breathing treatments, and early ambulation may all help to prevent atelectasis.

Postoperative Bronchospasm

Bronchospasm, contraction of lower airway smooth muscles resulting in obstruction, may occur following cardiopulmonary bypass because of activation of anaphylatoxin but may also occur with minimally-invasive procedures. Other causes may include an allergic response to medications (drug-induced histamine release), exacerbation of pre-existing pulmonary disorders (COPD, asthma), beta-adrenergic blockade, and bronchial irritation from presurgical smoking or recent respiratory infection. Additionally, repeated bronchospasms may occur with pulmonary embolism. Postoperative lung dysfunction may increase risk of bronchospasm due to the increased work of breathing, shallow respirations, and ineffective cough. Signs and symptoms of bronchospasm include increasing dyspnea, cough, prolonged expiration, cyanosis, inability to speak, anxiety, hypertension, tachycardia, and blood gas abnormalities leading to respiratory alkalosis. Initial treatment includes removing the irritant or causative agent if possible, inhaled bronchodilators (such as albuterol), and non-invasive ventilation. If there is an inadequate response, patients may require systemic bronchodilators (such as epinephrine) and/or steroids (methylprednisolone), and some patients may require reintubation and mechanical ventilation.

Pleural Effusion

Pleural effusion (fluid in the outer layers of the lungs) is common after cardiac surgery, occurring in 41–87% of patients; it appears as an opacity on a radiograph. A pleural effusion usually arises within the first 24 hours, especially if chest tubes are not placed in the most dependent part of the pleural space. Common indications include dyspnea, dry nonproductive cough, chest pain, and orthopnea, although small effusions (<500 mL) may remain asymptomatic. Pleural effusions are most common on the left but may occur bilaterally. Small pleural effusions resolve over time, but large pleural effusions (>50% of lung) may require thoracentesis (often with ultrasound guidance) to drain fluid and relieve dyspnea. Correct positioning of chest tubes during surgery can help reduce the incidence of pleural effusions. Large pleural effusions may result in cardiac tamponade and atrial or ventricular diastolic collapse.

Review Video: Pleural Effusions
Visit mometrix.com/academy and enter code: 145719

CHYLOTHORAX

In some cases, interruption of the lymphatic system of the thoracic duct in the left proximal mediastinum during mobilization of the left internal mammary artery results in chylothorax, an expanding pleural effusion with milky fluid, related to dietary fat. **Chylothorax** may occur after chest tube removal with the enlarging pleural effusion noted on radiograph. Chyle is found in the pleural fluid, which contains increased levels of lymphocytes and triglycerides (>110 mg/dL). The drainage may appear to be purulent, so chyle must be verified by laboratory analysis. Treatment includes chest tube drainage, nonfat diet, and medium-chain triglycerides. Octreotide, 50-100 μg, may be given subcutaneously every 8 hours to seal the leak if it does not clear within a few days. In some cases, thoracoscopic repair may be necessary.

HEMOTHORAX

Hemothorax occurs with bleeding into the pleural space. Draining of mediastinal blood into the pleural space after cardiac surgery may result in a hemothorax. Additionally, a hemothorax may result from vascular injury related to central venous pressure catheters. A small bleed may be self-limiting and seal, but a large tear or excessive bleeding can result in massive blood loss, followed quickly by hypovolemic shock. The pressure from the blood may result in an inability of the lung to ventilate and a mediastinal shift. Often a hemothorax occurs with a pneumothorax. Further symptoms include severe respiratory distress, decreased breath sounds, and dullness on auscultation. Treatment includes controlling bleeding, placement of a chest tube, or ensuring patency to drain the hemothorax. With large volumes, the pressure may be preventing exsanguination, which can occur abruptly as the blood drains and pressure is reduced. Autotransfusion may be used to replace blood lost.

COMPLICATIONS FROM PROLONGED MECHANICAL VENTILATION

Possible complications of prolonged mechanical ventilation include:

- **Ventilator-induced lung injury**: Includes atelectrauma, biotrauma, volutrauma, and oxygen toxicity as well as barotrauma (pneumothorax, pneumomediastinum, SC emphysema) and results from overdistention and rupture of alveoli because of excessive pressure or volume.
- **Ventilator-associated pneumonia**: ETTs increase the risk of bacterial contamination of the lungs and prevent coughing.
- **Auto-PEEP/Air trapping**: Lungs fail to return to baseline pressure at the end of exhalation.
- **Gastrointestinal bleeding**: Associated with stress ulcers, coagulopathy, thrombocytopenia, and multi-organ dysfunction. Preventive measures include antacids, PPIs, or H2 blockers.
- **Malnutrition**: Nutrition must be carefully managed because inadequate nutrition increases risk of pneumonia and weakness of respiratory muscles while excess calorie consumption increases production of carbon dioxide, resulting in increased ventilatory requirements.

- **Cardiovascular alterations**: Decreased venous return and cardiac output, hypotension.
- **Renal alterations**: Decreased urinary output and produced of atrial natriuretic peptide but increased production of antidiuretic hormone.
- **Acid-base alterations**: Respiratory acidosis or alkalosis.

TACO

Transfusion-associated circulatory overload (TACO) occurs when blood transfusions result in volume excess, usually associated with multiple transfusions in a short period of time but may be exacerbated by cardiovascular impairment. Indications include development of symptoms usually within about 6 hours (although it may occur in up to 24 hours) of transfusions: acute respiratory distress, hypertension, tachycardia, and pulmonary edema. The patient may exhibit orthopnea and cyanosis, and examination may find pulmonary rales, S3 cardiac sound, JVD, and peripheral edema. Patients at risk are children under age 3 and adults over age 60 (especially with cardiac disease, such as heart failure). Treatment includes discontinuing transfusions, respiratory support as needed, and diuretics to help to reduce pulmonary and peripheral edema. Patients with TACO are also at risk of transfusion-related acute lung injury (TRALI) and may have indications of both. Differentiating TACO from TRALI can be difficult because symptoms are similar. TACO is characterized by increased BNP and NT-pro-BNP.

PULMONARY DYSFUNCTION RESULTING FROM CARDIAC SURGERY

Pulmonary dysfunction can result from many factors related to cardiac surgery:

- General anesthesia and anesthetic agents, such as paralytic agents, result in decreased respiratory drive and impairment of the diaphragm and intercostal muscles. The supine position causes the chest wall to relax and changes in compliance.
- Cardiopulmonary bypass may result in pulmonary edema, interstitial pulmonary edema, and adult respiratory distress syndrome because of an inflammatory response and capillary leak. Inadequate ventilation of alveoli may result in atelectasis. The phrenic nerve injury from cooling may cause diaphragmatic paralysis.
- Sternotomy or thoracotomy may result in pain and splinting that impairs respirations.
- Internal mammary artery harvesting may cause impaired chest wall compliance because of incision into the pleura.
- Preexisting conditions, such as pulmonary disease or obesity, may further impair respirations.
- Habits, such as smoking, may cause increased bronchospasm and muscle weakness.
- Mechanical ventilation for over 48 hours increases the risk of pneumonia.

INJURY TO THE PHRENIC NERVE AND DIAPHRAGMATIC DYSFUNCTION

The **phrenic nerve** controls the action of the diaphragm and is essential to breathing. If the phrenic nerve is injured, this can cause unilateral or bilateral **diaphragmatic dysfunction** (paralysis). Injury (occurring in 1–30% of cardiac surgery patients) may result from iced slush used for myocardial protection during cardioplegic arrest. Damage to the nerve may also occur with harvesting of the left internal mammary artery or other surgical trauma. Unilateral injury is most common and usually does not severely impair ventilation, although lower lobe atelectasis, especially on the left, may occur. Symptoms include paradoxical movement of the diaphragm, nocturnal orthopnea, or dyspnea on exertion. Bilateral injuries may result in a longer duration of mechanical ventilation, difficulty weaning, prolonged nocturnal respiratory insufficiency, and in some cases acute respiratory failure. Plication of the diaphragm may be necessary to improve pulmonary function if the patient's respirations are severely compromised. Diagnosis is by chest x-ray, fluoroscopy, spirometry, nerve conduction studies, or ultrasound.

Acute Pulmonary Embolism

Acute pulmonary embolism occurs when a pulmonary artery or arteriole is blocked by a blood clot originating in the venous system or the right heart. While most pulmonary emboli are from thrombus formation, other causes may be air, fat, or septic embolus (from bacterial invasion of a thrombus). After cardiac surgery, most incidences are associated with deep venous thrombosis of the lower extremities. Other originating sites are the pelvic veins and the right atrium. Causes include stasis related to damage to the endothelial wall and changes in blood coagulation factors. Atrial fibrillation poses a serious risk because blood pools in the right atrium, forming clots that travel directly through the right ventricle to the lungs. The obstruction of the artery or arteriole causes an increase in alveolar dead space in which there is ventilation but impairment of gas exchange because of the ventilation–perfusion mismatching or intrapulmonary shunting. This results in hypoxia and the release of mediators that cause bronchoconstriction. Hypoxia leads to tachypnea which may present initially as respiratory alkalosis on early blood gas readings. In the case of severe hypoxia and systemic compromise that may ensue in later stages of a massive pulmonary embolism, a combination of metabolic and respiratory acidosis can occur. Metabolic acidosis occurs as a compensatory mechanism to the initial respiratory alkalosis, and in the case of systemic shut down and respiratory failure, respiratory acidosis can then result. If more than 50% of the vascular bed becomes excluded, pulmonary hypertension occurs.

Symptoms and Diagnostic Tests

Clinical manifestations of **acute pulmonary embolism (PE)** vary, according to the size of the embolus and the area of occlusion.

Symptoms include the following:

- Dyspnea with tachypnea
- Tachycardia
- Anxiety and restlessness
- Chest pain
- Fever
- Rales
- Cough (sometimes with hemoptysis)
- Hemodynamic instability

The following diagnostic tests for **PE** are used:

- Arterial blood gas analysis may show hypoxemia (decreased partial pressure of oxygen), hypocarbia (decreased partial pressure of carbon dioxide), and respiratory alkalosis (increased pH) in early stages that may transition to metabolic and respiratory acidosis in the later stages of severe cases.
- D-dimer will show elevation with PE.
- Electrocardiogram may show sinus tachycardia or other abnormalities.
- Echocardiogram can show emboli in the central arteries and can assess the hemodynamic status of the right side of the heart.
- Chest x-ray is of minimal value.
- Spiral computed tomography may provide a definitive diagnosis.

- Ventilation–perfusion scintigraphy can confirm the diagnosis.
- Pulmonary angiograms also can confirm the diagnosis.

Management

Medical management of pulmonary embolism starts with preventive measures for those at risk, including leg exercises, elastic compression stockings, and anticoagulation therapy (warfarin [Coumadin]). Most pulmonary emboli present as medical emergencies, so the immediate task is to stabilize the patient. Medical management may include the following:

- **Oxygen** to relieve hypoxemia
- **Intravenous infusions**
- **Dobutamine** (Dobutrex) or **dopamine** (Intropin) to relieve hypotension
- **Cardiac monitoring for dysrhythmias**
- **Medications** as indicated: Digitalis glycosides, diuretic, and antiarrhythmics
- **Intubation** and mechanical ventilation
- **Analgesia** (morphine sulfate) or sedation to relieve anxiety

Additional medical management of a pulmonary embolism may include the following:

- **Anticoagulants** can be administered to prevent recurrence, including heparin and warfarin (Coumadin), but they will not dissolve clots already present.
- **Placement of percutaneous venous filter** (Greenfield) in the inferior vena cava can prevent further emboli from entering the lungs if anticoagulation therapy is contraindicated.
- **Thrombolytic therapy**, recombinant tissue-type plasminogen activator or streptokinase, can be administered for those severely compromised with limited success; however, there is a danger of bleeding.

Hematology/Immunology

Bleeding

Upper GI Bleeding

Upper gastrointestinal (GI) bleeding can occur with both on-pump and off-pump cardiac surgeries, usually from development of a duodenal stress ulceration because of ischemia and hypoperfusion/reperfusion injury. Mortality rates associated with upper GI bleeding are 15–20%. Risk factors include a history of gastric disorders (i.e., gastritis, ulcers) and advanced age. Postoperative conditions that increase risk include decreased cardiac output, coagulopathy, anticoagulation, and prolonged mechanical ventilation. Indications include bright red drainage from a nasogastric (NG) tube, vomiting of blood, or bloody stools. Preventive measures include sucralfate, 1 g every 6 hours (PO or per NG tube) or proton pump inhibitors (pantoprazole, 40 mg IV or PO; omeprazole, 20 mg daily PO; lansoprazole, 15 mg daily PO; rabeprazole, 10 mg daily PO). Those receiving acetylsalicylic acid should receive enteric-coated preparations. Treatment includes upper GI endoscopy with laser bipolar coagulation and somatostatin infusion, 250 µg/hr for 3 days, for severe bleeding.

Lower GI Bleeding

Lower gastrointestinal (GI) bleeding can occur with mesenteric ischemia, ischemic colitis associated with extended hypoperfusion, *Clostridium difficile* or other super infection from antibiotics, anticoagulation (i.e., bleeding polyps, lesions), and intestinal angiodysplasia (i.e., Heyde's syndrome, which can occur with aortic stenosis). Indications include melena, blood-streaked stool, or frank rectal bleeding. Upper GI bleeding is ruled out with insertion of a nasogastric tube, followed by sigmoidoscopy or colonoscopy to identify the cause and site of bleeding. Underlying coagulopathy or another cause must be identified and treated. Treatment may include mesenteric angiography and vasopressin infusion; embolotherapy; octreotide, 50 µg over 50 minutes; or somatostatin, 50 µg bolus with follow-up infusion of 250 µg/hr. On rare occasions, surgical intervention may be necessary.

DIC

Disseminated intravascular coagulation (DIC), also known as consumption coagulopathy, is a secondary disorder that is triggered by another, such as trauma, congenital heart disease, necrotizing enterocolitis, sepsis, and severe viral infections. DIC triggers both coagulation and hemorrhage through a complex series of events that includes trauma that causes tissue factor (transmembrane glycoprotein) to enter the circulation and bind with coagulation factors, triggering the coagulation cascade. This stimulates thrombin to convert fibrinogen to fibrin, causing aggregation and destruction of platelets and forming clots that can be disseminated throughout the intravascular system. These clots increase in size as platelets adhere to them, causing blockage of both the microvascular systems and larger vessels, which can result in ischemia and necrosis. Clot formation triggers fibrinolysis and plasmin to breakdown fibrin and fibrinogen, causing destruction of clotting factors, resulting in hemorrhage. Both processes, clotting and hemorrhage, continue at the same time, placing the patient at high risk for death, even with treatment.

SIGNS, SYMPTOMS, AND TREATMENT

The onset of symptoms of disseminated intravascular coagulation (DIC) may be very rapid or progress slowly, resulting in a chronic form of the disease. Those who develop DIC from chronic disease usually have fewer acute symptoms and may slowly develop ecchymosis or bleeding wounds.

The following are **signs and symptoms** of DIC:

- Bleeding from surgical or venous puncture sites
- Evidence of gastrointestinal bleeding with distention and bloody diarrhea
- Hypotension and acute symptoms of shock
- Petechiae and purpura with extensive bleeding into the tissues
- Laboratory abnormalities:
    - Prolonged prothrombin and partial thromboplastin times
    - Decreased platelet counts and fragmented red blood cells
    - Decreased fibrinogen

The following **treatments** are used for DIC:

- Identifying and treating the underlying cause
- Replacement blood products, such as platelets and fresh frozen plasma
- Anticoagulation therapy (heparin) to increase clotting time
- Cryoprecipitate to increase fibrinogen levels
- Coagulation inhibitors and coagulation factors

THROMBOCYTOPENIA

Thrombocytopenia occurs when the platelet count drops to less than 50,000/mm^3, putting the patient at high risk for bleeding from trauma injury or conditions that affect blood coagulation (i.e., hemophilia, liver disease). Thrombocytopenia may occur with cardiac surgery because of hemodilution or destruction of platelets during extracorporeal circulation or from intra-aortic balloon pump (IABP). Platelet counts usually improve within a few days. Other causes include some medications (i.e., heparin, inamrinone) and sepsis. After surgery, thrombocytopenia may manifest as impaired hemostasis. When the platelet count drops below 20,000/mm^3, the patient may have spontaneous bleeding. Treatment includes platelet transfusions for counts less than 20,000–30,000/mm^3. If persistent bleeding occurs, transfusions are given if the count is less than 100,000/mm^3, although, with platelet dysfunction, transfusions may be administered at higher counts. If the patient is to undergo a planned surgical procedure, such as IABP removal, then transfusions are given at 60,000/mm^3 or less to reduce the risk of intraoperative and postoperative bleeding.

HIT/HITTS

Heparin-induced thrombocytopenia and thrombosis syndrome (HITTS) occurs in patients receiving heparin for anticoagulation. There are two types:

- **Type I** is a transient condition occurring within a few days and causing depletion of platelets (<100,000 mm³), but heparin may be continued as the condition usually resolves without intervention.
- **Type II** is an autoimmune reaction to heparin that occurs in 3–5% of those receiving unfractionated heparin and also occurs with low-molecular-weight heparin. It is characterized by low platelets (<50,000 mm³) that are ≥50% below baseline. Onset is 5–14 days but can occur within hours of heparinization. Death rates are <30%. Heparin-antibody complexes form and release platelet factor 4 (PF4), which attracts heparin molecules and adheres to platelets and endothelial lining, stimulating thrombin and platelet clumping. This puts the patient at risk for thrombosis and vessel occlusion rather than hemorrhage, causing stroke, myocardial infarction, and limb ischemia with symptoms associated with the site of thrombosis. Treatment includes:
    - Discontinuation of heparin
    - Direct thrombin inhibitors (lepirudin, argatroban)
    - Monitor for signs/symptoms of thrombus/embolus

Heparin-Rebound Effect

Protamine is a polypeptide derived from salmon sperm and is used for both on- and off-pump procedures to reverse the effects of heparin. Although protamine is given at the end of surgery to reverse heparin, a **heparin-rebound effect** may occur after surgery, causing a recurrence of anticoagulation and increased bleeding. After cardiopulmonary bypass, some heparin remains bound to tissues and protein, and as this slowly releases, the heparin-rebound effect occurs. Additional infusions of protamine will reduce this effect. Protamine (25 mg intravenously for two doses) is indicated for postoperative mediastinal bleeding if the partial thromboplastin time is elevated. Transesophageal echocardiography is indicated if there are concerns about cardiac tamponade. Packed red blood cells are indicated for a hematocrit of less than 26%. Desmopressin (0.3 μg/kg intravenously) is indicated for uremia or platelet dysfunction related to the use of aspirin.

Anaphylaxis Syndrome

Anaphylaxis syndrome is a sudden acute systemic immunoglobulin E (IgE)/G (IgG) or non-immunoglobulin E (non-IgE/non-IgG) inflammatory response affecting the cardiopulmonary and other systems.

- **IgE-mediated or IgG response** (anaphylactic shock) is an antibody–antigen reaction against an allergen, such as milk, peanuts, latex, insect bites, or fish (and fish-derived medications, such as protamine). This is the most common type.
- **Non–IgE-/non–IgG-mediated response** (anaphylactoid reaction) is a systemic reaction to infection, exercise, radio contrast material, or other triggers. While the response is almost identical to the other type, it does not involve IgE/IgG.

Typically, with IgE-mediated response, an antigen triggers release of substances, such as histamine and prostaglandins, which affect the skin and the cardiopulmonary and gastrointestinal systems. Histamine causes initial erythema and edema by inducing vasodilation. Each time the person has contact with the antigen, more antibodies form in response, so allergic reactions worsen with each contact. In some cases, initial reactions may be mild, but subsequent contact can cause severe life-threatening response.

PROTAMINE ANAPHYLACTIC REACTION

Protamine sulfate, a heparin antagonist, is comprised of strongly basic proteins derived from salmon sperm and some other fish, so allergies to fish can put the patient at risk for **protamine anaphylactic reaction**. Skin testing and prophylaxis with histamine blockers and steroids have not proven of value. There are three different types of reactions.

TYPE I

Hypotension may occur if protamine is given too rapidly (within 3 minutes) of discontinuation of cardiopulmonary bypass. This histamine-related response decreases systemic vascular resistance and pulmonary vascular resistance. This reaction is reversible with administration of an α agent. Protamine should be administered over 10–15 minutes to avoid this reaction. This reaction is common in diabetics who take protamine-containing insulin.

TYPE II

Reactions may be anaphylactic or anaphylactoid:

- **IIA**: An anaphylactic (IgE or IgG) reaction results in a systemic capillary leak and hypotension with pulmonary edema, usually within 10–20 minutes of administration.
- **IIB**: Immediate anaphylactoid reaction is seen.
- **IIC**: Reaction is delayed for 20 minutes or more. The patient may exhibit wheezing, pulmonary edema (noncardiogenic) related to capillary leak, hypotension, and hypovolemia.

TYPE III

SIGNS AND SYMPTOMS

The following are signs and symptoms of Type III protamine anaphylactic reaction:

- Sudden onset of weakness, dizziness, and confusion
- Urticaria
- Increased permeability of vascular system and loss of vascular tone
- Peripheral dilation with severe hypotension, leading to shock
- Laryngospasm/bronchospasm with obstruction of airway, causing dyspnea and wheezing
- Increased pulmonary artery pressure
- Nausea, vomiting, and diarrhea
- Seizures, coma, and death

Treatment

The following are treatments of Type III protamine anaphylactic reaction:

- Calcium chloride, 500 mg intravenously (IV), to increase systemic vascular resistance (SVR)
- α agents: phenylephrine/norepinephrine to increase SVR
- β agents: low-dose epinephrine, milrinone, inamrinone, and dobutamine to decrease pulmonary resistance
- Nitrates: nitroglycerin to decrease preload and pulmonary pressures
- Aminophylline: to control wheezing
- Heparin: to reverse protamine reaction
- Hydrocortisone, 100 mg IV, to reduce immune response
- Methylene blue, 1 mg/kg (in nitric acid involvement)

Anemia with Cardiac Surgery

Anemia is common with cardiac surgery because of hemodilution associated with cardiopulmonary bypass (CPB). Hematocrit levels are usually maintained at about 20% during CPB and at 22–24% in the postoperative period, although patients of advanced age may require transfusions to increase hematocrit if they experience marked fatigue or weakness, electrocardiographic abnormalities, or marked tachycardia. Usually, postoperative diuresis increases the hematocrit slowly, but the level may remain depressed as fluid moves from the blood into extracellular tissues. Additional extracorporeal circulation damages red blood cells, shortening their lifespans, and about 30% of red blood cells received by transfusion are lost within 24 hours. Patients with a hematocrit of less than 30% at the time of discharge should receive iron supplementation with ferrous sulfate or ferrous gluconate (300 mg three times daily for 4 weeks), although this may not be necessary if the patient has received multiple transfusions because of iron retained from hemolysis.

Neurological

Type I Neurological Deficits Associated with Cardiac Surgery

Type I neurological deficits associated with cardiac surgery include those with high morbidity: major focal neurological deficits, strokes, transient ischemic attacks, stupor, and coma. These occur in approximately 3% of cardiac surgery patients and result in a 21% mortality rate. Patients with type I neurological deficits tend to have an increased length of hospitalization and increased need for support after discharge. Risk factors include age over 70 years, with a history of pulmonary disease, hypertension, moderate-to-severe proximal aortic atherosclerosis, left main coronary stenosis, diabetes mellitus, or unstable angina. Other surgical risk factors include use of an intra-aortic balloon pump or a left ventricular assist device and perioperative hypoperfusion. Aortic lesions are of special concern as manipulation of the aorta during surgery may result in emboli, so risk increases with the number of aortic anastomoses.

Type II Neurological Deficits Associated with Cardiac Surgery

Type II neurological deficits associated with cardiac surgery include changes in mental status, confusion, loss of memory, agitation, disorientation, and seizures. Type II deficits are more common than the more severe type I deficits and may be more difficult to diagnose because the symptoms are more subtle and may be overlooked as simply a response to anesthesia or analgesia. While drugs may exacerbate symptoms, they persist even after the drugs are discontinued. Studies show that over half of patients undergoing coronary artery bypass graft experience type II neurological deficits. Risk factors for type II deficits include age over 70 years and a history of pulmonary disease, hypertension, or heart failure as well as a history of alcoholism. Other surgical risk factors include development of postoperative dysrhythmias, history of previous cardiac surgery, and episodes of hypoperfusion or hypotension.

Postoperative Impaired Cognition

Impaired cognition is very common after both on-pump and off-pump cardiac procedures with estimates reaching as high as 70%. Symptoms include forgetfulness, short attention span, impaired memory, inability to think of appropriate words, and reduced psychomotor function. Risk factors include preexisting cerebrovascular disease, diabetes, and advanced age. Impaired cognition is most pronounced in those with preoperative cognitive abnormalities. Early impaired cognition is believed to be related to cerebral microembolization and hypoperfusion or an inflammatory response to cardiopulmonary bypass, which may be reversible. Other possible causes include intraoperative hyperthermia and hyperglycemia. Delayed impaired cognition is more likely related to preexisting cerebrovascular disease and is more likely to be permanent.

Postoperative Spinal Cord Ischemia

Post-cardiac surgery spinal cord ischemia may result in paraplegia. The lumbo-sacral area of the spine is particularly vulnerable to hypoperfusion. Procedures that increase risk include those on the thoracic or abdominal aorta because aortic occlusion can result in distal hypotension and hypoperfusion of the spinal cord (usually below T9), since the spinal arteries originate in the aorta. Other procedures that carry risk are CABG, heart transplant, and valve repairs/replacements. Hypothermia is utilized during cardiopulmonary bypass to decrease the risk of spinal cord ischemia. However, extended periods of cardiopulmonary bypass (>240 minutes) and cross clamping (>150 minutes) increase risks. In some cases, intraoperative embolization with spinal cord infarction may occur, resulting in paralysis, usually at T4-T9. Spinal cord ischemia may also occur with hematomas (subadventitial/epidural). Diagnosis in those cases may be delayed because of patient sedation. Diagnosis is per neurological examination and MRI. Treatment is generally supportive although some neurological deficits may slowly resolve, depending on the severity of the injury.

Postoperative Vocal Cord Paralysis

Vocal cord paralysis post-cardiac surgery may result from a variety of causes:

- Prolonged intubation
- Trauma to the vocal cords
- Compression of recurrent laryngeal nerve (anterior) by excessive intracuff inflation
- Dysfunction of recurrent laryngeal nerve from hypothermia
- Compression of vagal and hypoglossal nerves at C1 during sternotomy if neck flexed laterally and hyperextended

Risk increases with procedures involving the aorta (and damage tends to be more severe), intubation of greater than 100 hours, history of hypertension, and prolonged surgical time. Paralysis may be permanent or may resolve over a period of weeks. Typical symptoms include hoarseness, stridor, impaired cough, breathy-sounding voices, dysphagia, and limited vocal range. Because of weakness and sedation following surgery, vocal cord paralysis may be overlooked initially. With bilateral injury, the patient is especially at risk for aspiration and increased mortality and may require tracheostomy and/or reintubation. Treatment options may include voice therapy, collagen injections, and/or surgical repair.

Cerebral Hypoxia and Anoxic Encephalopathy

Cerebral hypoxia (hypoxic encephalopathy) occurs when the oxygen supply to the brain is decreased. If hypoxia is mild, the brain compensates by increasing cerebral blood flow, but it can only double in volume and cannot compensate for severe hypoxic conditions. Hypoxia may be the result of insufficient oxygen in the environment, inadequate exchange at the alveolar level of the lungs, or inadequate circulation to the brain. Brain cells may begin dying within five minutes of deprived of adequate oxygenation, so any condition or trauma that interferes with oxygenation can result in brain damage, including the following:

- Near-drowning
- Asphyxia
- Cardiac arrest
- High altitude sickness
- Carbon monoxide
- Diseases that interfere with respiration, such as myasthenia gravis and amyotrophic lateral sclerosis
- Anesthesia complications

Symptoms include increasing neurological deficits, depending on the degree and area of damage, with changes in mentation that range from confusion to coma. Prompt identification of the cause and an increase in perfusion to the brain are critical for survival.

Anoxic encephalopathy, resulting from complete lack of oxygen to the brain, can occur with cardiac arrest, head trauma, asphyxia, increasing intracranial pressure, fat embolism, status epilepticus, and severe cerebral atherosclerosis. Biochemical changes occur in the brain within five minutes without oxygenation.

Metabolic Encephalopathy

Metabolic encephalopathy (hepatic encephalopathy) is damage to the brain resulting from a disturbance in metabolism, primarily hepatic failure to remove toxins from the blood. There may be impairment in cerebral blood flow, cerebral edema, or increased intracranial pressure. It can occur as the result of ingestion of drugs or toxins, which can have a direct toxic effect on neurons and can also occur with liver disease, especially when stressed by co-morbidities, such as hemorrhage, hypoxemia, surgery, trauma, renal failure with dialysis, or electrolyte imbalances. Symptoms may vary:

- Irritability and agitation
- Alterations in consciousness
- Dysphonia
- Lack of coordination and spasticity
- Seizures, commonly the presenting symptom
- Disorientation progressing to coma

Prompt diagnosis is important because the condition may be reversible if underlying causes are identified and treated before permanent neuronal damage occurs. Treatment varies, according to the underlying cause.

Risk Factors for Strokes Associated with Cardiac Surgery

Risk factors for strokes associated with cardiac surgery are multiple and can include preexisting conditions, habits, and health problems as well as factors related to the surgical procedure. The most common etiology is cerebral microembolization, occurring during coronary artery bypass graft surgery. **Risk factors** include the following:

- Preexisting carotid disease (present in about 30%)
- Female gender
- Surgery involving manipulation of the aorta
- Calcified aorta
- Advanced age
- History of previous stroke
- Critical condition and weakened state before surgery
- Compromised ventricular function
- History of diabetes mellitus or renal failure
- History of unstable angina, recent myocardial infarction, hypertension, and low-cardiac output syndrome
- Peripheral vascular disease
- Pulmonary hypertension
- Development of postoperative atrial fibrillation (increases risk two to five times)
- History of smoking
- Prolonged cardiopulmonary bypass surgery
- Reoperative (repeat) surgery

Embolic and Hemorrhagic Strokes

Up to 5% of cardiac surgery patients experience a stroke as a complication, usually within the first 24–48 hours. Most stokes are ischemic. Manipulation of the ascending aorta is a primary risk factor for developing intraoperative or postoperative (most common) **embolic strokes**. Strokes are also often preceded by a period of atrial fibrillation (Afib), especially if Afib persists for extended periods (48 hours). Afib is treated with cardioversion or pharmacological rate control with anticoagulation. However, **hemorrhagic strokes** may result from anticoagulation needed for cardiopulmonary bypass, causing a ruptured cerebral artery. This results in not only a lack of oxygen and nutrients but also edema that causes widespread pressure and damage. About 30% of infarcts may undergo hemorrhagic conversion. Multiple infarcts of varying sizes may occur following cardiac surgery. Serial computed tomography scans may be necessary for diagnosis as the initial scan may be negative. Diffusion weighted magnetic resonance imaging is most sensitive but may not be possible, and it may show preoperative undiagnosed infarcts.

Stroke Location

Strokes most commonly occur in the right or left hemisphere, but the exact location and the extent of brain damage determine the presenting symptoms. If the frontal area of either side is involved, there tends to be memory and learning deficits. Some symptoms are common to specific areas and help to identify the area involved.

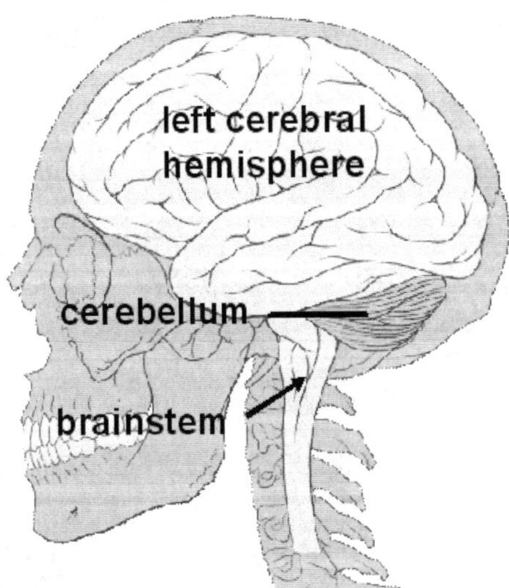

- A stroke in the **right hemisphere** of the brain results in left paralysis or paresis and a left visual field deficit that may cause spatial and perceptual disturbances so patients often have difficulty judging distance. Fine motor skills may be impacted, resulting in trouble dressing or handling tools. People may become impulsive and exhibit poor judgment, often denying impairment. Left-sided neglect (lack of perception of things on the left side) may occur. Depression, short-term memory loss, and difficulty following directions are common. Language skills usually remain intact.
- A stroke in the **left hemisphere** of the brain results in right paralysis or paresis and a right visual field defect. Depression is common, and people often exhibit slow, cautious behavior, requiring repeated instruction and reinforcement for simple tasks. Short-term memory loss and difficulty learning new material or understanding generalizations are common. Difficulty with mathematics, reading, writing, and reasoning may occur. Aphasia (e.g., expressive, receptive, global) is common.
- Because the **brain stem** controls respiration and cardiac function, a brain attack or stroke in the brain stem frequently causes death, but those who survive may have a number of problems, including respiratory and cardiac abnormalities. Strokes may involve motor or sensory impairment or both.
- The **cerebellum** controls balance and coordination. Strokes in the cerebellum are rare but may result in ataxia, nausea, vomiting, headaches, and vertigo.

Management of Stroke in Cardiac Surgery Patient

Stroke management in the cardiac surgery patient is usually aimed at support in the early stage and prevention of secondary complications. Supportive treatments include the following:

- Provide oxygen support to maintain oxygen saturation at 95% or more.
- Provide endotracheal intubation if necessary to maintain adequate ventilation.
- Prevent hyperthermia through methods such as antipyretics and cooling devices, as a 1–2 °C increase in brain temperature can cause damage.
- Monitor and maintain blood pressure (BP) at levels that allow for adequate perfusion. Hypertension should be controlled gradually, avoiding hypotension. In many cases, BP falls after a stroke without medications. Hypotension is treated with fluid boluses or vasopressor.
- Maintain glycemic control; hypoglycemia may present with symptoms similar to a stroke, and hyperglycemia increases morbidity from strokes. Serum glucose should be maintained at 80–140 mg/dL.
- Administer aspirin, as it may improve outcomes if not contraindicated.

Brachial Plexus Injury and Paraplegia Associated with Cardiac Surgery

Sternal retraction may result in brachial plexus injury, often associated with fracture of the first rib. Patients may complain of impaired sensation, including numbness, paresthesia, pain, and weakness related to T8–T1 injury, along the ulnar nerve distribution, often in the fourth and fifth fingers. Radial nerve deficits may also occur but are rare. Diagnosis is based on symptoms, electromyography results, motor and sensory conduction velocities, and somatosensory-evoked potentials. In most cases, no treatment is necessary as symptoms resolve over a few months, although a few patients may have persistent problems. Patients complaining of pain may get relief from amitriptyline, gabapentin, or carbamazepine.

Paraplegia is a rare complication of aortic dissection and may also result from use of an intra-aortic balloon pump. With the coronary artery bypass graft procedure, paraplegia usually occurs following an episode of hypotension in patients with preexisting hypertension and vascular compromise.

Saphenous and Radial Neuropathy

Saphenous neuropathy results from injury to branches of the saphenous nerve during harvesting of the saphenous vein. Indications include impaired sensation in the lower leg (medial aspect) and foot (to the great toe), especially if the vein is harvested distally to proximally. Endoscopic harvesting decreases the risk of saphenous neuropathy although it can still occur.

Radial neuropathy is common, occurring in 42–64% of patients during harvesting of the radial nerve. Indications include impaired sensation and paresthesia.

Gastrointestinal

Postoperative GI Complications

Gastrointestinal (GI) complications are rare following cardiac surgery, and most complications occur about a week after surgery. Risk factors for GI complications include prolonged mechanical ventilation, septic shock, and impaired renal function or complications. Those developing GI complications have an increased mortality rate (50%), so prevention is essential. Complications are commonly associated with splanchnic (visceral) hypoperfusion resulting from decreased cardiac output, with resulting vasoconstriction, hypoxia, and general hypoperfusion, leading to ischemia. Indications include decreased or absent bowel sounds, abdominal pain, abdominal distention, nausea, and vomiting. Other GI complications can include ileus, upper GI bleeding, hepatic failure, acute pancreatitis, and cholecystitis. Proton pump inhibitors are given to those with nasogastric tubes to reduce the incidence of bleeding.

Paralytic Ileus and Pseudo-Obstructions

Paralytic ileus is a bowel obstruction resulting from impairment of neural innervation of the intestines, usually related to infection, electrolyte imbalance, or surgical manipulation. Symptoms include decreased or absent bowel sounds, abdominal pain, inability to defecate, seepage of liquid feces, abdominal distention, nausea, vomiting, electrolyte imbalance, and dehydration. Paralytic ileus may be present for several days after cardiac surgery and usually clears by taking nothing by mouth with nasogastric suctioning. Total parenteral nutrition should be initiated, and medications that interfere with motility (e.g., narcotics, calcium channel blockers, anticholinergics) should be discontinued when possible. Metabolic imbalances must be corrected.

Pseudo-obstructions (acute and massive colonic dilatation) are treated with neostigmine, 2 mg intravenously, to decompress a distended colon rapidly. In persistent cases of colonic distention of 12 cm or more, decompressive colonoscopy or surgical intervention may be necessary.

Mesenteric Ischemia

Mesenteric ischemia is a rare complication of cardiac surgery, usually identified 5–10 days postoperatively. Most occurrences are nonocclusive, usually associated with splanchnic (visceral) ischemia, especially in older patients with atherosclerosis and dehydration. An intra-aortic balloon pump may cause atherosclerotic embolism, heparin-induced thrombocytopenia, and mesenteric thrombosis. Indications include paralytic ileus or severe acute abdominal pain. Patients may exhibit absent bowel sounds, and elevated lactate. Other complications, such as sepsis, hemodynamic instability, and gastrointestinal bleeding, may be present as well, obscuring the diagnosis. Mortality rate is high (>65%) without prompt identification and treatment. Surgical exploration and bowel resection may be necessary with intestinal necrosis.

Post-Cardiac Surgery Ischemic Bowel

Post-cardiac surgery ischemic bowel is a rare but potentially fatal complication. Risk factors include a history of peripheral vascular disease, steroid use, NYHA class 4, and cardiogenic shock as well as CABG procedure, hypothermic cardiopulmonary bypass, prolonged ventilator time (>24 hours postoperative), IABP, post-surgical CVI, post-surgical renal failure with serum creatinine greater than 200 micromol/L. Causes include hypoperfusion of splanchnic blood flow and mesenteric ischemia. The hypoperfusion may be exacerbated by the use of vasoconstrictors for >48 hours and the presence of atherosclerosis. Ischemic bowel may also occur with embolization/thrombosis, but less commonly. Symptoms may be non-specific, especially for patients under sedation, but may include sudden LLQ pain, the urge to defecate, and bloody stools or RLQ pain, usually without bleeding. Lack of bowel sounds is common but not universal. Patients may develop metabolic acidosis, elevated serum lactate, hyperkalemia, and increased WBC count. Perforation may occur, leading to peritonitis. Diagnostic studies may include colonoscopy, mesenteric angiography, and CT. Treatment may include vasodilators, restricted intake, and antibiotic therapy as well as complete or partial colectomy, depending on the severity of the ischemia.

Pharyngeal Dysfunction with Dysphagia Following Cardiac Surgery

Pharyngeal dysfunction with dysphagia occurs in 3% or fewer patients who undergo coronary artery bypass graft and increases the risk of aspiration, both silent and overt. Prolonged intubation increases the risk with about half of patients intubated for more than 48 hours experiencing dysphagia. Risk factors include advanced age, type 1 diabetes, renal impairment, chronic obstructive pulmonary disease, and a history or perioperative occurrence of stroke. The bedside swallowing test may help to identify overt aspiration. The patient is carefully observed while swallowing 50 mL of water. Indications of aspiration include a decrease in oxygen saturation per oximetry, coughing, or choking. Patients may require dietary modifications to reduce the risk of aspiration and referral to an occupational or speech therapist to improve swallowing. In severe cases, a feeding tube may be required to ensure adequate nutrition.

Hepatic Dysfunction

Hepatic dysfunction is common after cardiac surgery, especially with prolonged cardiopulmonary bypass and multiple procedures. It is characterized by transient low-grade elevation of liver function tests. About a quarter of patients will develop hyperbilirubinemia and jaundice with bilirubin over 3 mg/dL, but less than 1% progress to post-pump liver failure, which is characterized by coagulopathy, hypoglycemia, renal failure, encephalopathy, and refractory acidosis. Elevated bilirubin by itself is usually benign and self-limiting. Patients must be monitored carefully for coagulopathy during periods of hepatic dysfunction, as the impaired liver may not produce adequate clotting factors. Patients may exhibit jaundice or coagulopathy (i.e., a liver unable to produce sufficient clotting factors), hypoglycemia, renal failure, acidosis, or encephalopathy.

Treatment

Treatment includes the following:

- **Coagulopathy**: INR monitored and low doses of warfarin given, if anticoagulation is required
- **Stress ulcers**: Proton pump inhibitor, such as pantoprazole, 40 mg intravenously or orally daily, for prophylaxis
- **Hypoglycemia**: Careful monitoring and administration of glucose
- **Hyperammonemia/encephalopathy**: Restrict protein; rifaximin, 550 mg PO twice daily; zinc sulfate, 600 mg daily; and lactulose, 30 mL four times daily with sorbitol
- **Lactic acidosis**: Sodium bicarbonate if base deficit is over 10 mEq/L

Renal

RIFLE Criteria for Classifying Renal Failure

The RIFLE criteria for classifying renal failure helps to identify acute kidney injury and progressive renal dysfunction after cardiac surgery. **RIFLE classifications** include:

- **Risk** (most common) includes increased serum creatinine by 150% or decreased glomerular filtration rate (GFR) by 25% or more with urinary output of 0.5 mL/kg per hour or more over 6 hours.
- **Injury** includes increased serum creatinine by 200% or decreased GFR by 50% or more with urine output of 0.5 mL/kg per hour or less over 12 hours.
- **Failure** includes increased serum creatinine by 300%, decreased GFR by 75%, serum creatinine 4 mg/dL or more, or an acute rise in serum creatinine of 0.5 mg/dL or more with urine output 0.3 mL/kg per hour or less over 24 hours.
- **Loss** is acute renal failure persisting 4 weeks or more.
- **End-stage kidney disease** occurs after 3 months.

Prerenal, Intrarenal, and Postrenal Disorders

Acute renal failure is abrupt and almost complete failure of kidney function with a decreased glomerular filtration rate (GFR), occurring over a period of hours or days. It most commonly occurs in hospitalized patients but may occur in others as well. The blood urea nitrogen increases, and nitrogenous wastes are retained (azotemia). There are three primary categories, related to cause:

- **Prerenal disorders**, such as myocardial infarction, heart failure, sepsis, anaphylaxis, and hemorrhage result in hypoperfusion of the kidney and decreased GFR.
- **Intrarenal disorders** include burns, trauma, infection, transfusion reactions, and nephrotoxic agents that cause damage to glomeruli or kidney tubules, such as acute tubular necrosis. Burns and crush trauma injuries release myoglobin and hemoglobin from tissues, causing renal toxicity or ischemia. With transfusion reactions, hemolysis occurs, and the broken-down hemoglobin concentrates and precipitates in tubules. Medications, such as nonsteroidal anti-inflammatory drugs and angiotensin-converting enzyme inhibitors, may interfere with kidney function and cause hypoperfusion and ischemia.
- **Postrenal disorders** involve distal obstruction that increases pressure in tubules and decreases GFR.

Nonoliguric and Oliguric Renal Failure

Nonoliguric renal failure occurs when the serum creatinine increases, but urinary output remains 400 mL per 24 hours or more. This form of renal failure is most common after cardiac surgery and may occur in patients with a history of renal dysfunction or other risk factors. Renal damage is less pronounced than with oliguric failure, and mortality rate is relatively low (5-10%). Treatment includes hemodynamic support and fluids as well as high-dose diuretics.

Oliguric renal failure occurs with an increase in serum creatinine and a decrease in urinary output to 0.3-0.5 mL/kg per hour or more, persisting for 12-24 hours (usually an indication of RIFLE [risk, injury, failure, loss, end stage] criteria, category 3). Mortality rates are about 50%. Treatment includes renal replacement therapy. Risk factors include low-cardiac output, infections, stroke, and respiratory failure.

ACUTE TUBULAR NECROSIS

Acute tubular necrosis (ATN) occurs when a hypoxic condition causes renal ischemia that damages tubular cells of the glomeruli so that they are unable to filter the urine adequately, leading to acute renal failure. Causes include hypotension, hyperbilirubinemia, sepsis, surgery (especially cardiac or vascular), and birth complications. ATN may result from nephrotoxic injury related to obstruction or drugs, such as chemotherapy, acyclovir, and antibiotics, such as sulfonamides and streptomycin. Symptoms may be nonspecific initially and can include life-threatening complications.

Symptoms include:

- Lethargy
- Nausea and vomiting
- Hypovolemia with low-cardiac output and generalized vasodilation
- Fluid and electrolyte imbalance leading to hypertension, central nervous system abnormalities, metabolic acidosis, arrhythmias, edema, and congestive heart failure
- Uremia leading to destruction of platelets and bleeding, neurological deficits, and disseminated intravascular coagulopathy
- Infections, including pericarditis and sepsis
- Urinary sediment: tubular epithelial or granular (brown)

Treatment includes:

- Identifying and treating underlying cause and discontinuing nephrotoxic agents
- Supportive care
- Loop diuretics, such as furosemide (Lasix), in some cases
- Antibiotics for infection (e.g., pericarditis, sepsis)

TYPICAL PATTERNS OF ACUTE RENAL FAILURE AFTER CARDIAC SURGERY

After cardiac surgery, three typical patterns of acute renal failure occur:

- **Abbreviated**: This results from a transient episode of renal ischemia, occurring during surgery. The serum creatinine increases postoperatively, peaking at day 4 and then decreases. Urinary output generally remains adequate.
- **Overt**: This results from impairment of cardiac function and ischemia during surgery. Postoperatively, the serum creatinine level rises to a higher level and then decreases slowly to normal levels over 7-14 days.
- **Protracted**: This results from a period of ischemia during surgery followed by increased serum creatinine, but as the creatinine begins to return to normal levels, another injury to the kidneys occurs as the result of a complication, such as infection or hypoperfusion/hypotension, causing the creatinine to rise again.

Multisystem

Sepsis, Severe Sepsis, and Septic Shock

Infections can progress from bacteremia, septicemia, and systemic inflammatory response syndrome (SIRS) to the following:

- **Sepsis** is the presence of infection either locally or systemically in which there is a generalized life-threatening inflammatory response (SIRS). It includes all of the indications for SIRS as well as one of the following:
    - Changes in mental status
    - Hypoxemia (<72 mmHg) without pulmonary disease
    - Elevation in plasma lactate
    - Decreased urinary output of less than 0.5 mL/kg/hr for 1 hour or more
- **Severe sepsis** includes both indications of SIRS and sepsis as well as indications of increasing organ dysfunction with inadequate perfusion or hypotension.
- **Septic shock** is a progression from severe sepsis in which refractory hypotension occurs despite treatment. There may be indications of lactic acidosis.

Symptoms of Septic Shock

Septic shock is caused by toxins produced by bacteria and cytokines that the body produces in response to severe infection, resulting in a complex syndrome of disorders. **Symptoms** are wide-ranging:

- **Initial**: Temperature >38 °C or <36 °C with chills, tachycardia with increased pulse pressure, tachypnea, alterations in mental status (dullness), hypotension, hyperventilation with respiratory alkalosis (partial pressure of carbon dioxide ≤30 mmHg), increased lactic acid, unstable blood pressure, and dehydration with increased urinary output
- **Cardiovascular**: Myocardial depression and dysrhythmias
- **Respiratory**: Acute respiratory distress syndrome
- **Renal**: Acute renal failure with decreased urinary output and increased blood urea nitrogen
- **Hepatic**: Jaundice and liver dysfunction with an increase in transaminase, alkaline phosphatase, and bilirubin
- **Hematologic**: Mild or severe blood loss (from mucosal ulcerations), neutropenia or neutrophilia, decreased platelets, and disseminated intravascular coagulation
- **Endocrine**: Hyperglycemia and hypoglycemia (rare)
- **Skin**: Cellulitis, erysipelas, fasciitis, and acrocyanotic and necrotic peripheral lesions

Diagnosis and Treatment of Septic Shock

Septic shock is most common in patients over 50 years of age and those who are immunocompromised. There is no specific test to confirm a **diagnosis** of septic shock, so diagnosis is based on clinical findings and tests that evaluate hematologic, infectious, and metabolic states: a complete blood count, disseminated intravascular coagulation panel, electrolytes, liver function tests, blood urea nitrogen, creatinine, blood glucose, arterial blood gases, urinalysis, electrocardiogram, radiographs, and cultures of blood and urine. **Treatment** must be aggressive and includes the following:

- Oxygen and endotracheal intubation as necessary.
- Intravenous (IV) access with two large bore catheters and a central venous line.
- Rapid fluid administration of 1-2 L isotonic crystalloid bolus within the first minutes to hours. Additional fluids must be weighed against risks for fluid overload.
- Monitoring urinary output to an optimum of more than 30 mL/hr.
- Inotropic agents (e.g., dopamine, dobutamine, norepinephrine) if no response to fluids or fluid overload.
- Empiric IV antibiotic therapy (usually with two broad-spectrum antibiotics for both gram-positive and gram-negative bacteria) until cultures return, at which point antibiotics may be changed.
- Hemodynamic and laboratory monitoring.
- Removing source of infection (abscess, catheter).

MODS

Multi-organ dysfunction syndrome (MODS) is the progressive deterioration and failure of 2 or more organ systems with mortality rates of 45-50% with 2 organ systems involved and 80-100% if there are 3 or more systems failing. Trauma patients and those with severe conditions, such as shock, burns, and sepsis, are particularly vulnerable, especially in those >65. MODS may be primary or secondary:

- **Primary MODS** relates directly to the injury/disorder (including cardiovascular surgery) of the organ systems, resulting in dysfunction, such as with thermal injuries, traumatic pulmonary injuries, and invasive infections.
- **Secondary MODS** relates to dysfunction of organ systems not directly involved in the injury/disorder but that developed as the result of a systemic inflammatory response syndrome (SIRS) as the patient's immune and inflammatory responses become dysregulated (which can occur with cardiopulmonary bypass).

In some patients, failure of organ systems is sequential, usually progressing from the lungs, the liver, the gastrointestinal system, and the kidneys to the heart. However, in other cases, various organ systems may fail at the same time.

Invasive Blood Gas Monitoring

Invasive blood gas monitoring options include the following:

- **Arterial blood gas (ABG)** is the most informative measurement of blood gas status. If an arterial catheter is in place, it is easily obtained by aspirating 1-2 mL of blood.
- **Venous blood gas (VBG)** is easier to obtain if an arterial catheter is not in place. In order to compare the values in the VBG with an ABG, make the following calculations:
  - Add 0.05 to the pH of the VBG.
  - Subtract 5-10 mmHg from the PCO_2 of the VBG.
- **Capillary blood gas (CBG)** can be obtained with a heel stick, without a venous or arterial line, but the values obtained in a CBG are the least accurate and are rarely useful. This is used most often in neonates.

COMPONENTS OF A BLOOD GAS READING

The following are components of a blood gas reading:

- **pH** measures the circulating acid and base levels. Neutral pH for humans is 7.4. A value below 7.35 indicates acidosis and a value greater than 7.45 indicates alkalosis.
- **pCO_2** is the partial pressure of carbon dioxide and it determines the respiratory component of pH. An elevated pCO_2 lowers the pH. A low pCO_2 raises the pH. The pCO_2 value is dependent on adequate pulmonary ventilation and respiration. Changes in respiratory status quickly alter this value. Normal value range for pCO_2 is 35-45 mmHg.
- **pO_2** is the partial pressure of oxygen, which indicates how well the individual is transporting oxygen from the lungs into the bloodstream. Normal value is 75-100 mmHg.
- **HCO_3^-** is bicarbonate, the metabolic component of pH. This value may slowly change in response to abnormal pH, or a disease process may cause an elevation or depression. Low values decrease the pH and high values raise the pH. Normal value for bicarbonate is 22-26 mEq/L.

Review Video: Acid-Base Balance & Blood Gas Interpretation
Visit mometrix.com/academy and enter code: 611909

METABOLIC AND RESPIRATORY ACIDOSIS

PATHOPHYSIOLOGY

- Metabolic acidosis
  - Increase in fixed acid and inability to excrete acid, or loss of base, with compensatory increase of CO_2 excretion by lungs
- Respiratory acidosis
  - Hypoventilation and CO_2 retention with renal compensatory retention of bicarbonate (HCO_3) and increased excretion of hydrogen

LABORATORY

- Metabolic acidosis
  - Decreased serum pH (<7.35) and PCO_2 normal if uncompensated and decreased if compensated
  - Decreased HCO_3
- Respiratory acidosis
  - Decreased serum pH (<7.35) and increased PCO_2
  - Increased HCO_3 if compensated and normal if uncompensated

CAUSES

- Metabolic acidosis
  - DKA, lactic acidosis, diarrhea, starvation, renal failure, shock, renal tubular acidosis, starvation
- Respiratory acidosis
  - COPD, overdose of sedative or barbiturate (leading to hypoventilation), obesity, severe pneumonia/atelectasis, muscle weakness (Guillain-Barré), mechanical hypoventilation

Symptoms

- Metabolic acidosis
  - Neuro/muscular: Drowsiness, confusion, headache, coma
  - Cardiac: Decreased BP, arrhythmias, flushed skin
  - GI: Nausea, vomiting, abdominal pain, diarrhea
  - Respiratory: Deep inspired tachypnea
- Respiratory acidosis
  - Neuro/muscular: Drowsiness, dizziness, headache, coma, disorientation, seizures
  - Cardiac: Flushed skin, VF, ↓BP
  - GI: Absent
  - Respiratory: Hypoventilation with hypoxia

Metabolic and Respiratory Alkalosis

Pathophysiology

- Metabolic alkalosis
  - Decreased strong acid or increased base with possible compensatory CO_2 retention by lungs
- Respiratory alkalosis
  - Hyperventilation and increased excretion of CO_2 with compensatory HCO_3 excretion by kidneys

Laboratory

- Metabolic alkalosis
  - Increased serum pH (>7.45)
  - PCO_2 normal if uncompensated and increased if compensated
  - Increased HCO_3
- Respiratory alkalosis
  - Increased serum pH (>7.45)
  - Decreased PCO_2
  - HCO_3 normal if uncompensated and decreased if compensated

Causes

- Metabolic alkalosis
  - Excessive vomiting, gastric suctioning, diuretics, potassium deficit, excessive mineralocorticoids and $NaHCO_3$ intake
- Respiratory alkalosis
  - Hyperventilation associated with hypoxia, pulmonary embolus, exercise, anxiety, pain, and fever
  - Encephalopathy, septicemia, brain injury, salicylate overdose, and mechanical hyperventilation

Symptoms

- Metabolic alkalosis
    - Neuromuscular: Dizziness, confusion, nervousness, anxiety, tremors, muscle cramping, tetany, tingling, seizures
    - Cardiac: Tachycardia and arrhythmias
    - GI: Nausea, vomiting, anorexia
    - Respiratory: Compensatory hypoventilation
- Respiratory alkalosis
    - Neuro/muscular: Light-headedness, confusion, lethargy
    - Cardiac: Tachycardia and arrhythmias
    - GI: Epigastric pain, nausea, and vomiting
    - Respiratory: Hyperventilation

Electrolyte Imbalances

Hyponatremia

Sodium regulates fluid volume, osmolality, acid-base balance, and activity in the muscles, nerves, and myocardium. It is the primary cation (positive ion) in extracellular fluid (ECF), necessary to maintain ECF levels that are needed for tissue perfusion (normal value: 135–145 mEq/L). Hyponatremia (<135 mEq/L)

Hyponatremia may result from inadequate sodium intake or excess loss, through diarrhea, vomiting, or nasogastric suctioning. It can occur as the result of illness, such as severe burns, fever, syndrome of inappropriate antidiuretic hormone, acute respiratory failure, and ketoacidosis. Medications that cause hyponatremia include thiazide diuretics and nonsteroidal anti-inflammatory drugs. In the postsurgical cardiac patient, hyponatremia is almost always associated with hyperglycemia. Hyponatremia may occur with severe heart failure and may develop with hypovolemia, normovolemia, or hypervolemia.

Symptoms vary and include the following:

- Irritability to lethargy and alterations in consciousness
- Nausea and vomiting
- Generalized muscle weakness
- Cerebral edema with headache, seizures, and coma
- Dyspnea with Cheyne-Stokes respirations to respiratory failure

Treatment: The underlying cause is identified and treated, and sodium replacement is provided.

Hypernatremia

Hypernatremia (>145 mEq/L) may result from renal disease, diabetes insipidus, and fluid depletion. Hypernatremia is uncommon after cardiac surgery but is associated with hyperventilation and increases the risk of mortality to 40–60%. It may also result from dehydration from fever, diarrhea, diabetes, or osmotic diuretics.

Symptoms include the following:

- Irritability to lethargy to confusion to coma
- Seizures and flushing
- Muscle weakness and spasms
- Thirst
- Disorientation
- Poor skin turgor and dry oral mucosa and tongue

Treatment includes identifying and treating the underlying cause, monitoring sodium levels carefully, and replacing intravenous fluids. With levels of 150 mEq/L, tromethamine is used to treat metabolic acidosis rather than sodium bicarbonate, which may increase sodium levels more. A too rapid decrease in sodium levels may result in cerebral edema.

Hypokalemia

Potassium is the primary electrolyte in intracellular fluid (ICF) with about 98% inside cells and only 2% in extracellular fluid (ECF), although this small amount is important for neuromuscular activity. Potassium influences activity of the skeletal and cardiac muscles. Its level is dependent on adequate renal functioning because 80% is excreted through the kidneys and 20% through the bowels and sweat (normal values: 3.5–5.5 mEq/L).

Hypokalemia (<3.5 mEq/L; critical value: <2.5 mEq/L) is caused by a loss of potassium through diuresis after cardiac surgery and cardiopulmonary bypass, diarrhea, vomiting, gastric suction, diuresis, alkalosis, decreased potassium intake with starvation, nephritis, diuresis without adequate potassium replacement, insulin used to treat hyperglycemia, and metabolic/respiratory alkalosis. **Symptoms** include the following:

- Lethargy and weakness
- Paresthesias
- Dysrhythmias with abnormalities on the electrocardiograph: premature ventricular contractions, prolonged PR interval, ST-segment depression, and flattened T waves with U waves
- Muscle cramps with hyporeflexia
- Hypertension (with ventricular dysrhythmias) and hypotension
- Tetany

Hypokalemia is caused by a loss of potassium through diuresis after cardiac surgery and cardiopulmonary bypass, diarrhea, vomiting, gastric suction, diuresis, alkalosis, decreased potassium intake with starvation, nephritis, diuresis without adequate potassium replacement, insulin used to treat hyperglycemia, and metabolic/respiratory alkalosis.

The underlying cause is identified and treated, and potassium chloride is replaced by central line at 10–20 mEq/hr in a mix of 20 mEq potassium chloride in 0.45% normal saline. (Dextrose solutions may stimulate the production of insulin and lower potassium levels.)

HYPERKALEMIA

Hyperkalemia (>5.5 mEq/L; critical value: >6.5 mEq/L) can result from high-potassium cardioplegic solutions, low cardiac output with oliguria, tissue ischemia, acute or chronic renal insufficiency, and medications (e.g., nonsteroidal anti-inflammatory drugs, angiotensin receptor blockers, β-blockers, angiotensin-converting enzyme inhibitors, potassium-sparing diuretics).

The **primary symptoms** relate to the effect on the cardiac muscle:

- Ventricular arrhythmias with increasing changes in the electrocardiogram, leading to cardiac and respiratory arrest.
- Weakness with ascending paralysis and hyperreflexia.
- Diarrhea.
- Increasing confusion.

Hyperkalemia treatment includes identifying the underlying cause and discontinuing sources of increased potassium:

- Calcium gluconate (10 mL/10% solution over 2–3 minutes) to decrease cardiac effects.
- Furosemide (20–40 mg intravenously [IV]) to increase potassium secretion.
- Sodium bicarbonate shifts potassium into the cells temporarily.
- Insulin (10 U regular IV in 50 mL 50% dextrose) and hypertonic dextrose shift potassium into the cells temporarily.
- Albuterol (10–20 mg) per nebulizer to move potassium into cells.
- Cation exchange resin (sodium polystyrene sulfonate [Kayexalate]) enema (50 g/150 mL water) every 2–4 hours to decrease potassium.
- Hemodialysis.

HYPOCALCEMIA

More than 99% of calcium is in the skeletal system with 1% in serum, but it is important for transmitting nerve impulses and regulating muscle contraction and relaxation, including the myocardium. Calcium activates enzymes that stimulate chemical reactions and has a role in coagulation of blood (normal values: 8.2–10.2 mg/dL).

Hypocalcemia (<8.2 mg/dL; critical value: <7 mg/dL)

Hypocalcemia may be caused by hypoparathyroidism and occurs after thyroid and parathyroid surgery, pancreatitis, renal failure, inadequate vitamin D, alkalosis, magnesium deficiency, and low serum albumin. After cardiac surgery, hypocalcemia may be caused by cardiopulmonary bypass, hemodilution, multiple transfusions of citrated blood products, low cardiac output, and sepsis.

Symptoms include the following:

- Tetany, tingling, seizures, and altered mental status
- Ventricular tachycardia
- Laryngeal spasm and inspiratory and expiratory wheezing

Decreased myocardial contractility and cardiac output, hypotension, prolonged QT interval, bradycardic dysrhythmias, and muffled heart sounds

Chvostek's Sign and Trousseau's Sign for Tetany

Tetany is the most common manifestation of hypocalcemia and hypomagnesemia. It includes a range of neuromuscular symptoms related to spontaneous discharge in both the sensory and motor peripheral nerves. Muscle spasms and twitching may cause pain, and there may be sensations of tingling in the fingers and perioral area. Seizures may occur. Two signs are present with tetany:

- **Chvostek's sign** is elicited by tapping the muscles enervated by the facial nerves about 2 cm in front of the earlobe just inferior to the zygomatic arch. A positive response is twitching of the muscle. A positive response may also occur with respiratory alkalosis.
- **Trousseau's sign** is elicited by applying a blood pressure cuff to the upper arm and inflating it 20 mm Hg above systolic and leaving it in place for 5 minutes or less. A positive response occurs with increasing ischemia of the ulnar nerve: carpopedal spasm with the thumb adducted, the wrist and metacarpophalangeal joints flexed, and the interphalangeal joints extended with the

Hypercalcemia

Hypercalcemia (>10.2 mg/dL; critical value:>12 mg/dL) is not usually a complication of cardiac surgery but relates to increased intestinal or bone absorption or decreased calcium elimination. Hypercalcemia may be caused by acidosis, kidney disease, hyperparathyroidism, prolonged immobilization, and malignancies. Hypercalcemia may also result from some medications (e.g., thiazide diuretics, lithium carbonate) and acidosis. Crisis carries a 50% mortality rate. Symptoms include the following:

- Increasing muscle weakness with hypotonicity
- Anorexia, nausea, and vomiting
- Decreased renal function, polyuria, and polydipsia
- Constipation
- Bradycardia and cardiac arrest, shortened QT segments, depressed T waves, and heart block (e.g., first, second, third, bundle branch block)
- Altered mental status, psychosis, lethargy, and coma (if untreated)

The underlying cause is identified and treated, and loop diuretics, intravenous (IV) calcitonin, and IV fluids are given.

Hypophosphatemia

Phosphorus, or phosphate (PO_4), is necessary for neuromuscular and red blood cell function and the maintenance of acid–base balance; it also provides structure for teeth and bones. About 85% is in the bones, 14% in soft tissue, and 1% or less in extracellular fluid (normal values: 2.4–4.5 mEq/L).

Hypophosphatemia (<2.4 mEq/L; critical value:<1 mEq/L) occurs with severe protein–calorie malnutrition; excess antacids with magnesium, calcium, or albumin; hyperventilation; severe burns; and diabetic ketoacidosis. Most commonly, hypophosphatemia results from increased renal elimination of phosphorus related to respiratory alkalosis or stress related to surgery. Hypophosphatemia is often associated with hypomagnesemia and hypercalcemia. Symptoms include the following:

- Irritability, tremors, and seizures leading to coma
- Muscle pain, weakness, and tenderness
- Apprehension and anxiety
- Hemolytic anemia
- Decreased myocardial function, hypotension, and decreased stroke volume

Respiratory depression and failure (Respiratory rate falls with rising phosphorus levels, but with respiratory alkalosis, respiratory rate increases.)

The underlying cause is identified and treated, and phosphorus is replaced. Phosphorus infusion may result in rebound hyperphosphatemia, characterized by heart block or flaccid paralysis.

Hyperphosphatemia

Hyperphosphatemia (>4.5 mEq/L; critical value: >5 mEq/L) occurs with renal failure, hypoparathyroidism, excessive intake, and neoplastic disease, diabetic ketoacidosis, muscle necrosis, and respiratory acidosis. Most cases relate to decreased renal function and glomerular filtration rate, 50 mL/min or less. At this point, the kidneys cannot effectively metabolize phosphorus. Respiratory acidosis results in rising carbon dioxide levels, which causes phosphorus to move from intracellular to extracellular fluid compartments. Metabolic acidosis (as in diabetic ketoacidosis) also leads to hyperphosphatemia. **Symptoms** can include the following:

- Tachycardia, hypotension, muffled heart sounds, prolonged QT interval, and pericardial friction rub
- Altered mental status
- Muscle cramping, hyperreflexia, paresthesia, and tetany
- Nausea and diarrhea

The underlying cause is identified and treated; hypocalcemia is corrected; normal saline intravenous fluids and antacids are provided; and emergent renal replacement therapy is given, if necessary.

Hypomagnesemia

Magnesium is the second most common intracellular electrolyte (after potassium); it activates many intracellular enzyme systems. Magnesium is important for carbohydrate and protein metabolism, neuromuscular function, and cardiovascular function (electrical conduction), producing vasodilation and directly affecting the peripheral arterial system. Hypomagnesemia is often associated with hypophosphatemia, hypocalcemia, and hypokalemia (normal values: 1.6–2.4 mEq/L).

Hypomagnesemia (<1.6 mEq/L; critical value: <1.2 mEq/L) occurs from hemodilution during cardiopulmonary bypass (CPB) but also occurs in an open-pump coronary artery graft procedure; it is also associated with low-cardiac output syndrome and prolonged mechanical ventilation. It is common in cardiac surgery patients, especially those undergoing CPB or diuretics.

Hypomagnesemia symptoms include the following:

- Neuromuscular excitability/tetany.
- Confusion, headaches, dizziness, seizure, and coma.
- Tachycardia with atrial and ventricular arrhythmias.
- Respiratory depression.
- Nonspecific changes in T waves, U waves, prolonged QT interval, widened QRS complex, and ST-segment depression (Peaked T waves and torsade de pointes may be evident.)
- Insulin resistance.

The underlying cause is identified and treated, and magnesium replacement is provided with magnesium sulfate (2 g/100 mL solution) to raise the level to 2 mEq/L or more. The infusion is stopped if urinary output falls to less than 100 mL/4 hr.

HYPERMAGNESEMIA

Hypermagnesemia (>2.4 mEq/L; critical value: >4.9 mEq/L; fatal value: >10 mEq/L) can occur with hypercarbia; it decreases respiratory muscle function and is associated with respiratory failure/ventilator dependence as well as renal failure or inadequate renal function, diabetic ketoacidosis, hypothyroidism, and Addison's disease.

Symptoms include the following:

- Muscle weakness and lethargy.
- Dilated pupils.
- Seizures.
- Decreased or absent bowel sounds.
- Anorexia.
- Hypotension and shallow respirations, and periods of apnea.
- Ventricular dysrhythmias, bradycardia, or prolonged PR interval.
- Complete heart block and cardiac arrest.
- Dysphagia with decreased gag reflex.
- Tachycardia with hypotension.

The underlying cause is identified and treated; seizure precautions are taken; and infusion of insulin and glucose, calcium gluconate (10–20 mEq over 10 minutes) loop diuretics, fluid resuscitation, and dialysis are provided. If a patient develops severe respiratory depression, mechanical ventilation may be necessary. Some patients require a temporary pacemaker for marked bradycardia.

Behavioral

Adjustment Disorders Post-Cardiac Event/Surgery

Adjustment disorders, such as depression and anxiety, can affect patients post cardiac event/surgery, increasing the risk of morbidity (including postoperative delirium) and mortality. Up to 40-50% of patients undergo some type of depression with a loss of interest in social activities and lack of pleasure. Patients may experience sleep disturbance, appetite disturbance, difficulty concentrating and/or suicidal ideation. Some patients show improvement after surgery, but others have persistent symptoms, perhaps related to stress or fear of recurrence. Some patients experience primarily anxiety or a combination of depression and anxiety, and may have symptoms consistent with generalized anxiety disorder, PTSD, and panic disorders. Some may limit social and work activities because of fear of another cardiac event, and others may believe they are actually experiencing one due to fear. Self-screening may help to identify patients in need of monitoring or intervention, such as SSRIs (used for both anxiety and depression), anxiolytics, therapy (such as CBT), and support groups.

Agitation After Cardiac Surgery

Agitation is common in the post-cardiac surgery period and is characterized by a state of arousal, irritability, and tension that is usually fleeting but may persist for extended periods. Agitation may be associated with recovery from anesthesia in the immediate postoperative period. Some agitated patients may appear confused and exhibit behavior change, acting in a combative manner, with severe restlessness, turning back and forth, moving legs, and pulling at tubes and IVs. Other patients may become hypoactive and inattentive. Confusion and other symptoms are generally less acute, less fluctuating, more benign, and shorter lasting than with delirium, which may include severe mood swings. Agitation is often associated with severe anxiety, and patients may exhibit signs of both. Precipitating factors include hypoxia, dementia, the effect of drugs, infection, metabolic disorders, fear, pain, a full bladder, noise, and constipation. Interventions include identifying and resolving problems, such as pain or constipation, maintaining a quiet and calm environment as much as possible, staying with the patient, and talking quietly to the patient. Antipsychotics, often prescribed for delirium, are usually not required.

Delirium

Delirium is an acute sudden change in consciousness, characterized by a reduced ability to focus or sustain attention, language, memory disturbance, disorientation, confusion, audiovisual hallucinations, sleep disturbance, agitation, and psychomotor activity disorder. Delirium differs from disorders with similar symptoms in that it is fluctuating. Delirium is the most common neurological disorder associated with cardiac surgery, occurring in 3–7% of patients with onset of symptoms most common 48–72 hours after surgery. Risk factors include preexisting psychological disorders, alcohol abuse, left ventricular ejection fraction less than 30%, 65 years of age or older, cerebral artery disease, emergent surgery, circulatory arrest over 30 minutes, electrolyte imbalances, and hypothermia (<25 °C). Medications also increase the risk (e.g., β-blockers, calcium channel blockers, angiotensin-converting enzyme inhibitors, diuretics, antiarrhythmic drugs, statins). **Treatment** includes the following:

- Identifying and treating underlying cause
- Providing supportive measures, such reducing sensory input and promoting sleep
- Treating symptoms, usually with haloperidol (initial dose of 1–2 mg every 2–4 hours), lorazepam, or trazodone
- Barbiturates should be avoided, and benzodiazepines should be restricted to those going through alcohol withdrawal

CONFUSION ASSESSMENT METHOD

The Confusion Assessment Method is used to assess the development of delirium and is intended for those without psychiatric training to help differentiate delirium from other types of confusion. The tool covers nine factors. Some factors have a range of possibilities, and others are rated only as to whether the characteristic is present, not present, uncertain, or not applicable. The tool provides room to describe abnormal behavior. Factors indicative of delirium include the following:

- **Onset**: Acute change in mental status
- **Attention**: Inattentive, stable, or fluctuating
- **Thinking**: Disorganized, rambling conversation, switching topics, or illogical
- **Level of consciousness**: Altered, ranging from alert to coma
- **Orientation**: Disoriented (person, place, time)
- **Memory**: Impaired
- **Perceptual disturbances**: Hallucinations or illusions
- **Psychomotor abnormalities**: Agitation (tapping, picking, moving) or retardation (staring, not moving)
- **Sleep-wake cycle**: Awake at night and sleepy in the daytime

This tool indicates delirium if there is an acute onset with fluctuating inattention and disorganized thinking or altered level of consciousness.

Important Terms

Inspiratory Reserve Volume: Inspiratory reserve volume (IRV) is the amount of air that can be taken into the lungs with forced inhalation after a normal resting inspiratory effort.

Expiratory Reserve Volume: Expiratory reserve volume (ERV), conversely, is the amount of air that can be exhaled through forced exhalation after a normal resting exhalation.

Residual Volume: Residual volume (RV) is the volume of air remaining in the lungs after ERV is completed.

Tidal Volume: Tidal volume (Vt) is the volume of air that is inhaled or exhaled in a single breath.

Inspiratory Capacity: Inspiratory capacity (IC) is the maximum volume of air that can be inhaled from a resting exhalation. It can be calculated by the equation Vt + IRV = IC, or it can be measured directly.

Functional Residual Capacity: Functional residual capacity (FRC) is the combination of the expiratory reserve volume and the residual volume. This is defined as the volume of air in the lungs at resting tidal exhalation.

Vital Capacity: Vital capacity (VC) is the maximum amount of air that can be forced out of the lungs following a maximum inhalation. It is defined as IRV + Vt + ERV = VC.

Total Lung Capacity: Total lung capacity (TLC) is the total sum of all of the air that the lungs can contain. It is defined as IRV + Vt + ERV + RV = TLC.

Alveolar Hypoventilation: Alveolar hypoventilation occurs when the effectiveness of alveolar gas exchange reduces so the partial pressures of oxygen and carbon dioxide both increase. The failure to eliminate carbon dioxide displaces oxygen in the alveolar sacs.

Physiologic Shunting: Physiologic shunting is venous blood in the lung bypassing the alveoli and re-entering the arterial system. This normally occurs with 2–3% of venous blood but may increase with alveolar congestion related to pulmonary edema, atelectasis, or other disorder.

Intrapulmonary Shunting: Intrapulmonary shunting involves alveolar perfusion without ventilation, so the oxygenated blood reaches the alveolus but cannot exchange for carbon dioxide because the alveolus is damaged or diseased.

Refractory Hypoxemia: Refractory hypoxemia occurs when there is so much loss of alveoli that oxygen administration is unable to correct the hypoxemia.

Dead Space: Dead space occurs when a well-ventilated alveolus cannot be perfused because of blockage by an embolus, capillary compression, or other damage.

Ventilation–Perfusion (V/Q) Mismatch: Ventilation–perfusion mismatch occurs when well-ventilated alveoli lack adequate perfusion (creating partial dead space) or poorly ventilated alveoli have adequate perfusion (creating partial shunts).

Therapeutic Interventions

Cardiovascular

Antidysrhythmics

Classes

Antidysrhythmics include a number of drugs that act on the conduction system, the ventricles or the atria to control dysrhythmias. There are four classes of drugs that are used as well as some that are unclassified:

- **Class I:** Three subtypes of sodium channel blockers (1A: quinidine procainamide, disopyramide; IB: lidocaine, mexiletine, phenytoin; IC: propafenone and flecainide)
- **Class II:** β-adrenergic blockers (esmolol, propranolol)
- **Class III:** Slows repolarization (amiodarone, ibutilide, dofetilide, sotalol, dronedarone)
- **Class IV:** Calcium channel blockers (diltiazem, verapamil)
- Unclassified: adenosine

Group 1A Antidysrhythmics

Group 1A antidysrhythmics, such as quinidine, procainamide, and disopyramide, are sodium channel blockers, which alter the cell membranes of the myocardium, interfering with the autonomic nervous system control of pacemaker cells. Blocking sodium results in the following:

- Decreased automaticity of ectopic foci (abnormal sites of pacemaker activity).
- Increased refractory period.
- Decreased conduction speed.
- Procainamide and disopyramide are most frequently used after cardiac surgery. Sodium channel blockers are used to treat atrial fibrillation, premature ventricular contractions, and ventricular tachycardia. Adverse effects include gastrointestinal upset (i.e., nausea, vomiting, diarrhea), hypotension, dizziness, confusion, tinnitus, delirium, fever, chills, thrombocytopenia, and dysrhythmias, and heart failure.
- Contraindications include complete atrioventricular block, conduction defects, and myasthenia gravis. Sodium channel blockers must be used with caution in patients with renal or hepatic impairment.

Procainamide

Procainamide (Pronestyl), a group 1A sodium channel blocker, is used primarily to treat life-threatening ventricular arrhythmias and to prevent atrial fibrillation and less frequently to convert, although its use has been supplanted by amiodarone. Other indications include suppression of premature atrial/ventricular complexes and treatment of Wolff-Parkinson-White syndrome. Procainamide slows conduction, decreases systemic vascular resistance, and decreases cardiac conductivity. Dosage is 100 mg every 5 minutes to a maximum dosage of 1000 mg followed by a maintenance infusion of 2–4 mg/min to a therapeutic level of 4–10 µg/mL. The infusion rate should not exceed 25–50 mg/min. Adverse effects include nausea, hypotension, anorexia, hallucinations, psychosis, depression, fever, rash, and lupus syndrome.

Disopyramide

Disopyramide (Norpace), a group 1A sodium channel blocker, is used to:

- Treat atrial and ventricular arrhythmias (especially life-threatening ventricular arrhythmias, paroxysmal supraventricular tachycardia) and Wolff-Parkinson-White syndrome.
- Treat and prevent atrioventricular reentry tachycardia.
- To prevent or convert atrial fibrillation.

Disopyramide decreases the rate of diastolic depolarization, reduces automaticity, prolongs the refractory period of myocardial cells, and decreases the rate of the rise of the action potential. Dosage is 100–200 mg orally every 6 hours to a therapeutic level of 2–5 μg/mL. Adverse effects include torsades de points, ventricular tachyarrhythmias, urinary retention, constipation, nausea, dizziness insomnia, blurred vision, dry mouth, impotence, rash, itching, muscle weakness, heart failure, hypotension, and cardiac conduction disturbances.

Group 1B Antidysrhythmics

Lidocaine

Lidocaine is a group IB antidysrhythmic that is used to manage acute ventricular arrhythmias associated with cardiac surgery or myocardial infarction. Lidocaine is also used as a local or infiltrating anesthetic. As an antidysrhythmic, lidocaine decreases diastolic depolarization, decreases automaticity of ventricular cells, and increases the threshold of ventricular fibrillation. Dosage is 1 mg/kg intravenously initially followed by a maintenance infusion of 2–4 mg/min with a bolus of 0.5 mg/kg in 15 minutes or when the infusion rate is increased. The therapeutic level is 1–5 μg/mL. Lidocaine is contraindicated with heart failure, cardiogenic shock, second- or third-degree heart block, Stokes-Adams syndrome, and Wolff-Parkinson-White syndrome. Lidocaine should be used cautiously with hepatic or renal impairment. Adverse effects include dizziness, tremors, vision changes, seizures, cardiac arrhythmias, cardiac arrest, vasodilation and hypotension, nausea, vomiting, respiratory depression or arrest, and malignant hyperthermia.

Group IC Antidysrhythmics

Propafenone

Group IC antidysrhythmics block sodium at the cell membrane, depressing automatic firing of the sinus node and slowing impulses to the atria, atrioventricular node, ventricles, and Purkinje fibers. They are used for ventricular arrhythmias, atrial fibrillation, and atrial flutter. Drugs include propafenone and flecainide . After cardiac surgery, **propafenone** can be used to slow ventricular response and convert to sinus rhythm. Adverse effects include headache, dizziness, dysrhythmias, tremor, visual disturbances, and exacerbation of heart failure. In some cases, propafenone may cause new dysrhythmias or worsen those that are preexisting. Propafenone is contraindicated with heart block and must be administered with care for those with heart failure, impaired hepatic function, and potassium imbalances. Potassium levels should be monitored routinely.

Group II Antidysrhythmics

β-Adrenergic Blockers

Group II antidysrhythmics, **β-adrenergic blockers (β-blockers),** slow the heart rate, reduce hypertension, prevent dysrhythmias, and reverse ventricular remodeling, so they are classified as both antidysrhythmics and antihypertensives. β-Blockers block β_1 and β_2 receptors by competing with norepinephrine. Negative inotropic and chronotropic effects reduce blood pressure. They slow sinus node conduction and prolong conduction through the atrioventricular node, decreasing the ventricular rate, and improving contractility and cardiac output. They are effective in reducing tachycardia associated with exercises or stress because they block excessive sympathetic nervous stimulation at the sinus node. β-Blockers should not be used during decompensation and should be monitored carefully for those with airway disease, uncontrolled diabetes, slow irregular pulse, or heart block. Adverse effects include bradycardia, hypostatic hypotension, heart failure, hypoglycemia, nausea, vomiting, diarrhea, sleep disorders, and edema. Commonly used drugs after cardiac surgery include metoprolol (ventricular dysrhythmias), sotalol (ventricular tachycardia), esmolol (sinus tachycardia, supraventricular tachycardia, and postoperative hypertension), and labetalol (postoperative hypertension). Because β-blockers may precipitate heart block, pacemaker backup should be readily available during treatment with intravenous β-blockers.

β-Blockers: Labetalol

Labetalol is a β-blocker with combined α_1-, β_1-, and β_2-blocking properties (β:α is 7:1 intravenous [IV] and 3:1 oral). The combination helps to prevent reflex tachycardia that can occur with some α-blocking drugs. Onset of action (IV) is within 10–15 minutes, but duration is 6 hours. Labetalol is especially indicated both pre- and postoperatively for aortic dissection. Dosage is 0.25 mg/kg bolus with follow-up doses of 0.5 mg/kg every 5 minutes (to a maximum of 300 mg) or a continuous infusion at 1–4 mg/min until blood pressure stabilizes. Labetalol is contraindicated with sinus bradycardia, second- or third-degree heart block, heart failure, cardiogenic shock, or asthma and should be used cautiously with diabetes or hypoglycemia. Adverse effects include dizziness, vertigo, fatigue, heart failure, cardiac arrhythmias, peripheral vascular insufficiency, gastric pain, flatulence, constipation, nausea, vomiting, diarrhea, impotence, decreased libido, dyspnea, and cough. Labetalol may increase the risk of atrioventricular heart block if given concomitantly with calcium channel blockers.

β-Blockers: Esmolol

Esmolol is a β_1 selective adrenergic blocker that decreases the sympathetic nervous system influence on the heart, reducing the heart's excitability and cardiac output. Esmolol blocks the release of renin and lowers blood pressure and heart rate. Onset of action is within 2 minutes; it peaks in 5 minutes, with a reversal in 10–20 minutes; thus, it is the preferred drug in the initial postoperative period for control of transient hypertension, although it is contraindicated with low-cardiac output. Dosage is initially 0.25 mg/kg or less to determine response and a repeat dose up to 5 mg/kg with a maintenance infusion of 50–100 μg/kg/min. As an antidysrhythmic, esmolol is used to treat sinus tachycardia and supraventricular dysrhythmias. Dosage is 500 μg/kg load followed by a maintenance infusion of 50–200 μg/kg/min. Both toxic and therapeutic effects are increased if esmolol is given concomitantly with verapamil. Adverse effects of esmolol include lightheadedness, midscapular pain, weakness, rigors, hypotension, bradycardia, urine retention, local inflammation, fever, and flushing.

β-Blockers: Metoprolol

Metoprolol is a β_1 selective adrenergic blocker that decreases the sympathetic nervous system influence on the heart, reducing the heart's excitability and cardiac output. Esmolol blocks the release of renin and lowers blood pressure and heart rate. Metoprolol is commonly given to prevent atrial fibrillation (Afib) [oral dose 25–100 mg twice daily] with an additional intravenous dose of 5 mg every 5 minutes for three doses if Afib occurs. Onset of action is within 2–3 minutes, peak in 20 minutes, and duration up to 5 hours. Metoprolol may be given long-term for treatment of angina pectoris (50 mg twice daily initially increasing to 200 mg or less twice daily as needed). Metoprolol is also sometimes used for early or late treatment of myocardial infarction. Metoprolol should be withheld if bradycardia is less than 45 bmp, heart block is present, or systolic pressure is less than 100 mm Hg. Adverse effects include laryngospasm, heart failure, cardiac arrhythmias, gastric pain, flatulence, constipation, nausea, vomiting, diarrhea, impotence, decreased libido, arthralgia, dyspnea, and bronchospasm.

Group III Antidysrhythmics

Group III antidysrhythmics are **potassium channel blockers** that may be used to convert atrial fibrillation (Afib) to sinus rhythm:

- **Amiodarone** (most effective) converts Afib and provides rate control. Amiodarone prolongs repolarization and the refractory period, increases the ventricular fibrillation threshold, and decreases peripheral resistance. Amiodarone is contraindicated with sinus node dysfunction, hypokalemia, and severe bradycardia. Adverse effects include hypotension (rapid infusion), pulmonary and hepatic toxicity, visual disturbances, heart failure, cardiac arrest, and cardiac arrhythmias.
- **Ibutilide** is effective for both Afib and atrial flutter. Adverse effects include ventricular arrhythmias, hypotension, hypertension, tachycardia, headache, and dizziness. It is contraindicated with quinidine, procainamide, amiodarone, and sotalol.
- **Dofetilide** selectively blocks potassium channels and may be used for those with contraindications to class I drugs because of left ventricular dysfunction or β-blockers because of bradycardia or chronic obstructive pulmonary disease. It is used to convert Afib or flutter to normal sinus rhythm and to maintain sinus rhythm. It is contraindicated with heart block and must be used cautiously with ventricular arrhythmias and renal or hepatic impairment. Adverse effects include headache, tingling in the arms, dizziness, nausea, diarrhea, ventricular arrhythmias, hypotension, and hypertension.

Group IV Antidysrhythmics

Group IV antidysrhythmics, **calcium channel blockers (CCBs)**, which can also be used as vasodilators, act as antidysrhythmics to prevent and treat supraventricular arrhythmias. CCBs block the flow of positive calcium ions into cells, relax smooth arterial muscles, decrease myocardial contraction, slow atrioventricular (AV) conduction, reduce heart rate, decrease coronary vascular resistance, dilate coronary arteries, and increase blood flow to coronary arteries, while reducing myocardial oxygen demand. Commonly used medications include the following:

- **Verapamil (Calan):** Used for supraventricular tachycardia; depresses myocardium and prolongs AV conduction time.
- **Diltiazem (Cardizem**): Used to treat paroxysmal supraventricular tachycardia, AV node reentry tachycardia, and Wolf-Parkinson-White syndrome.

Adverse effects include constipation (common), nausea, muscle cramps, orthostatic hypotension, bradycardia, heart block, myocardial infarction, headache, dyspnea, and hepatic toxicity. CCBs may exacerbate heart failure and should be avoided. CCBs should be used with caution with hypotension, marked bradycardia, aortic stenosis, severe left ventricular impairment, and liver or kidney disease. Patients with heart failure must be monitored carefully.

Review Video: Calcium Channel Blockers and Antiarrhythmics
Visit mometrix.com/academy and enter code: 942825

Antidysrhythmics Used for Supraventricular Tachycardia

The following are antidysrhythmics used for supraventricular tachycardia:

- **Adenosine** affects the conduction system and may cause transient flushing, decreased blood pressure, and shortness of breath.
- **Diltiazem** (Cardizem) affects the conduction system and may cause brady-cardia, atrioventricular block, and decreased blood pressure (BP).
- **Esmolol** (Brevibloc) affects the con-duction system and may cause decreased BP, brady-cardia, and heart failure.
- **Propranolol** (Inderal) affects the conduction system and may cause brady-cardia, heart block, and heart failure.
- **Procainamide** (Pronestyl) affects the atria and ventricles and may cause decreased BP and electro-cardiographic abnormalities (widening of QRS and QT).

Antidysrhythmics Used for Paroxysmal Supraventricular Tachycardia, Sinus Tachycardia, Premature Ventricular Contractions

Paroxysmal Supraventricular tachycardia	Adenosine Digoxin (Lanoxin) affects the conduction system and may cause bradycardia, heart block, nausea, vomiting, and central nervous system (CNS) depression. Verapamil (Calan) affects the conduction system and may cause decreased blood pressure, bradycardia, and heart failure.
Sinus tachycardia	Esmolol (Brevibloc)
Premature ventricular contractions	Lidocaine affects the ventricles and may cause CNS toxicity with nausea and vomiting. Procainamide (Pronestyl)

Antidysrhythmics Used for Atrial Fibrillation or Atrial Flutter

Antidysrhythmics for atrial fibrillation or atrial flutter include the following:

- **Digoxin (Lanoxin)** affects the conduction system and may cause bradycardia, heart block, nausea, vomiting, and central nervous system depression.
- **Diltiazem (Cardizem)** affects the conduction system and may cause bradycardia, atrioventricular block, and decreased blood pressure (BP).
- **Ibutilide (Corvert)** affects the conduction system and rarely has side effects.
- **Amiodarone (Cordarone)** affects the atria and ventricles and may cause decreased BP and adverse hepatic effects.
- **Metoprolol (Lopressor)** blocks β-adrenergic cardiac receptors, decreasing response to sympathetic nervous system. It may cause laryngospasm, heart failure, arrhythmias, peripheral vascular insufficiency, hypotension, and pulmonary edema.
- **Carvedilol (Coreg)** lowers BP and prevents reflex tachycardia seen with many other drugs. It is used to treat hypertension, heart failure, and left ventricular dysfunction after myocardial infarction. It may cause dizziness, tinnitus, bradycardia, orthostatic hypertension, cardiac arrhythmias, pulmonary edema, and hypotension.
- **Sotalol** (Betapace) blocks sympathetic response and decreases cardiac excitability, reducing cardiac output and oxygen consumption. It may cause heart failure, dizziness, tinnitus, disorientation, heart failure, cardiac arrhythmias, sinoatrial or atrioventricular nodal block, peripheral vascular insufficiency, pulmonary edema, and hypotension.
- **Magnesium sulfate** has few adverse effects.

Antidysrhythmics Used for Ventricular Tachycardia and Ventricular Fibrillation

Antidysrhythmics used for the following rhythms:

Ventricular tachycardia	Lidocaine Amiodarone (Cordarone) Procainamide
Ventricular fibrillation	Lidocaine

Cardiac Arrest

Management

Cardiac arrest may occur during cardiac surgery or in the postoperative period. Management includes the following:

- Establish airway, and manually ventilate with positive pressure ventilation at a rate of 8–10 breaths/min.
- Provide chest compressions at 100/min after three attempts at defibrillation for ventricular tachycardia (VT)/ventricular fibrillation (VF) or pacing for asystole. Perform until stable or the chest can be opened.
- For VT/VF that is not responsive to defibrillation, perform cardiopulmonary resuscitation (CPR), and give epinephrine, 1 mg, and vasopressin, 40 U.
- For recurrent VT/VF after three shocks, give amiodarone, 300 mg; lidocaine, 1–1.5 mg/kg bolus; or both, and give magnesium sulfate, 1–2 g in 10 mL 5% dextrose in water for torsades de pointes/hypermagnesemia. Give a single shock every 2 minutes until resternotomy.
- When asystole is not responsive to pacing, give atropine, 3 mg, and perform external pacing and CPR until resternotomy.
- Perform defibrillation for ventricular fibrillation and pulseless ventricular tachycardia. Emergency sternotomy should be done within 10 minutes of arrest if other methods are ineffective.
- Assess for cause (e.g., cardiac tamponade, hypovolemia, pacing failure, pneumothorax, myocardial infarction). Provide oxygen with facemask, and intubate. Review chest tube drainage, x-rays, medications, and doses, and evaluate the cardiac monitor and the electrocardiogram.

Causes

Cardiac arrest may result from a number of different **causes**:

- Acidosis (hydrogen ion): Administer sodium bicarbonate.
- Hypovolemia: Fluid resuscitation is necessary to maintain fluid balance and increase blood pressure.
- Hypoxia: Patients should receive hand ventilation with supplementary oxygen at 100%.
- Potassium imbalance: Administer calcium chloride, glucose, insulin, bicarbonate for hyperkalemia, and an infusion of potassium chloride for hypokalemia.
- Hypothermia: Use warming blankets, and increase ambient temperature as indicated.
- Cardiac tamponade: Perform pericardiocentesis or emergent sternotomy.
- Pneumothorax (tension): Perform a needle decompression and insertion of chest tube.
- Myocardial infarction: Perform emergent cardiac catheterization, intra-aortic balloon pump, and treatment as indicated.

- Pulmonary embolism: Administer oxygen and anticoagulant. Embolectomy or an inferior vena cava umbrella may be indicated.
- Medications: Overdose of drugs may require activated charcoal and gastric lavage or antidote. Treat digoxin toxicity with digoxin immune Fab (Digibind). Treat toxicity from β-blockers and calcium channel blockers with inotropes and pacing.

Emergency Defibrillation

Emergency defibrillation is done to treat acute ventricular fibrillation or ventricular tachycardia in which there is no audible or palpable pulse. A higher voltage is generally used for defibrillation than is used for cardioversion, causing depolarization of myocardial cells, which can then repolarize to regain a normal sinus rhythm. Defibrillation delivers an electrical discharge usually through paddles applied to both sides of the chest. Defibrillation may be repeated, usually up to three times, at increasing voltage, but if the heart has not regained a sinus rhythm by then, cardiopulmonary resuscitation and advanced life support are required. Medications, such as epinephrine or vasopressin may be administered, and cardiopulmonary resuscitation continued for 1 minute, after which defibrillation is again attempted. Additional medications, such as amiodarone, magnesium, or procainamide, may be necessary if there are persistent ventricular dysrhythmias.

Internal Defibrillation

Internal defibrillation for life-threatening ventricular tachycardia/ventricular fibrillation that does not respond to external defibrillation requires that the chest is opened similar to emergent resternotomy and that advanced cardiac life support is initiated. Sterile internal defibrillator paddles are prepared, and the paddles are placed on the heart, one over the right side (atrium or ventricle) and the other over the heart apex. The paddles are charged to 5–20 joules (usually 20 joules), and all employees are reminded to stand clear of the patient and equipment during defibrillation. Upon completion, the patient is assessed for conversion to sinus rhythm or the presence of a pulse. If no conversion occurs or the patient remains pulseless, then defibrillation is repeated. If the pericardium has not been opened, the repeat defibrillations may be done at 40 and 60 joules, but 20 joules is the recommended maximum if the pericardium is removed.

Cardioversion

Cardioversion is a timed electrical stimulation to the heart to convert a tachydysrhythmia (e.g., atrial fibrillation) to a normal sinus rhythm. Usually anticoagulation therapy is administered for at least 3 weeks before elective cardioversion to reduce the risk of emboli, and digoxin is discontinued for at least 48 hours before cardioversion. During the procedure, the patient is usually sedated or anesthetized. Electrodes in the form of gel-covered paddles or pads are positioned in the left chest and left back (in front of and behind the heart), connected by leads to a computerized electrocardiogram (ECG) and cardiac monitor with a defibrillator. The defibrillator is synchronized with the ECG so that the electrical current is delivered during ventricular depolarization (QRS). The timing must be precise to prevent ventricular tachycardia or ventricular fibrillation. Sometimes, drug therapy is used in conjunction with cardioversion; for example, antiarrhythmics (e.g., diltiazem [Cardizem], amiodarone [Cordarone]) may be given before the procedure to slow the heart rate.

Emergent Reopening of the Chest

Indications

An hourly bleeding rate of more than 400 mL in 1 hour indicates the need for **emergent reopening of the chest**. Reopening should be considered any time there is a sudden onset of excessive bleeding (> 300 mL/hr) because delay is associated with increased morbidity and death, increased need for transfusions, hemodynamic instability, and the risk of cardiac arrest. Other indications for emergent reopening of the chest include signs of cardiac tamponade and bleeding criteria:

- More than 300 mL/hr for 2–3 hours
- More than 200 mL/hr for 4 hours

Emergent resternotomy is also indicated for those who cannot be resuscitated after cardiac arrest, within 10 minutes of arrest, and tamponade with impending cardiac arrest. Because emergent sternotomy may be necessary after minimally invasive procedures, sternal saws should be available for emergencies. Resternotomy can be done up to 10 days after surgery.

Resternotomy Procedure

A sternotomy surgical pack should be available at all times for cardiac surgery patients in addition to all necessary surgical equipment (e.g., drapes, antiseptics, cauterizers) and personal protective equipment (e.g., gowns, gloves, face masks). The **resternotomy procedure** includes the following:

- Apply ground pads for electrocautery device to patient's skin.
- Remove sternal dressing, and pour antiseptic on patient's skin.
- Apply draping.
- Open wound with scalpel, and cut sternal wires with wire cutters.
- Expose the heart with sternal retractors.
- Suction and control bleeding as indicated.
- Carry out manual massage or internal defibrillation as indicated.
- Irrigate the mediastinum with warm normal saline or antibiotic solution.
- Close the sternum.
- Secure epicardial pacing wires, and apply protective dressing.
- Secure chest tubes.
- Upon closure of the wound, the patient must be monitored for hemodynamic status at least every 15 minutes until the patient's condition stabilizes. Assessment of the chest tube drainage, wound, coagulation, and hematology should be ongoing.

Temporary Transvenous Pacemakers

Transvenous pacemakers, comprised of a catheter with a lead at the end, may be used prophylactically or therapeutically on a temporary basis to treat a cardiac abnormality, especially bradycardia. The catheter is inserted through a vein at the femoral or neck area and attached to an external pulse generator. Transvenous pacemakers are used to:

- Treat persistent dysrhythmias not responsive to medications.
- Increase cardiac output with bradydysrhythmia by increasing rate.
- Decrease ventricular or supraventricular tachycardia by "overdrive" stimulation of contractions.
- Treat secondary heart block caused by myocardial infarction, ischemia, and drug toxicity.
- Improve cardiac output after cardiac surgery.
- Provide diagnostic information through electrophysiology studies, which induce dysrhythmias for purposes of evaluation.

- Provide pacing when a permanent pacemaker malfunctions.
- Complications are similar to implanted pacemakers and include increased risk of pacemaker syndrome.

Review Video: Pacemaker Care
Visit mometrix.com/academy and enter code: 979075

Transcutaneous Pacing

Transcutaneous pacing is used temporarily to treat bradydysrhythmia that does not respond to medications (atropine) and results in hemodynamic instability. Generally, an arterial line is placed, and the patient is provided with oxygen before the pacing. The placement of pacing pads (large self-adhesive pads) and electrocardiogram leads varies somewhat, according to the type of equipment, but usually one pacing pad (negative) is placed on the left chest, inferior to the clavicle, and the other (positive) on the left back, inferior to the scapula, so the heart is sandwiched between the two pads so that the myocardium is depolarized through the chest wall. Lead wires attach the pads to the monitor. The rate of pacing is usually set between 60 and 70 bpm. Current is increased slowly until capture occurs—a spiking followed by the QRS sequence—then the current is readjusted downward if possible, just to maintain capture. Both demand and fixed modes are available, but the demand mode is preferred. Patients may require analgesia, especially if a higher current setting is needed.

Five-Letter Format Pacemaker Code for Classifying Pacemakers

Temporary pacing modes for code positions I, II, and III after cardiac surgery include:

- Asynchronous atrial pacing: AOO.
- Atrial demand pacing: AAI.
- Ventricular demand pacing: VVI.
- Atrioventricular (AV) sequential pacing (ventricular demand): DVI.
- AV sequential pacing (biventricular): DDD.

North American Society of Pacing and Electrophysiology and British Pacing & Electrophysiology Group Pacemaker Codes

I Chambers paced	II Chambers sensed	Response to sensing
A = atrium	A = atrium	T = triggers pacing
V = ventricle	V = ventricle	I = inhibits pacing
D = dual	D = dual	D = dual function (both T and I)
S = single chamber	S = single chamber	O = none
O = none	O = none	

III Programmable functions/rate response	IV Antiarrhythmic functions
O = none	O = none
R = rate responsive	P = paced (antitachycardia)
P = simple programmable	S = shock
M = multiprogrammable	D = dual function (P and S)
C = communicating	

Epicardial Pacing

Placement of Wires

Epicardial pacing wires may be attached directly to the exterior atria, ventricles, or both at the conclusion of surgery for cardiopulmonary bypass or valve repair or for patients with a risk of atrioventricular (AV) block because of medications used to control atrial fibrillation. Cold cardioplegia may precipitate transient sinus node or AV node dysfunction. While some surgeons avoid placing epicardial pacing wires because of concerns about bleeding and cardiac tamponade on removal, recommendations include placing at least one ventricular pacing wire. A typical configuration for pacing wires is atrial pacing wires placed in a plastic disk that is sutured low on the right atrium. The two ventricular wires are attached over the right ventricular wall. Atrial pacing wires may be used to record atrial activity and, with a standard electrocardiogram, can help to distinguish atrial, junctional, and ventricular arrhythmias. Pacing wires can also be used therapeutically to increase the heart rate to about 90 bpm to achieve optimal hemodynamics.

Asystole or Pulseless Electrical Activity

Patients with epicardial pacing may develop **pulseless electrical activity** if ventricular fibrillation (VF) occurs; the pacer should be turned off briefly to check for VF if asystole occurs. If there is no VF, then the pacing wires should be connected and epicardial pacing initiated in the DDD mode/90 bpm. If the arrest was witnessed, then the wires should be connected before initiating cardiopulmonary resuscitation (CPR) [1 minute delay]. If pacing is not successful in reestablishing a pulse within a minute, then external CPR should begin. After resuscitation efforts have begun, transcutaneous pacing may be attempted. Medications include the following:

- Bradycardia: epinephrine, 1 mg intravenous (IV) bolus every 3–5 minutes or an infusion of 2–10 μg/min, OR vasopressin, 40 U IV. Atropine, 1 mg IV every 3–5 minutes (to a total of 0.4 mg/kg)
- Bradycardia nonresponsive to epicardial pacing: atropine, 0.5 mg IV initially with 0.5–1 mg every 3–5 minutes (total dose of 3 mg) and attempt transcutaneous pacing; other medications: epinephrine, 2–10 μg/min, and dopamine infusion, 2–10 μg/kg/min).

Atrial Pacing

Atrial (AV) pacing provides the best support for hemodynamics. Additionally, biatrial pacing after surgery may reduce the incidence of atrial fibrillation. To initiate atrial pacing, both atrial electrodes are connected to the pacemaker machine and the modes set at AOO (most common) or AAI. Pulse amplitude is usually 10–20 mA in the asynchronous mode; the pulse rate is set faster than the underlying rate. Normal AV conduction is necessary for atrial pacing, and it is ineffective for atrial fibrillation (Afib) or flutter. Indications include the following:

- Sinus bradycardia is treated by increasing heart rate with settings higher than the underlying rate.
- Premature ventricular contractions are suppressed with pacing faster than the sinus mechanism.
- Premature atrial complexes or prevention of Afib is suppressed with dual atrial pacing.
- Junctional rhythm is suppressed.
- Overdrive of supraventricular tachycardias is accomplished by interrupting the circuit and converting to sinus rhythm.

Atrial Overdrive Pacing

Atrial overdrive pacing at high rates (≤ 800 bpm) may be used to control supraventricular tachycardias, such as atrial flutter, paroxysmal atrial or atrioventricular junctional reentrant tachycardia, with initial pacing set at 10–15 bpm higher than the ventricular rate to ensure that the atria only are being paced. The electrocardiogram should be monitored during overdrive pacing and bipolar pacing used. The pacer is set to 20 mA (full current), and the rate is set at 10 bmp faster than the rate of flutter or tachycardia. After atrial capture, the rate is increased slowly until change occurs in flutter waves (usually at 20–30% higher than the atrial flutter rate) with pacing continued for 1 minute; then the pacer is turned off immediately, and the patient's rate and rhythm are assessed. If the tachycardia converts to marked bradycardia, then the pacemaker may be set at about 60 mA until the sinus mechanism stabilizes.

Atrioventricular Pacing

Atrioventricular (AV) pacing may shorten the AV delay typically found after cardiac surgery. To initiate AV pacing, both atrial and ventricular wires are attached to the AV pacer with both outlets set at 10–20 mA with a PR interval of 150 ms. With atrial activity, the DDD mode is used. Without atrial activity, DDD or DVI modes can be used. AV pacing is indicated for heart block (i.e., complete, first-degree, second-degree). Patients who have normal conduction should have atrial pacing alone. AV pacing is usually better than ventricular pacing because the atria are important for filling and 20–30% of cardiac output. Left ventricular systolic and diastolic functions are improved with biventricular pacing. Atrial fibrillation during AV pacing may be signaled by abrupt hemodynamic instability.

Ventricular Pacing

Ventricular pacing increases the risk of atrial fibrillation (Afib), but it can be used to slow the ventricular response to Afib or when atrial pacing is unable to maintain an adequate heart rate or to overdrive ventricular tachycardia. To initiate ventricular pacing, both ventricular wires are connected to the pulse generator for bipolar pacing, or one wire is connected to the negative pole and a different electrode (e.g., an atrial wire) to the positive for unipolar pacing. The mode is set at VVI with a ventricular output of 10–20 mA in the demand (synchronous) mode. The sensing threshold must be monitored as undersensing may cause incorrect pacing, and oversensing may inhibit pacing. The rate is adjusted according to the problem for which pacing is initiated. Left ventricular systolic and diastolic functions are improved with biventricular pacing. Care must be taken that ventricular pacing wires are not inappropriately sensing as this can result in ventricular tachycardia (VT). VT is treated with rapid ventricular pacing.

Complications Related to Pacemaker Use

Pacemakers, transvenous, temporary, and permanent, are invasive foreign bodies and as such can cause a number of different complications.

- Infection, bleeding, or hematoma may occur at the entry site of leads for temporary pacemakers or at the subcutaneous area of implantation for permanent generators.
- Puncture of the subclavian vein or internal mammary artery may cause a hemothorax.
- The endocardial electrode may irritate the ventricular wall, causing ectopic beats or tachycardia.
- Dislodgement of the transvenous lead may lead to malfunction or perforation of the myocardium. This is one of the most common early complications.
- Dislocation of leads may result in phrenic nerve or muscle stimulation (which may be evidenced by hiccupping).
- Cardiac tamponade may result when epicardial wires of temporary pacing are removed.
- General malfunctioning of the pacemaker may indicate dislodgement, dislocation, interference caused by electromagnetic fields, and the need for new batteries or generator.
- Pacemaker syndrome may result.

Pacemaker Syndrome

Pacemaker syndrome can occur with any type of pacemaker if there is inadequate synchronicity between the contractions of the atria and ventricles, resulting in a decrease in cardiac output, and inadequate atrial contribution to the filling of ventricles. Total peripheral vascular resistance may increase to maintain blood pressure, but hypotension occurs if it decreases.

Mild	Pulsations evident in neck and abdomen Cardiac palpitations Headache and feeling of anxiety General malaise and unexplained weakness Pain or "fullness" in the jaw or chest
Moderate	Increasing dyspnea on exertion with accompanying orthopnea Dizziness, vertigo, and increasing confusion Feeling of choking
Severe	Increasing pulmonary edema with dyspnea even at rest and crackling rales Syncope Heart failure

Problems Associated with Pacemakers

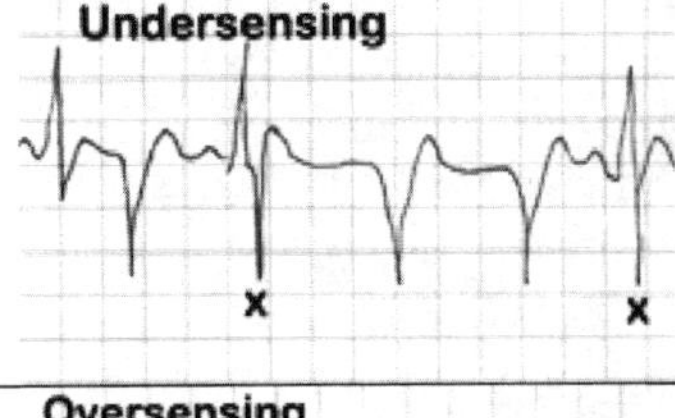	**Undersensing:** The sensitivity is too low to detect cardiac depolarizations and triggers unneeded contractions, competing with the patient's native rhythm. This may be related to dislodging a lead, incorrect positioning of a lead, or a low-amplitude cardiac signal.
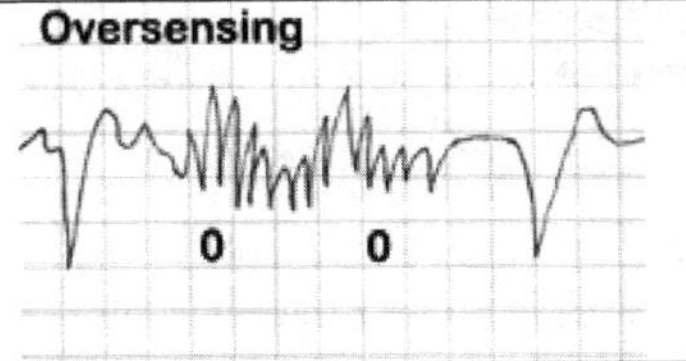	**Oversensing:** The sensitivity is too high, misinterpreting artifacts, such as muscle contractions, and nondepolarization events, such as contractions, and fails to trigger, resulting in decreased cardiac output because of interruption in contractions. This may result from damage or disconnection of a lead.

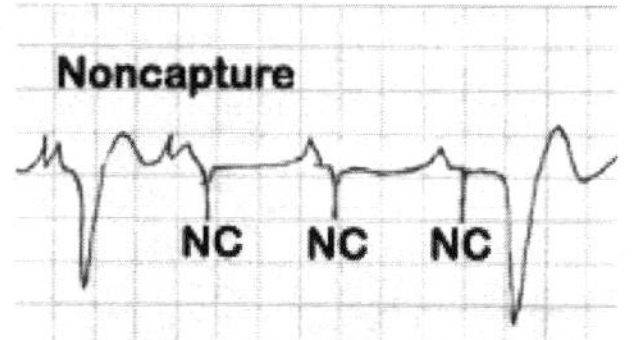	**Noncapture:** The pacemaker does not trigger contractions. This may be related to settings, lead disconnection, low battery, or metabolic changes.

Troubleshooting Methods for Problems Associated with Epicardial Pacing

Nonfunctioning	Wires may be defective or connections faulty. Electrodes may not be positioned properly or may have become dislodged. Atrial fibrillation may be occurring and causing atrial capture to fail. Battery may be low.
Threshold changes	Changes in condition (e.g., edema, inflammation, scar tissue near electrodes, thrombus formation) may cause the threshold to rise after surgery. If heart block continues for a number of days, a permanent transvenous pacemaker may need to be inserted.
Oversensing	In DDD pacing, atrial fibrillation and flutter may result in a fast-ventricular rate. The upper rate should be programmed lower or the pacemaker mode changed to VVI. VVI pacing may be inhibited by oversensing T waves.
Ventricular tachycardia (VT)/ ventricular fibrillation (VF)	Asynchronous ventricular pacing may trigger VT/VF. Ventricular pacing must be done in demand mode, and unused wires should be isolated and capped so they do not inadvertently trigger contractions.
Mediastinal bleeding	Mechanical irritation of the bypass graft can occur if wires are placed too close to surgical areas. Additionally, bleeding can occur from the atrial and ventricular surfaces where the wires are secured if the sutures are too tight or near small vessels. Pacing wires should not be removed until heparin is discontinued and INR is stable to reduce the chance of bleeding. Patients must be monitored carefully for cardiac tamponade.
Competing rhythm	Atrial or ventricular ectopic beats may occur with asynchronous pacing if the pacemaker's rate is too close to the patient's intrinsic rate. Turning the pacemaker off should relieve this situation.
Difficulty in removing wires	If pacing wires are secured too tightly or get caught under other sutures or wires, they may dislodge easily. Holding loose traction may help to dislodge the wires, but if this is not successful, the wire should be pulled out gently as far as possible and cut off at the skin. Once cut and the traction stopped, the wire should retract.

Fluid Balance/Fluid Deficit

Body fluid is primarily intracellular fluid (ICF) or extracellular fluid (ECF). By 3 years of age, the **fluid balance** has stabilized and remains the same throughout adulthood.

- ECF: 20–30% (interstitial fluid, plasma, transcellular fluid)
- ICF: 40–50% (fluid within the cells)

The fluid compartments are separated by semipermeable membranes that allow fluid and solutes (i.e., electrolytes, other substances) to move by osmosis. Fluid also moves through diffusion, filtration, and active transport. In fluid volume deficit, fluid is out of balance, and ECF is depleted; an overload occurs with an increased concentration of sodium and retention of fluid. Signs of a **fluid deficit** include the following:

- Thirsty
- Restless to lethargic
- Increased pulse rate and tachycardia
- Depressed fontanelles (infants)
- Decreased urinary output
- Normal blood, pressure progressing to hypotension
- Dry mucous membranes
- A 3–10% decrease in body weight

Hypovolemia/Fluid Volume Deficit

Hypovolemia/fluid volume deficit occurs when the loss of extracellular fluid is greater than the intake of fluid. Fluid and electrolytes are lost in equal proportions so serum electrolyte levels usually remain within a normal range unless there are other complications. Fluid volume deficit is classified by percentage of total body weight lost:

- Mild: 2%.
- Moderate: 2–5%
- Severe: 8% or more

Hypovolemia is characterized by increased heart rate and arterial hypotension and decreased pulmonary arterial wedge pressure, central venous pressure, capillary refill time, and urinary output; there is also increased osmolality, specific gravity, hemoglobin, hematocrit, and blood urea nitrogen, and a serum creatinine ratio of over 30:1. Hypotension (postural or prolonged) and tachycardia are common. Hypovolemia may result from a net loss of blood during surgery, surgical hypothermia (resulting in vasodilation as the body warms), and intravenous fluid loss into interstitial spaces because of increased permeability of capillary beds. Hypovolemia is the most common cause of decreased cardiac output in the postsurgical period. Treatment includes fluid replacement, usually initially crystalloid and then colloid. Packed red blood cells may be required for hemodilution.

Estimating Loss of Fluids

Patients may have preexisting fluid deficit (e.g., from presurgical fasting) as well as fluid maintenance requirements. **Estimating loss of fluids** is done by multiplying the normal maintenance rate (calculated according to weight) by the number of hours of fasting:

- 10 kg or less: 4 mL/kg/hr
- 11–20 kg: additional 2 mL/kg/hr
- 21 kg or more: additional 1 mL/kg/hr

Surgical wound fluid losses (e.g., blood loss) or "third-space" losses must also be estimated, and fluids added to compensate. Surgeries are usually classified, according to the degree of trauma and expected fluid loss from redistribution, evaporation, and blood loss:

- Minimal (e.g., hernia repair): 2–4 mL/kg/hr
- Moderate (e.g., cholecystectomy): 4–6 mL/kg/hr
- Severe (e.g., colectomy): 6–8 mL/kg/hr

Additionally, fluids may need to be added in conditions in which there is excessive fluid loss preoperatively, such as from severe diarrhea, ascites, or fever. Blood loss should be estimated, based on suctioned blood and saturated dressings:

- 4 x 4 = 10 mL/blood.
- Laparotomy pad = 100–150 mL/blood.

Fluid Shifts Associated with Cardiac Surgery

Fluid shifts between spaces are controlled by differences in hydrostatic and colloid osmotic pressure (COP). While water usually moves freely among intracellular, intravascular, and interstitial spaces, sodium moves freely only between the intravascular and interstitial spaces and does not move passively into the intracellular spaces unless serum osmolality and sodium concentration decrease, pulling fluid into the intracellular space. Cardiac surgery results in decreased COP by increasing capillary permeability, shifting fluid from intravascular to interstitial spaces. Cardiopulmonary bypass (CPB) results in a 20–30% increase in extracellular volume and increased sodium retention and potassium excretion. Each hour of CPB results in 800 mL fluid buildup; a 50% decrease is COP. Low levels of serum sodium postoperatively usually indicate total body fluid overload. Increased pulmonary capillary wedge pressure or decreased serum albumin pressures shifts fluid from the intravascular space to the interstitial space, resulting in pulmonary and tissue edema. Extracellular fluid (intravascular serum and interstitial fluid) is more easily lost than intracellular fluid. Electrolyte values reflect plasma levels and indicate the status of extracellular fluid.

Postoperative Fluid Management

Postoperative fluid management after cardiac surgery presents numerous challenges. Cardiopulmonary bypass (CPB) results in total body fluid and sodium overload, causing increased weight; this is not reflected in cardiac filling pressures because of capillary leak, decreased plasma and colloid osmotic pressure, and impaired myocardial function. Despite fluid overload, low-filling pressures are common with hypovolemia. Fluid administration is usually indicated to maintain intravascular volumes and adequate hemodynamics. Blood products and colloids are more effective in expanding intravascular volume than hypotonic solutions or crystalloids. If patients are well oxygenated, up to 1 L of crystalloid may be administered, followed by colloids if the response is not adequate. Colloids may include 5% albumin, which has less effect on coagulation than hydroxyethyl starches. Colloids with 5% albumin may increase interstitial fluid and cause decreased intracellular fluid. Hypertonic 25% albumin solutions reduce the amount of fluid necessary. Hydroxyethyl starch preparations are excellent volume expanders but may have adverse effects on renal function. Hypertonic saline solutions (3%) can increase intravascular volume but may cause hypernatremia.

Use of Diuretics for Fluid Management

Diuretics are usually avoided for the first 6 postoperative hours, but once the patient has stabilized, diuretics may be used to excrete the sodium and fluid overload caused by cardiopulmonary bypass. Loop diuretics, such as furosemide, are the diuretics of choice for **fluid**

management. Loop diuretics inhibit reabsorption of sodium and tubular water and may also improve the glomerular filtration rate (GFR). The usual dose for those with adequate renal function is 10–20 mg intravenously (IV); this dose can be repeated in 4 hours, although one dose may be sufficient for some patients. If hemodynamic status is unstable, an initial bolus of 40 mg may be followed by an infusion of 0.1–0.5 mg/hg/hr. If patients have developed tolerance to diuretics, a thiazide, such as chlorothiazide, 500 mg IV, may be given in conjunction with furosemide. Dopamine, 2–3 μg/kg/min, will also increase GFR and renal blood flow and may reduce the need for diuretics in patients with normal kidney function.

Fluid Replacement

Colloids

Colloids are solutions (usually isotonic saline but available with glucose and in hypertonic solutions) with dissolved high-molecular-weight (large) non-crystalline molecules and electrolytes. Colloids stay in the intravascular space more readily than crystalloids, so they are effective volume expanders. They are used primarily for fluid replacement with severe intravascular deficits, such as from hemorrhage and in conditions with severe hypoalbuminemia or where protein loss is probable, such as severe burns. Colloids are derived from plasma proteins or synthetic glucose polymers. Colloids obtained from plasma contain albumin (5% or 25% solutions) and plasma protein fractions (5%). Jehovah Witnesses may object to receiving these solutions. Colloids obtained from synthetic glucose contain hydroxyethyl starches and gelatin. Colloids have more safety concerns than crystalloids. Allergic reactions (including anaphylaxis) may be caused by dextran, hydroxyethyl, and (to a lesser degree) albumin. Bleeding may also result from a reduction in platelet aggregation, factor VII, and von Willebrand factor and prolonged partial thromboplastin time, so colloids should be avoided in patients with coagulopathies.

Crystalloid Solutions

Both colloids and **crystalloid solutions** (or a combination) are used as intravenous fluid therapy during surgery. Crystalloids are solutions of inorganic small molecules, glucose, or saline, dissolved in water. There are many types of crystalloid solutions:

- **Hypotonic solutions** are maintenance solutions used to replace water loss. Dextrose in water (D5W) is commonly used when patients have a water deficit and for those with sodium restriction.
- **Hypertonic solutions** are used for hyponatremia (3% saline) and severe hypovolemic shock (3–7.5% saline).
- **Isotonic solutions** are replacement solutions for loss of water and electrolytes. Isotonic crystalloids, such as normal saline (0.9%), Ringer's lactate (contains potassium), and Plasma-Lyte (contains potassium) are most commonly used. Different solutions contain different electrolytes (e.g., sodium, chloride, potassium, calcium, lactate, magnesium), so monitoring electrolytes is essential.

Crystalloids are effective in restoring fluid volume, but blood replacement requires 3:1 administration of crystalloids, while colloids are 1:1 replacement, and rapid crystalloid administration may result in tissue edema. Crystalloids are usually given as initial resuscitation fluid in emergencies. Glucose in some solutions may prevent ketosis and hypoglycemia.

Hypertonic Saline Solution

Hypertonic saline solution (HSS) has a sodium concentration higher than 0.9% (normal saline) and is used to reduce intracranial pressure/cerebral edema. Concentrations usually range from 2–23.4%, but 3% solutions may be used with cardiac surgery patients to treat total body fluid overload. HSS draws fluid from the tissue through osmosis. As edema decreases, circulation improves. HSS also expands plasma, increasing cerebral perfusion pressure, and counteracts hyponatremia that can occur in the brain after injury, causing increased intracranial pressure. It is administered as follows:

- Peripheral lines: HSS 3% or less only
- Central lines: HSS 3% or more

HSS can be administered continuously at rates varying from 30–150 mL/hr. Rates must be carefully controlled. Fluid status must be monitored to prevent hypovolemia, which increases the risk of renal failure. Laboratory monitoring includes the following:

- Sodium (every 6 hours) is maintained at 145–155 mmol/L. Higher levels can cause heart, respiratory, and renal failure.
- Serum osmolality (every 12 hours) is maintained at 320 mOsmol/L. Higher levels can cause renal failure.

Mannitol

Mannitol is an osmotic diuretic that increases excretion of both sodium and water and reduces intracranial pressure and brain mass. Mannitol may also be used to shrink the cells of the blood-brain barrier to help other medications breach this barrier. Mannitol is administered by intravenous infusion. It may be used during cardiopulmonary bypass to control blood pressure. Additionally, mannitol, 500 mL of 20%, is given with furosemide, 1 g, and dopamine, 2–3 μg/kg/min, to produce diuresis within 6 hours of onset of oliguria. Fluid and electrolyte balances must be carefully monitored as well as intake, output, and body weight. Concentrations of 20–25% require a filter. Crystals may form if the mannitol solution is too cold, and the mannitol container may require heating (in 80°C water) and shaking to dissolve crystals; the solution should be cooled to body temperature or less before administration. Mannitol cannot be administered in polyvinylchloride bags as precipitates form. Side effects include fluid and electrolyte imbalance, nausea, vomiting, hypotension, tachycardia, fever, and urticaria.

Intravenous Fluid Warmers

Intravenous fluid (IV) warmers warm fluids to body temperature to avoid inducing or worsening hypothermia, especially in geriatric patients. In cases of severe hypothermia, warmed fluids (104°F–108°F) may be administered to raise core temperature. Also, medications are absorbed more effectively in warmed fluids. There are numerous types of fluid warmers. Simple warmers warm fluid in the tubing as the tubing passes through the warming device. Some units are disposable and battery powered, and some are approved for both blood and fluids. Some units require special tubing or equipment. All must be monitored carefully. Special heating chambers may heat a number of IV fluid bags at one time in a cabinet-type structure. Intraoperative warming of IV fluids may prevent anesthesia-associated hypothermia.

IABP

The **intra-aortic balloon pump (IABP)** is the most commonly used circulatory assist device. The IABP improves hemodynamic status and controls and prevents ischemia pre- and postoperatively. Indications include the following:

- Postsurgical left ventricular failure and low cardiac output.
- Unstable angina.
- Refractory ischemia and hemodynamic instability.

- Myocardial infarction with complications or persistent angina.
- Cardiogenic shock.
- Papillary muscle dysfunction or rupture with mitral regurgitation or ventricular septal rupture.
- Nonresponsive ventricular dysrhythmias.

Contraindications include aortic regurgitation or dissection and severe atherosclerosis (aortic/peripheral).

Insertion

The **intra-aortic balloon pump (IABP)** is a catheter with an inflatable balloon from the tip and lengthwise down the catheter. The catheter is usually inserted through the femoral artery but may be placed during surgery or through a cut-down. The catheter is threaded into the descending thoracic aorta, and the balloon inflates distal to the left subclavian artery during diastole to increase circulation to the coronary arteries; it then deflates during systole to decrease afterload.

Removal

Anticoagulation is reduced and usually discontinued before removal of the IABP. When an IABP is removed percutaneously, initial pressure is applied distal to the insertion site for a few heartbeats to flush out the wound. Pressure is then applied slightly proximal to the insertion site as the artery puncture site is slightly cephalad to the skin puncture site. Steady pressure should be maintained for 45 minutes or more without interruption to prevent the formation of thrombus. The D-STAT dry hemostatic bandage, which contains bovine thrombin, may be used to improve surface hemostasis.

Complications

Complications associated with an intra-aortic balloon pump (IABP) include the following:

- Dysrhythmias (may interfere with ballooning).
- Peripheral ischemia from femoral artery occlusion.
- Balloon perforation or rupture, requiring immediate removal; migration; or inadequate ballooning.
- Vascular injury, including aortic dissection/rupture, thrombosis, vascular occlusion, and embolization.
- Renal ischemia if the balloon is placed too distally.
- Thrombocytopenia from damage to circulating platelets, so a daily platelet count is necessary.
- Distal ischemia is the most common complication, so distal pulses/Doppler signals must be assessed routinely. Ischemia may result from thrombosis near the site of insertion. Ischemia is most common in those with prolonged IABP use and in older female patients, diabetics, and patients with preexisting peripheral vascular disease. Cool extremities in the initial postoperative period may result from hypothermia, peripheral vasoconstriction, or low cardiac output, but this should reverse with treatment.

Timing of Balloon Inflation and Deflation

The **timing** of balloon inflation and deflation with the intra-aortic balloon pump (IABP) is done using the electrocardiogram (ECG) or arterial waveform:

- ECG: Inflation occurs at the peak of the T wave, and deflation occurs before or on the R wave.
- Arterial waveform: Inflation occurs at the dichrotic notch, and deflation occurs just before the aortic upstroke.

Most commonly the ECG is used as a trigger; the R wave indicates ventricular systole, and the arterial waveform is used to determine timing. Initially, the setting of inflation is 1:2 with every other heartbeat receiving assistance for comparison purposes. Then, the timing is set at 1:1 or other settings as needed by the patient. Criteria for optimal inflation include the following:

- Distinct V-shape occurs at the dicrotic notch.
- Augmented diastolic pressure is more than or equal to the previous systolic pressure.

Criteria for optimal deflation include:

- Assisted end-diastolic pressure is 5–10 mm Hg lower than the unassisted end-diastolic pressure.
- Assisted systolic pressure is 5–10 mm Hg lower than unassisted systolic pressure.

Timing Errors

While timing is carried out automatically, waveforms should be monitored carefully as manual adjustments may be required. Equipment varies, so manufacturer's directions should always be consulted. Correctly timing inflation is especially important. **Timing errors with the intra-aortic balloon pump** include early or late inflation and deflation.

- **Early inflation:** aortic regurgitation from early valve closing and decreased stroke volume, increasing end-diastolic volume and the need for myocardial oxygen (waveform loses V shape).
- **Late inflation:** decreased coronary artery perfusion pressures (diastolic augmentation after dicrotic notch).
- **Early deflation:** Increased afterload and need for myocardial oxygen (sharp drop-off in waveform with U curve before systolic upstroke).
- **Late deflation:** Loss of afterload reduction as balloon blocks left ventricular ejection of blood (systolic waveform widened and slow rise in the next assisted systole).

Monitoring Patients

Monitoring patients with intra-aortic balloon pumps (IABPs) involves checking the hemodynamic status every 15 minutes initially, then hourly, and then as indicated. The electrocardiogram and chest x-ray are performed daily, and intravenous therapy is maintained to ensure adequate preload. IABP settings must be checked and documented hourly with a waveform tracing printed every 12 hours or with changes. Distal pulses and sensorimotor function are checked every 15–30 minutes and then every hour; an ankle-brachial index is checked every 4 hours. A left radial pulse is monitored as an absence indicates upward migration of the catheter. Heparin levels are maintained with anticoagulation studies every 6 hours. Respiratory status is monitored every 4 hours with incentive spirometry every 2 hours, and the head of bed is maintained at 30°–45° to prevent aspiration. Patients should be advised to avoid flexing the hip on the affected side and may need a leg immobilizer. Patients should be log rolled for skin care.

WEANING CRITERIA

When the **intra-aortic balloon pump (IABP)** is initially placed, the inflation ratio is usually set at 1:2, with alternate beats assisted, but this may be changed to 1:1 if necessary. The ratio may be decreased to 1:3 or 1:4 or more as the patient's condition improves and is weaned from the IABP. **Weaning criteria** include the following:

- Normal or acceptable serum lactate, electrolytes, and hemoglobin/hematocrit levels.
- Absence of chest pain, dyspnea, or indications of decreased cerebral perfusion (e.g., confusion, restlessness, anxiety, altered mental status).
- Normal or near-normal heart rate without significant dysrhythmia.
- Stable hemodynamic status:
    - Mean arterial pressure over 65–70 mm Hg
    - Pulmonary artery occlusion pressure less than 18 mm Hg
    - Cardiac index over 2 L/min/m^2
    - Systemic vascular resistance less than 2000 dynes/sec/cm^{-5}
    - Urinary output over 0.5 mL/kg/hr
    - Venous oxygen saturation 60–80%

Both the ratio of assisted beats and the amount of gas in the balloon are decreased during weaning. Gas volume is usually reduced about 20% at each step in the weaning process; however, volume reduction increases the risk of thrombus formation, so the ratio is decreased more rapidly.

ABI

The **ankle-brachial index (ABI)** examination is done to evaluate peripheral arterial disease of the lower extremities:

1. Apply blood pressure cuff to one arm, palpate brachial pulse, and place conductivity gel over the artery.
2. Place the tip of a Doppler device at a 45° angle into the gel at the brachial artery, and listen for the pulse sound.
3. Inflate the cuff until the pulse sound ceases, and then inflate the cuff 20 mm Hg above that point.
4. Release air, and listen for the return of the pulse sound. This reading is the brachial systolic pressure.
5. Repeat the procedure on the other arm, and use the higher reading for calculations.
6. Repeat the same procedure on each ankle with the cuff applied above the malleoli and the gel over the posterior tibial pulse to obtain the ankle systolic pressure.
7. Divide the ankle systolic pressure by the brachial systolic pressure to obtain the ABI.
8. Sometimes, readings are taken both before and after 5 minutes of walking on a treadmill.

INTERPRETING RESULTS

Once the **ankle-brachial index (ABI)** examination is completed, the ankle systolic pressure must be divided by the brachial systolic pressure. Ideally, the blood pressure at the ankle should be equal to that of the arm or slightly higher. With peripheral arterial disease, the ankle pressure falls, affecting the ABI. Additionally, some conditions that cause calcification of arteries, such as diabetes, can cause a false elevation. Calculation is simple: If the ankle systolic pressure is 90 mm Hg and the brachial systolic pressure is 120 mm Hg, then 90/120 = .75. The degree of disease relates to the score.

Ankle-brachial Index Score

> 1.3	Abnormally high, may indicate calcification of vessel wall.
1–1.1	Normal reading, asymptomatic.
< 0.95	Indicates narrowing of one or more leg blood vessels.
< 0.8	Moderate, often associated with intermittent claudication during exercise.
< 0.6–0.8	Borderline perfusion.
0.5–0.75	Severe disease, ischemia.
< 0.5	Pain even at rest and limb threatened.
0.25	Critical limb-threatening condition.

Extracorporeal Circulation

The following are different types of extracorporeal circulation:

- **Ventricular assist devices (VADs)**: VADs are devices that support circulation with afferent conduits attached to the apex of the left ventricle and an efferent conduit attached to the ascending aorta; each conduit contains a porcine valve that directs flow of blood in one direction. The pump usually rests on the external chest wall and has an attached external pneumatic power source as well as a control circuit.
- **Deep hypothermic circulatory arrest (DHCA)**: DHCA is used primarily for surgery involving the aorta when the aorta cannot be clamped to protect the brain. The patient is cooled to 18°C with the patient's head packed and administration of methylprednisolone (20 mg/g) before clamping the arterial line and draining the blood. Antegrade cerebral perfusion or retrograde cerebral perfusion may also be used.
- **Assisted right-heart bypass**: Assisted right-heart bypass is sometimes used for off-pump procedures, especially with hypertrophy that interferes with filling of the right ventricle. Devices drain blood from the right atrium and return it to the pulmonary artery.
- **Extracorporeal membrane oxygenation (ECMO)**: ECMO is a modification of the cardiopulmonary bypass equipment that can provide support for the heart and lungs by pumping blood outside of the body for oxygenation. Typically, cannulas are placed in large vessels, and the blood is pumped to the machine for gas exchange; it is then heated and returned to the arterial system with the venous–arterial type of ECMO or to the venous system with the venous–venous type of ECMO.
- **Left-heart bypass**: Left-heart bypass may be done for thoracic aortic surgery. Blood is drained from the left side of the heart either from the left atrium or inferior pulmonary vein (preferred) with blood returned to the femoral artery or distal aorta (below clamp).

Short-Term Mechanical Circulation Devices and Ventricular Assist Devices

Short-term mechanical circulation devices may be used for an emergent bridge to transplant. These include the Abiomed pumps, which require sternotomy and can be used for right, left, or bilateral ventricular support. The TandemHeart PTVA system is inserted percutaneously into the femoral vein and threaded to the left atrium. Oxygenated blood from the left atrium is returned to the femoral artery by an arterial cannula. This device has been used to treat cardiogenic shock after cardiotomy. Extracorporeal membrane oxygenation may also be used for days or weeks, oxygenating the blood while bypassing the heart and lungs.

Ventricular assist devises (VADs) can provide support to the left ventricle (most common), right ventricle, or both. With most devices, blood drains from the base of the left ventricle into the pump through an inflow cannula and back into the aorta through an outflow cannula. The pump is placed preperitoneally in the abdomen with electrical cables and an air vent tunneled through a percutaneous line to the external controller. Left VADs require good right ventricular function.

Indications for Ventricular Assist Devices

In some cases, after cardiac surgery, patients cannot be weaned from cardiopulmonary bypass even with medications and use of an intra-aortic bypass pump. In that case, a **ventricular assist device (VAD)** may be inserted. Other indications include acute myocardial infarction with cardiogenic shock, metabolic abnormalities, and a cardiac index less than 1.8 L/min/m^2.

- **Left VAD (LVAD)** decompresses the left ventricle and provides systemic perfusion. Systolic blood pressure is less than 90 mm Hg, left atrial pressure is more than 20 mm Hg, and systemic vascular resistance is more than 2100 dynes/cm^5, with decreased urinary output of less than 20 mL/hr.
- **Right VAD (RVAD)** decompresses the right ventricle and provides pulmonary blood flow. Mean right atrial pressure is more than 20 mm Hg, left atrial pressure is less than 15 mm Hg, and there is no indication of tricuspid regurgitation.
- **Right and left VAD (BiVAD)** provides both systemic and pulmonary blood flow support. Left atrial pressure is more than 20 mm Hg, right atrial pressure is more than 20–25 mm Hg, and there is no tricuspid regurgitation. For those with LVAD, the BiVAD is indicated if the LVAD cannot maintain flow more than 2 L min/m^2 with right atrial pressure more than 20 mm Hg.

Monitoring of Patient with VAD

After the insertion of a **ventricular assist device (VAD)**, the patient must be **monitored** carefully:

- Infection: Dressings over drive-line exit sites must be changed daily and the drainage and wound conditions noted. Any changes in temperature (< 36°C or > 28.5°C) or erythema, purulent discharge, foul odor, or skin separation must be reported immediately. Trauma is prevented by applying abdominal binders to secure the cannulas.
- Albumin levels must be monitored (maintain > 2.5 g/dL) to promote healing.
- Right ventricular (RV) failure, including right arterial pressure and central venous pressure, may occur in which case RV support (dobutamine, 3–5 mcg/kg/min, or milrinone, 0.135–0.375 mcg/kg/min) must be provided. Nitric oxide may also improve RV function.
- Renal function for patients with left VAD must be monitored as renal function may decrease postoperatively, especially with heart failure.
- Hepatic function must be monitored for patients with heart failure or those who received intraoperative transfusions.

Vasodilators

Smooth Muscle Relaxants

Vasodilators may be used for arterial or venous dilation to improve cardiac function. These drugs may be used to treat pulmonary hypertension or generalized systemic hypertension. They may be used for patients who cannot tolerate angiotensin-converting enzyme inhibitors or angiotensin receptor blockers. Vasodilators may dilate arteries, veins, or both:

- Arterial dilation reduces afterload, improving cardiac output.
- Venous dilation reduces preload, reducing filling pressures.

Smooth muscle relaxants decrease peripheral vascular resistance but may cause hypotension and headaches.

- Sodium nitroprusside (Nipride) dilates both arteries and veins. It is rapid in action and used for the reduction of hypertension and afterload in heart failure.
- Nitroglycerin (Tridil) primarily dilates veins and is used intravenously to reduce preload for acute heart failure, unstable angina, and acute myocardial infarction. Nitroglycerin may also be used prophylactically after percutaneous coronary intervention to prevent vasospasm.
- Hydralazine (Apresoline) dilates arteries and is given intermittently to reduce hypertension.

Review Video: Muscle Relaxants
Visit mometrix.com/academy and enter code: 862193

Calcium Channel Blockers

Calcium Channel Blockers are primarily arterial vasodilators that may affect the peripheral and coronary arteries. General side effects include lethargy, flushing, abdominal and peripheral edema, and indigestion.

Dihydropyridine, such as nifedipine (Procardia), which should be avoided in older adults, and nicardipine (Cardene) are primarily arterial vasodilators, affecting both coronary and peripheral arteries, used to treat acute postoperative hypertension. Nicardipine may cause headache, nausea, vomiting, peripheral edema, and tachycardia. Clevidipine (Cleviplex) acts as a smooth muscle relaxant and arterial vasodilator, decreasing mean arterial pressure and systemic vascular resistance. Clevidipine is used postoperatively to treat hypertension without compromising cardiac function. Side effects are similar to nicardipine but can include atrial fibrillation and acute renal failure.

Benzothiazepine, such as diltiazem (Cardizem) and phenylalkylamine, such as verapamil (Calan), dilate primarily coronary arteries and are used for angina and supraventricular tachycardias.

Angiotensin-Converting Enzyme (ACE) Inhibitors

ACEIs limit the production of the peripheral vasoconstricting angiotensin, resulting in vasodilation, which can cause a precipitous fall in blood pressure, so use must be carefully monitored. ACEIs result in decreased and increased cardiac output but usually do not affect heart rate. They are often the first line of drugs to be used for acute hypertension and heart failure and are used to prevent nephropathy in patients with diabetes. After surgery, ACEIs may be administered in the initial period for those with mild left ventricular dysfunction, even with mild-to-moderate renal impairment, although serum creatinine levels should be monitored. Hyperkalemia may occur with inhibition of aldosterone.

- **Captopril** (Capoten) and **enalapril** (Vasotec) decrease afterload and preload for heart failure.
- **Enalapril** promotes vasodilation and decreases systemic vascular resistance. Adverse effects include cough, hyperkalemia, and renal failure.

Enalapril (Vasotec) is an angiotensin-converting enzyme inhibitor with antihypertensive action, inhibiting the renin–angiotensin system and decreasing vasoactive substances that usually increase with cardiopulmonary bypass. Enalapril provides both venous and arterial vasodilation, reducing preload and afterload without increasing heart rate. Onset of action for intravenous [IV] administration is 15 minutes with a peak in 1–4 hours and a duration of 6 hours. Oral medications have an onset of 1 hour, with a peak in 4–6 hours and a duration of 24 hours. Intravenous enalapril may be given for patients with impaired ventricular function and persistent hypertension if they are unable to take oral medications. Usual dose is 0.625–1.25 mg IV over 5 minutes every 6 hours (with a repeat dose after 1 hour if the response is inadequate, although peak action may be delayed for 4 hours in some patients). Adverse effects include headache, dizziness, fatigue, syncope, palpitations, hypotension (in sodium- or volume-depleted patients), nausea, vomiting, diarrhea, decreased hemoglobin and hematocrit, cough, and muscle cramps.

B-Type Natriuretic Peptides

B-type natriuretic peptides (nesiritide [Natrecor]) A new type of vasodilator (noninotropic), which is a recombinant form of a peptide of the human brain. It decreases filling pressure and vascular resistance and increases urinary output but may cause hypotension, headache, bradycardia, and nausea. It is used short term for worsening decompensated congestive heart failure.

Selective Specific Dopamine D_1-Receptor Agonists

Selective specific dopamine D1-receptor agonists, such as fenoldopam (Corlopam) are peripheral dilators affecting renal and mesenteric arteries and can be used for patients with renal dysfunction or those at risk for renal insufficiency. Fenoldopam is a rapid-acting peripheral and renal vasodilator that can be used to treat postoperative hypertension and is useful in patients with renal insufficiency as it increases glomerular filtration rate, renal blood flow, and excretion of sodium. It may cause a reflex tachycardia and hypokalemia.

Fenoldopam is rarely used postoperatively to treat hypertension but is usually used to protect the kidneys during surgery or to control hypertension when an immediate response (within 5 minutes) is necessary. Small doses used for renoprotective purposes usually do not result in hypotension.

Hydralazine

Hydralazine is an antihypertensive and peripheral vasodilator that acts on smooth muscle to cause arterial vasodilation, decreasing peripheral resistance. Hydralazine helps to maintain or increase both renal and cerebral blood flow. Hydralazine is commonly used as needed to control blood pressure when pressure remains unstable after the patient is transitioned to oral medications. Dosage is usually 10 mg intravenously (IV) injected slowly over 1 minute or 20–40 mg intramuscularly every 15 minutes until blood pressure responds and then every 6 hours. Hydralazine is fairly rapid acting with onset at 5–10 minutes (peaking at 20 minutes). Adverse effects include headache, peripheral neuritis, palpitations, tachycardia, angina, anorexia, nausea, vomiting, diarrhea, rash, arthralgia, fever, and nasal congestion. Hydralazine increases the effects of β-blockers, so the dosage of a concomitant β-blocker may need to be adjusted. Oral medications should be given with food. Medication should be withdrawn slowly to prevent rebound hypertension. Patients may experience orthostatic hypotension, especially in the morning, during hot weather, and with exercise or ingestion of alcohol.

α-Adrenergic Blockers

ARBs block α receptors in the arteries and veins, causing vasodilation but may cause orthostatic hypotension and edema from fluid retention. Blocking the angiotensin receptors results in decreased aldosterone, which can lead to increased renal sodium and water secretion. ARBs are used to manage hypertension and are contraindicated in patients with bilateral renal artery stenosis. Commonly used medications include:

- **Labetalol (Normodyne)** is a combination peripheral α-blocker and cardiac β-blocker and is used to treat acute hypertension, acute stroke, and acute aortic dissection.
- **Phentolamine (Regitine)** is a peripheral arterial dilator that reduces afterload and is used for pheochromocytoma.

VASOPRESSORS

ADRENERGIC AGONISTS

Adrenergic agonists are vasopressors (vasoconstrictors) with effects similar to norepinephrine or epinephrine. Adrenergic agonists can bind directly to adrenergic receptors to promote the release of norepinephrine, block norepinephrine reuptake, or inhibit activation of norepinephrine. Adrenergic agonists are used to control hypotension in the cardiac surgery patient when the patient is unresponsive to other measures. Following cardiac surgery, about 40% of patients require vasopressor support and 20% inotropic support.

Two classifications of adrenergic agonists include the following:

- **Catecholamines**: Epinephrine, norepinephrine, dopamine, and dobutamine.
- Noncatecholamines: Phenylephrine.

Adrenergic agonists usually have specific actions or combined actions, depending on the particular agent, and the action may be dose dependent; thus, the same drug at different dosages may have different actions. Adrenergic agents are classified according to which receptors they stimulate and the resultant action:

- α_1: vasoconstriction.
- α_2: inhibition of norepinephrine release and vasodilation.
- β_1: increased heart rate, blood pressure, contractility, cardiac output, automaticity, and conduction velocity.
- β_2: bronchodilation.
- D_1: vasodilation.
- D_2: inhibition of norepinephrine release and vasodilation.
- V_1: increased pulmonary vascular resistance and vasoconstriction (capillaries/arterioles).

PHENYLEPHRINE

Phenylephrine, a selective α_1-adrenergic agonist, increases both systolic and diastolic blood pressure but has little effect on β receptors in the heart. It is used postoperatively to manage mild-to-moderate hypotension, especially for patients with a high cardiac index and marked vasodilation. It can treat vascular failure associated with shock or drug-induced hypotension/hypersensitivity. With phenylephrine, systemic vascular resistance usually increases while cardiac output decreases, and heart rate may increase or decrease. Dosage depends on the clinical picture but usually ranges from 2–200 mcg/min. Adverse effects can include hypoperfusion with resultant splanchnic and renal ischemia. Phenylephrine may increase myocardial oxygen consumption and worsen metabolic acidosis. Other adverse effects include necrosis with extravasation, decreased urine formation and dysuria, cardiac arrhythmias, nausea, vomiting, dizziness, headache, tremors, and central nervous system depression. Phenylephrine is contraindicated with monoamine oxidase inhibitors, severe hypertension, ventricular tachycardia, pulmonary edema, and narrow-angle glaucoma. Phenylephrine is used with caution in diabetics and asthmatics. Adequate fluid resuscitation should be given before administration of phenylephrine.

EPINEPHRINE

Epinephrine stimulates α_1, β_1, and β_2 receptors and is used postoperatively primarily for inotropic effects to improve cardiac function and increase stroke volume, to control refractory hypotension, to increase heart rate, or to treat cardiac arrest. The effects on different receptors vary according to dosage:

- Low dose (< 0.2 mcg/kg/min): Stimulation of β_2 receptors results in bronchodilation and vasodilation.
- Moderate dose (0.008–0.06 mcg/kg/min): Stimulation of β_1 receptors increases blood pressure, cardiac output, and contractility.
- High dose (0.5–4.0 mcg/min): Stimulation of β_1 receptors (for a chronotropic effect) increases heart rate.
- Highest dose (> 2 mcg/min): Stimulation of α_1 receptor results in vasoconstriction.

Adverse effects relate to dosage with high dosages more likely to cause severe hypertension, myocardial ischemia, tachycardias, and tachyarrhythmias. Other adverse effects include hyperglycemia (sometimes requires insulin drip), metabolic acidosis (with serum bicarbonate levels, 17–21 mEq/L), especially if epinephrine is administered within 6–8 hours of surgery. Extravasation may result in tissue necrosis. Heart and glucose monitoring must be done continuously.

NOREPINEPHRINE

Norepinephrine stimulates α_1 and β_1 receptors, resulting in both vasoconstriction and inotropic action. Norepinephrine also has some stimulation of β_1 receptors, resulting in bronchodilation. Norepinephrine is used postoperatively for severe hypotension when volume replacement is not adequate and may be given with fluid resuscitation. It is the most frequently used vasopressor to treat hypotension/shock associated with cardiopulmonary bypass. The dosage usually begins at 2–20 mcg/min with dosages titrated to reach optimal response (mean arterial pressure of at least 70 mm Hg). Adverse effects include increased myocardial oxygen consumption and workload, hyperglycemia, and metabolic acidosis. Reception of α_1 receptors may result in visceral ischemia and renal damage. High doses may cause vasoconstriction that impairs peripheral perfusion and can lead to necrosis, so peripheral pulses, capillary refill time, and skin temperature and color should be assessed frequently.

VASOPRESSIN

Vasopressin is released in the body in response to cardiopulmonary bypass (CPB), sometimes resulting in post-CPB vasoconstriction, but the levels fall with prolonged hypotension; some people have low levels of vasopressin. Vasopressin is a potent vasoconstrictor that is used to treat vasodilatory shock after CPB when other measures (e.g., fluid resuscitation, inotropes, norepinephrine) are unsuccessful. Vasopressin may also be used for cardiac arrest associated with ventricular fibrillation or pulseless ventricular tachycardia and for milrinone-related hypotension. Vasopressin stimulates V_1 receptors and causes vasoconstriction of capillaries and small arterioles and increases secretion of corticotropin, which, in turn, stimulates the adrenal cortex to produce cortisol, helping to regulate blood pressure. Dosage varies from 0.01–0.1 U/min per intravenous infusion. Adverse effects relate to hypoperfusion and ischemia with end-organ damage, hyponatremia, and increased systemic vascular resistance. Vasopressin must be used very cautiously in patients with preexisting vascular disease.

Inotropic Agents

Dopamine

Inotropic agents increase cardiac output and improve contractility of the myocardium for heart failure. Intravenous inotropic agents may increase the risk of death but may be used when other drugs fail. Oral forms of these drugs are less effective than intravenous.

Dopamine stimulates α1, α2, and β2, D1, and D2 receptors although β2 stimulation is less than with other adrenergic drugs. Dopamine can be used for vasoconstriction or inotropic and chronotropic effects, depending on dosage:

- Low doses (< 8 mcg/kg/min) stimulate D1 and D2 receptors, resulting in inhibition of norepinephrine and vasodilation.
- Doses of 0.5–3.0 mcg/kg/min result in renal vasodilation.
- Doses of 4–10 mcg/kg/min stimulate β1 receptors, providing positive inotropic and chronotropic effects.
- High doses of 10 mcg/kg/min or more stimulate α1 receptors, providing vasoconstriction by stimulating endogenous norepinephrine.

Dopamine is used to improve cardiac output, increase blood pressure and renal perfusion, and treat shock. Adverse effects include hypertension, chest pain, tachyarrhythmias, dyspnea, ventricular dysrhythmias, and gangrene. Dopamine is contraindicated with pulmonary hypertension and tachyarrhythmias.

Dobutamine

Dobutamine, a synthetic catecholamine that is primarily a β1 agonist but also has some stimulation of α1 and β2 receptors. Dobutamine improves cardiac output, treats cardiac decompensation, lowers systemic vascular resistance and blood pressure, and increases heart rate, improving contractility. Dobutamine is indicated especially for patients who cannot tolerate vasodilators and have decreased cardiac output but high systemic vascular resistance or pulmonary vascular resistance. Patients with mitral valve replacement or high pulmonary pressures may have more benefit from dobutamine than dopamine. Dosage is usually 2–20 mcg/kg/in with rapid response. Adverse effects include increased systolic blood pressure and heart rate as well as premature ventricular contractions (5%), hypotension, and local reactions. Dobutamine should be avoided with hypovolemia.

Phosphodiesterase III Inhibitors

Milrinone (Primacor) Milrinone (preferred drug) increases the strength of contractions and causes vasodilation, decreasing systemic vascular resistance and pulmonary vascular resistance, especially indicated for patients with right ventricular failure. Other actions include increased cardiac output/cardiac index and stroke volume and decreased pulmonary artery occlusion pressure. Milrinone improves myocardial oxygenation. Milrinone usually has minimal effects on the heart rate. The initial dose is 50–75 mcg/kg with a maintenance infusion of 0.25–0.75 mcg/kg/min. Adverse effects include ventricular arrhythmias, hypotension, and headaches. Patients may need an adrenergic agonist to counteract pronounced vasodilation and replacement of potassium and magnesium to prevent dysrhythmias. Hypotension may occur during treatment, so patients must be monitored closely.

Inamrinone (Inocor) Inamrinone acts as a venous and arterial vasodilator and has hemodynamic effects that are similar to milrinone. The initial loading dose is 50–75 mg/kg over 2–3 minutes followed by a maintenance infusion of 10–30 mg/kg/min (total dose not to exceed 10 mg/kg/d) or repeat loading doses. Adverse effects include thrombocytopenia, nephrogenic diabetes mellitus, impaired liver function, and exacerbation of dysrhythmias.

Assessment of Peripheral Perfusion

Assessment of peripheral perfusion can indicate venous or circulatory impairment:

- **Venous refill:** Begin with the patient lying supine for a few moments, and then position the feet in a dependent position. Observe the veins on the dorsum of the foot, and count the seconds before normal filling. Venous occlusion is indicated with times of 20 seconds or more.
- **Capillary refill:** Grasp the toenail bed between the thumb and index finger, and apply pressure for several seconds to cause blanching. Release the nail, and count the seconds until the nail regains normal color. Arterial occlusion is indicated with times of 2–3 seconds or more. Check both feet and more than one nail bed.
- **Skin temperature:** Using the palm of the hand and fingers, gently palpate the skin, moving distally to proximally, comparing both legs. Circulatory impairment is indicated by decreased temperature (coolness) or a marked change from proximal to distal.

Methylene Blue for Vasodilatory Shock

Methylene blue inhibits nitric oxide, which is released in the body after cardiopulmonary bypass. Nitric acid can cause severe vasoplegia with marked peripheral vasodilation and hypotension associated with normal- or high-cardiac output, low central venous pressure, pulmonary artery occlusion pressure, and lower pulmonary vascular resistance. Methylene blue is used to treat vasodilatory shock although it is not approved by the Food and Drug Administration for this purpose. Methylene blue is also used to treat type III protamine reaction that results in catastrophic pulmonary vasoconstriction, cyanide poisoning, and drug-induced methemoglobinemia. Usual dosage for vasodilatory shock is 1–2 mg/kg intravenously over 20 minutes. Adverse effects include hypertension, temporary (about 10 minutes) low oxygen saturation, hypotension, dizziness, headache, nausea, vomiting, diarrhea, and abdominal pain. Patients must be carefully monitored for hypertension, urine discoloration, oxygen saturation, and methemoglobin levels and may need to have a reduced rate of norepinephrine infusion. Methylene blue should be used cautiously in those with glucose-6-phosphate dehydrogenase deficiency, anemias, and renal impairment.

Digitalis

Digitalis, an inotrope most commonly administered in the form of digoxin (Lanoxin), is derived from the foxglove plant and is used to increase myocardial contractility and left ventricular output and slow conduction through the atrioventricular (AV) node, decreasing rapid heart rates and promoting diuresis. Digoxin does not affect mortality but increases tolerance to activity and reduces hospitalizations for heart failure. Therapeutic levels (0.5–2.0 ng/mL) should be maintained to avoid digitalis toxicity, which can occur even if digoxin levels are within the therapeutic range, so observation of symptoms is critical. Potassium imbalance may cause toxicity.

Symptoms of toxicity include the following:

- Early signs
- Increasing fatigue, lethargy, depression, nausea, and vomiting
- Sudden change in heart rhythm, such as regular or irregular rhythm, and palpitations
- Sinoatrial or AV block, new ventricular dysrhythmias, and tachycardia (atrial, junctional, ventricular)
- Bradycardia

Treatment includes:

- Discontinue medication.
- Monitor serum levels and symptoms.
- Digoxin immune Fab (Digibind) may be used to bind to digoxin and inactivate it if necessary.

Note: A number of drugs, including amiodarone, may increase digoxin levels.

Pulmonary

Chest Tubes/Drains

Chest (pleural and mediastinal) tubes/drains are placed during surgery to drain blood or air that may accumulate at the surgical site. Typically, 2 to 3 tubes/drains are placed and sutured to the skin. The negative pressure tubes/drains are left in place until drainage subsides and then removed, usually within 72 hours. The tubes/drains are used to prevent complications, such as cardiac tamponade or pneumothorax, and to detect signs of excess bleeding. Changing the patient's position may result in increased drainage from the chest tube because of pooling of blood. Acute onset of bleeding is characterized by bright red blood and continuous steady discharge. Dark red blood suggests older blood rather than active bleeding, especially if discharge slows after initial increase. Chest tube/drain output should be monitored hourly and should not exceed 200 mL in 2 to 6 hours. Excess bleeding may require coagulations studies, repeat chest ray to evaluate the width of the mediastinum, and transesophageal echocardiogram if cardiac tamponade is suspected. With cardiac tamponade, a sudden decrease in chest tube/drain drainage may occur as blood and clots accumulate in the pericardial sac.

Readiness for Extubation

During **extubation**, the oxygen saturation should be 92–94% or more on a fraction of inspired oxygen of 40% and a positive end-expiratory pressure of 5 cmH_2O. Methods used to determine **readiness for extubation** include:

- **Compliance, resistance, oxygenation, pressure (CROP) index:** This identifies parameters that predict extubation success based on respiratory rate, compliance, arterial oxygen, maximum inspiratory pressure, and relative inspiratory effort.
- Intermittent mandatory ventilation (IMV)/synchronized IMV (SIMV): The rate of ventilation is gradually reduced.
- **Pressure support ventilation (PSV):** Inspiratory support is gradually reduced. In some cases, a minimum tidal volume is set per ventilator-assisted breath. PSV may be combined with IMV/SIMV.
- **Spontaneous breathing trial (SBT):** SBT is usually in the morning for a prescribed period (30–120 minutes) after the patient exhibits some spontaneous triggering of respirations, and sedation is reduced. The ventilator rate is adjusted to 0, and pressure support is decreased. The SBT is discontinued if respiratory distress occurs.

Ventilation Extubation

Criteria

Extubation from ventilation in the initial postoperative period should be done after the patient meets the weaning criteria. Extubation can be done from continuous positive air pressure (CPAP) or T-piece. Ventilation extubation criteria include the following:

- Patient meets weaning criteria.
- Patient is able to maintain an awake state without stimulation.
- Respiratory mechanics are acceptable:
- Tidal volume is 5 mL/kg ideal body weight or more.
- Negative inspiratory force is 25 cmH_2O or more.
- Vital capacity is 10–15 mL/kg or more.
- Respirations (spontaneous) are 24 breath/min or less.
- Blood gases are acceptable (on ≤ 5 CPAP/pressure support ventilation)
- Partial pressure of oxygen is 70 torr or more (with a fraction of inspired oxygen of ≤ 0.5).
- Partial pressure of carbon dioxide is 48 torr or less.
- pH is 7.32–7.45.

After an extended period of ventilation, patients should meet the criteria related to respiratory mechanics and blood gases and should have a respiratory rate of 35 breaths/min or more without agitation or diaphoresis and should be mentally alert and able to cough. A **cuff leak of 110** or more should be present with the cuff deflated.

Failure Criteria

About 5% of cardiac surgical patients fail extubation. **Failure criteria for ventilator extubation** include the following:

- Decreased oxygen saturation of less than 90%. Agitation, diaphoresis, or increased somnolence.
- Change in systolic blood pressure by more than 20 mm Hg/min or a rise to 160 mm Hg or more.
- Heart rate increase or decrease of more than 20% or tachycardia of 120 bpm.
- Need for vasoactive medications to maintain status. Development or worsening of arrhythmias. Increased respiratory rate of 10 breaths/min or a rise to 35 breaths/min or more for a 5-minute period.
- Partial pressure of oxygen of less than 60 torr (with a fraction of inspired oxygen of 0.5).
- Partial pressure of carbon dioxide of more than 50 torr with a pH of less than 7.30 (indicating respiratory acidosis).

Patients who are agitated may require more sedation and prolonged ventilation with weaning attempted when patient is stabilized. Avoid extubation at night if intubation was difficult in the event reintubation is necessary. Older patients with a slow metabolism may awaken more slowly, but reversal agents (e.g., naloxone) should be avoided as use may markedly increase pain. Small amounts of a reversal agent may be indicated after 24–36 hours to determine if the patient has suffered a stroke or other impairment.

Postextubation Management

Patients must be monitored carefully **postextubation**. Patients who did not exhibit a cuff leak during positive pressure ventilation with the cuff deflated may have laryngotracheal edema that can lead to obstruction of the upper airway, especially after several days of ventilation. Patients may need oxygen (humidified at 40–70%) because of decreased compliance of the chest wall, atelectasis, and pain inhibiting deep breathing. Patients with inadequate oxygenation may require a nonrebreather mask with oxygen at 8–15 L/min.

Bilevel positive airway pressure, continuous positive airway pressure (CPAP), or intermittent positive pressure breathing should be used for several days after surgery as they expand the lungs better than incentive spirometry. CPAP with a nasal mask may be used for patients with cardiogenic pulmonary edema. Dysphagia may occur, especially in patients with ventilation for over 48 hours, putting them at risk for aspiration. When hemodynamically stable, intravenous furosemide is administered to promote diuresis. Adequate analgesia is critical for recovery. Antiembolism stockings or devices and early mobilization can prevent thromboembolism. Antibiotics are needed for a positive sputum culture, and bronchodilators are needed for bronchospasm).

BiPAP

Bilevel positive airway pressure (BiPAP) devices deliver two levels of pressure, which can be preset. Inspiratory positive airway pressure (IPAP) is set at a higher level than expiratory positive airway pressure (EPAP). This allows for the pressure needed to open the airway during inspiration but reduces pressure to facilitate expiration. Typically, BiPAP devices do not compensate for altitude and can be used with humidification. Some have software and downloadable memory to generate reports of sleep events. Spontaneously timed (BiPAP ST) devices have two pressure settings for each breath as well as settings for the number of respirations so that they can trigger inspiration if the respiratory rate falls below a preset level, an important consideration for central sleep apnea and other pulmonary disorders. Settings include *spontaneous mode*, which triggers increased pressure after the person attempts to breath, and *timed mode,* which triggers increased pressure to initiate respiration within a preset time. Autotritrating BiPAP devices are also available and can vary both IPAP and EPAP automatically as needed to promote adequate ventilation.

Determining Continuous Positive Airway Pressure

All positive airway pressure devices have air blowers that deliver pressurized room air to an interface or mask. Pressure can be increased or decreased by adjusting the speed or the amount of airflow, with most machines generating pressure ranging from 2–20 cm water pressure. Carbon dioxide is expelled through a vent or nonrebreather valve on expiration. A wide range of equipment is available for **continuous positive airway pressure (CPAP)**, starting with the most basic relatively inexpensive machines to expensive computerized equipment.

Basic CPAP machines may be large or small, but all have filters in the back and can be used with a variety of masks (e.g., oral, nasal, orofacial, nasal pillow). Some have built-in heated humidifiers, and all can be used with cool passover or heated humidifiers. Many basic machines do not adjust for environmental factors, such as altitude, and many do not have an internal memory to generate sleep reports. Some may switch between 110 and 200 volts. Even basic machines allow for a gradual rise to selected pressure.

More sophisticated CPAP machines usually have software and downloadable memories and can provide reports regarding respiratory events. Altitude compensation is usually automatic.

Inhaled Vasodilators and Intravenous Vasodilators

Inhaled pulmonary vasodilators, most commonly nitric oxide (NO) or prostacyclins (such as iloprost), are used in the treatment of heart failure with left heart disease and pulmonary hypertension and after placement of a left ventricular assist device to improve ventilation-perfusion matching. They increase cardiac output and decrease pulmonary vascular resistance. Inhaled vasodilators selectively affect well-ventilated alveolar pulmonary capillaries. NO has a very short half-life so it must be administered continuously to avoid rebound effects and poses the risk of methemoglobinemia, while iloprost is administered every 3 to 4 hours with fewer adverse effects. While useful to improve oxygenation and reduce pulmonary artery pressure, inhaled pulmonary vasodilators have not demonstrated an effect on mortality.

Intravenous pulmonary vasodilators, such as nitroglycerine, epoprostenol, and nitroprusside, are non-selective, have greater systemic effects than inhaled pulmonary vasodilators, and are more likely to result in hypotension although they can reduce pulmonary artery pressure. However, IV vasodilators may increase blood flow to poorly-ventilated alveoli, increasing ventilation-perfusion mismatching.

Primary Respiratory Functions

The body's cells obtain energy from the oxidation of carbohydrates, fats, and proteins, a process that requires oxygen and generates carbon dioxide as a by-product. The primary **respiratory function** is to facilitate this process:

Oxygen transport	Blood circulates to carry oxygen to the cells and to remove carbon dioxide by diffusion at the capillary level.
Respiration	Gas exchange occurs between the atmospheric air and the blood and between the blood and the body cell. The capillaries in the lungs have a lower concentration of oxygen than the alveoli, so oxygen diffuses into the blood. The capillaries have a higher concentration of carbon dioxide than the alveoli, so carbon dioxide diffuses into the alveoli.
Ventilation	Air flows into the lungs during inspiration and back into the atmosphere during expiration with airflow governed by variances in air pressure, airway resistance, and compliance.

Airway Clearance

Airway clearance, the ability to move secretions or foreign particles from the upper airway and prevent aspiration, depends on an intact and functioning mucociliary system and the ability to cough effectively. Mucus provides barrier protection to the tissues, and the cilia mechanically move mucus and particles upward. Inflammation, asthma, chronic obstructive pulmonary disease, cystic fibrosis (CF), and mechanical ventilation can alter the viscosity of the mucus and impair its effectiveness. CF, lung transplantation, mechanical irritation, and smoking can damage cilia. Patients with tracheotomies or mechanical ventilation tend to retain secretions, impairing the exchange of oxygen and increasing the effort required to breathe, leading to increased inflammation and infection that further impair lung function. Both increased and retained secretions lead to decreased forced expiratory volume (in 1 second) and higher mortality rates. Cough is impaired by mechanical ventilation as well as restrictive and obstructive respiratory diseases. Airway clearance measures include the following:

- Directed cough, chest physiotherapy (if not on ventilator)
- Positioning with head of bed elevated
- Suctioning as needed (limited to 5 seconds in duration)
- Antibiotics for infection

- Bronchodilators
- Airway clearance devices

Factors Related to Ventilation

The following are factors related to ventilation:

- Air pressure variances:
  - Inspiration: The thorax expands and lowers the pressure in the thoracic cavity relative to atmospheric pressure, drawing air into the alveoli.
  - Expiration: The diaphragm relaxes, the lungs contract, and pressure inside the alveoli increases relative to atmospheric pressure, causing air to flow out of the lungs.
- Airway resistance: Resistance directly relates to the size of the airway, so changes in size can increase resistance, requiring an increased effort of breathing:
  - Bronchial contraction, smooth muscles (asthma)
  - Mucosal hyperplasia (chronic bronchitis)
  - Airway obstruction (tumor, mucus, foreign body)
  - Dilation, loss of elasticity (chronic obstructive pulmonary disease [COPD])
- Compliance
  - The elasticity and expandability of the lungs and thoracic cavity determine the volume/pressure relationship:
    - ❖ Compliance decreases when lung expansion is limited or "tight" (e.g., pneumothorax, pulmonary edema, atelectasis, acute respiratory distress disorder), requiring an increased effort of breathing.
    - ❖ Compliance increases with overdistention of the thorax or loss of elasticity (e.g., COPD).

Review Video: Mechanical Ventilators
Visit mometrix.com/academy and enter code: 679637

Terms Related to Oxygen Administration

Flow rate (FR)	The FR is the number of liters of oxygen flow per minute. During titration, flow may be adjusted, according to the patient's response by using the least amount required to obtain optimal oxygen saturation.
Fraction of inspired oxygen (FiO_2)	The FiO_2 is the percentage of oxygen in the mixture of air provided to the patient. This ranges from that of room air, 21%, to 100%, but is usually maintained at less than 60%. FiO_2 may be expressed as a decimal or percentage: 0.50 equals 50%. When ordering oxygen for titration, the physician may not specify the exact FiO_2 but rather the target oxygen saturation.
Liters per minute (LPM)	LPM measures the liters of oxygen administered.
Room air (RA)	RA is 21% oxygen. This is the usual air provided by positive airway pressure.

Negative Inspiratory Pressure, Tidal Volume, Minute Ventilation, Intrapulmonary Shunt, and Alveolar-Arterial Oxygen Gradient

Negative inspiratory pressure is the pressure generated in a forced inspiration with obstructed airflow. It assesses the patient's ability to cough hard enough to mobilize and expel secretions.

Tidal volume is the volume of air expelled with normal exhalation (not forced).

Minute ventilation is the volume of gas exchange (including both inhaled and exhaled) in 1 minute.

Intrapulmonary shunt (IPS) is the percentage of cardiac output that does not go through gas exchange because it does not come in contact with ventilated alveoli. This may result from atelectasis or hypoxemia after cardiac surgery. The usual intrapulmonary shunt is 5% or less, although those with acute respiratory distress syndrome may have shunts up to 50%. Oxygen is not effective in treating IPS.

Alveolar-arterial (A-a) oxygen gradient is the difference in the percentage of alveolar oxygen and the percentage of arterial oxygen. The A-a gradient can help to identify the cause of hypoxemia and to identify IPS. A simplified formula is: **$PAO_2 - PaO_2$.**

Oxyhemoglobin Dissociation Curve

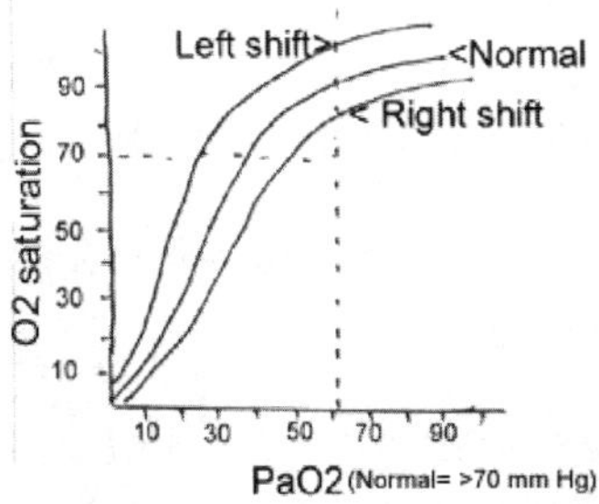

The **oxyhemoglobin dissociation curve** is a graph that plots the percentage of hemoglobin saturated with oxygen (Y axis) and different partial pressures of oxygen (PaO_2 levels, X axis). A curve shift to the right, as occurs with acidosis, represents conditions where hemoglobin has less affinity for oxygen, and greater amounts of oxygen are released into the tissues. Low pH shifts the curve to the right, enabling increased off-loading of hemoglobin to tissues. A shift to the left, which occurs with hypothermia and alkalosis, has the opposite implications, increased binding of oxygen but less release to the tissues. Blood transfusions and elevated oxygen shifts the curve to the left, causing increased affinity of hemoglobin for oxygen in the lungs. Normal PaO_2 is 80–100 mm Hg, equal to 95–98% oxygen saturation. Levels less than 40 mm Hg are dangerous.

Arterial Oxygen

Arterial oxygen is carried in the red blood cells by hemoglobin. Each hemoglobin molecule can carry four molecules of oxygen, with 1 g of hemoglobin equal to 1.39 mL of oxygen (100 mL arterial blood carries 0.3 mL oxygen). When the hemoglobin is fully saturated (4 oxygen molecules per molecule of hemoglobin), then arterial oxygen saturation is 100%. A small amount of oxygen remains dissolved in blood (partial pressure of oxygen [PaO_2] x 0.003), but this has little effect on arterial oxygen content. The formula to determine arterial oxygen (CaO_2) is described below:

$$CaO_2 = (\text{hemoglobin} \times SaO_2 \times 1.39) + (PaO_2 \times 0.003)$$

A simplified formula is sometimes used to evaluate oxygen delivery (O_2D):

$$O_2D = (\text{stroke volume x heart rate}) \text{ x oxygen saturation } (SpO_2).$$

Perfusion pressure is estimated by the systolic blood pressure:

$$\text{Systolic blood pressure} = \text{cardiac output x systemic vascular resistance}.$$

Because the oxygen in the blood is related to hemoglobin levels, correcting anemia more effectively increases PaO_2 than increasing the fraction of inspired oxygen.

Factors Affecting Partial Pressure of Carbon Dioxide

There are many factors that can affect the **partial pressure of carbon dioxide ($PaCO_2$)** level in the blood, including conditions that relate to respiratory acidosis and metabolic alkalosis:

- Increased $PaCO_2$ and acute respiratory acidosis may occur with central nervous system depression caused by medications (e.g., sedatives), stroke, head trauma, neuromuscular diseases (e.g., Guillain-Barré, myasthenia gravis, muscular dystrophy), lung disorders (e.g., pleural effusion, pneumothorax), airway obstruction, and acute respiratory disorders (e.g., pneumonia, hyperventilation, pulmonary edema).
- Increased $PaCO_2$ and chronic respiratory acidosis may occur with chronic disorders, such as chronic obstructive pulmonary disease, kyphoscoliosis, and scleroderma.
- Decreased $PaCO_2$ and metabolic alkalosis may occur with diabetic ketoacidosis, uremia, hyperalbuminemia, ethyl alcohol ingestion, salicylate poisoning, hypokalemia, uretero-sigmoidostomy, renal tubular acidosis, angiotensin-converting enzyme inhibitors, and hyperkalemia.
- Increased $PaCO_2$ to 70 mm Hg is an indication of imminent respiratory failure, requiring intubation. This is especially true if the $PaCO_2$ is rebounding from a previous lack of carbon dioxide in the arterial sampling. This is common in hyperventilating asthmatics who are tiring and headed for respiratory arrest.

Prolonged Postoperative Ventilation

Predictors for the need for prolonged postoperative ventilation after cardiac surgery:

Preoperative	**Preexisting conditions:** diabetes, recent myocardial infarction, pulmonary edema, previous cardiac surgery, peripheral vascular disease, left ventricular impairment with an ejection fraction of less than 40%, increased serum creatinine, cardiogenic shock, sepsis, chronic obstructive pulmonary disease, class III or IV congestive heart failure, aortic aneurysm, valvular disease, and need for intubation. **Age and gender:** 75 years of age or older and female
Intraoperative	Deep hypothermic circulatory arrest, prolonged cardiopulmonary bypass over 4–6 hours, extended duration of surgery, abnormal serum glucose levels, coagulopathy, multiple procedures, perioperative heart failure, and severe myocardial dysfunction
Postoperative	Impaired mentation, excessive mediastinal bleeding, hemodynamic instability, need for intra-aortic balloon pump, pulmonary edema, hypoxia, respiratory failure, stroke, parenteral nutrition, acute respiratory distress syndrome, and need for inotropic agents or transfusions

Mechanical Ventilation Modes

Control mode (CM)	Inspiration and expiration as well as tidal volume (Vt) and rate are preset, and the patient cannot initiate breaths or alter pattern. This mode is rarely used, and patients may require sedation to prevent competition with ventilation.
Continuous mandatory ventilation (CMV)	The Vt and rate are preset, but the patient can initiate breaths but cannot alter the Vt. This is frequently used after anesthesia. Patients may need sedation to decrease spontaneous breaths.
Synchronized intermittent mandatory ventilation (SIMV)	The Vt and rate are preset and synchronized with the patient's spontaneous breathing in this primary ventilation mode. This mode is often used to wean patients from the ventilator. Respiration rates of less than 6 breaths/min can cause increased work of breathing.
Pressure support ventilation (PSV)	Positive pressure is supplied during spontaneous inspiration. This mode does not have a preset rate, so patients must be monitored closely for fatigue or apnea. This mode is used for higher pressures and to wean patients with chronic obstructive pulmonary disease.

Postoperative Ventilator Settings

Postoperative **ventilator settings** include:

- **Type of ventilation:** synchronized intermittent mandatory ventilation, assist control, pressure support, or pressure control
- **Control mode:** controlled ventilation, assisted ventilation, synchronized intermittent mandatory (allows spontaneous breaths between ventilator-controlled inhalation/exhalation), positive end-expiratory pressure (PEEP) [positive pressure at end of expiration], continuous positive airway pressure, and bilevel positive airway pressure
- **Tidal volume (Vt):** set in relation to respiratory rate, 8–12 mL/kg ideal body weight. An increase may decrease carbon dioxide, and a decrease may increase carbon dioxide levels.
- **Inspiratory-expiratory ratio (I:E):** ranges from 1:2 but may vary
- **Respiratory rate:** depends on Vt and partial pressure of carbon dioxide ($PaCO_2$) target, 8–18 breaths/min.
- mL/kg/min
- **Fraction of inspired oxygen (FiO_2):** the percentage of oxygen in the inspired air, usually ranges from 21–100% and maintained at less than 40% to avoid toxicity; depends on arterial blood gas and oxygen saturation (0.4–1.0).
- **Sensitivity:** determines the effort needed to trigger inspiration.
- **Pressure:** controls the pressure exerted in delivering Vt, 5–10 cmH_2O.
- **Rate of inspiratory flow:** controls the liters per minute speed of Vt, 30–60 L/min.
- **Minute volume:** 100–120.
- **PEEP:** 5–10 cmH_2O.

Positive Pressure Ventilators

Positive pressure ventilators assist respiration by applying pressure directly to the airway, inflating the lungs, forcing expansion of the alveoli, and facilitating gas exchange. Generally, endotracheal intubation or tracheostomy is necessary to maintain positive pressure ventilation for extended periods. There are three basic kinds of positive pressure ventilators:

- **Pressure cycled:** This type of ventilation is usually used for short-term treatment after extubation. The intermittent positive pressure breathing machine is the most common type. This delivers a flow of air to a preset pressure and then cycles off. Airway resistance or changes in compliance can affect the volume of air and may compromise ventilation.
- **Time cycled:** This type of ventilation regulates the volume of air the patient receives by controlling the length of inspiration and the flow rate.
- **Volume cycled:** This type of ventilation provides a preset flow of pressurized air during inspiration and then cycles off and allows passive expiration, providing a fairly consistent volume of air.

Preventing Complications from Mechanical Ventilation

Methods to **prevent complications** from mechanical ventilation include:

- Elevate the patient's head and chest to 30° to prevent aspiration and ventilation-associated pneumonia.
- Reposition patient every 2 hours.
- Provide deep venous thrombosis prophylaxis, such as external compression support or heparin (5000 U subcutaneously two to three times daily).
- Administer famotidine (20 mg twice a day by nasogastric [NG] tube or intravenously [IV]) or sucralfate (1 g per NG tube four times day) to prevent gastrointestinal bleeding.
- Decrease and eliminate sedation/analgesia as soon as possible.
- Follow careful protocols for pressure settings to prevent barotrauma. Tidal volumes are usually maintained at 8–10 mL/kg ideal body weight.
- Monitor for pneumothorax or evidence of barotrauma.
- Conduct nutritional assessment (including lab tests) to prevent malnutrition.
- Monitor intake and output carefully, and administer IV fluids to prevent dehydration.
- Do daily spontaneous breathing trials, and discontinue ventilation as soon as possible.

Criteria for Ventilator Weaning

Ventilator weaning has three phases: removal of the ventilator, extubation, and finally removal of supportive oxygen. Criteria for ventilator weaning in the early postoperative period include the following:

- Patient awake without stimulation, not shivering, and able to grip hand or lift head for 5 seconds.
- Neuromuscular blockade reversal evident and patient moving.
- Core temperature stable at 35.5°C or higher.
- Stable systolic blood pressure of 100–140 mm Hg.
- Heart rate stable at less than 120 bpm without arrhythmias.
- Cardiac index 2.2 L/min/m^2 or more.
- Chest tube drainage less than 50–100 mL/hr.
- Minute ventilation of about 6 L/min (respiratory rate x tidal volume).
- Rapid shallow breath index less than 100 breaths/min/L.

- Partial pressure of oxygen (PaO_2)/fraction of inspired oxygen (FiO_2) more than 150 (PaO_2 > 75 torr on FiO_2 of 0.5).
- Partial pressure of carbon dioxide ($PaCO_2$) less than 50 torr.
- pH 7.3–7.5.

When patients have been on prolonged ventilation, the underlying disease process should be stable, and the patient should be awake and alert enough to breathe independently. Hemodynamic status should be stable with no vasoactive drugs, and hemoglobin and metabolic status satisfactory. Arterial blood gases should be stable with a respiratory rate less than 35 breaths/min and rapid shallow breathing index of less than 100. Criteria for oxygen weaning: FiO_2 is reduced until PaO_2 is 70–100 mm Hg on room air. Supplemental oxygen is necessary with a PaO_2 of less than 70 mm Hg.

Review Video: Ventilator Weaning
Visit mometrix.com/academy and enter code: 346956

Endocrine

Management of Hyperglycemia After Cardiac Surgery

Both nondiabetics and diabetics may exhibit **hyperglycemia** because of hormonal stress, causing insulin resistance, total parenteral nutrition, or sepsis and is associated with an increased risk of osmotic diuresis, impaired wound healing, impaired cognitive function, and atrial fibrillation; thus, blood glucose levels must be monitored carefully and maintained at less than 180 mg/dL (usually 110–150 mg/dL) during the first 48 hours postoperatively although stringent methods to keep blood glucose less than 120 mg/dL are contraindicated. Novolin R, fast-acting regular insulin, is used most frequently with a bolus followed by an infusion (100 U/100 mL normal saline). Potassium should be monitored as well and maintained between 4 and 4.5 mEq/L. Patients with preexisting diabetes type 1 may receive a low dose (about 50% of normal dose) of intermediate or long-acting insulin supplemented with regular insulin. Patients with diabetes type 2 may require regular insulin after surgery and should resume oral medications when able to eat a normal diet. Note that hypoglycemia and diabetic ketoacidosis rarely occur after cardiac surgery.

Use of Insulin After Cardiac Surgery

Insulin is used to metabolize glucose after cardiac surgery to control hyperglycemia induced by hormonal stress and insulin resistance. Duration of action may vary, according to the individual's metabolism, intake, and level of activity. The types of insulin commonly used for hyperglycemia after cardiac surgery include the following:

- **Humalog (Lispro H)** is a fast-acting, short-duration insulin that acts within 5–15 minutes, peaks between 45-90 minutes, and lasts 3–4 hours.
- **Novolog (Aspart)** is a fast-acting, short-duration insulin that acts within 5–10 minutes, peaks in 1–3 hours, and lasts 3–5 hours.
- **Regular (R)** is a relatively fast-acting insulin that acts within 30 minutes, peaks in 2–5 hours, and lasts 5–8 hours.
- **NPH (N)** is an intermediate-acting insulin that acts in 1–3 hours, peaks at 6–12 hours (Humulin N) or 4–12 hours (Novolin N), and lasts 16–24 hours.
- **Lantus (Glargine)** is a long-acting insulin that acts in 1 hour and lasts 24 hours with no peak.

Acute Hypoglycemia

Acute hypoglycemia (hyperinsulinism) results from the use of insulin to control hyperglycemia after cardiac surgery. Hyperinsulinism can cause damage to the central nervous system and cardiopulmonary system, interfering with brain function and causing neurological impairment. Causes include the following:

- Severe infections, such as Gram-negative sepsis or endotoxic shock.
- Too much insulin for body needs.
- Too little food.

Symptoms include the following:

- Blood glucose less than 50–60 mg/dL
- Central nervous system: seizures, altered consciousness, lethargy, poor feeding with vomiting, myoclonus, respiratory distress, diaphoresis, hypothermia, and cyanosis
- Adrenergic system: diaphoresis, tremor, tachycardia, palpitation, hunger, and anxiety

Treatment includes:

- Treatment depends on the underlying cause and includes the following:
    - Glucose/glucagon administration to elevate blood glucose levels
    - Diazoxide (Hyperstat) to inhibit release of insulin
    - Somatostatin (Sandostatin) to suppress insulin production
    - Careful monitoring

Hematology/Immunology

Blood Products Commonly Used for Transfusions

Red blood cells	Red blood cells (RBCs) may be administered after cardiac surgery primarily to increase the oxygen-carrying function of blood to prevent ischemia. RBCs are usually administered when the hematocrit falls to 26% or less. Blood filters with pore sizes of 170 µm or more should be used with all transfusions, and blood lines should be flushed with isotonic solutions (usually normal saline). Lactated Ringer's solution and dextrose 5% in water may result in red cell hemolysis.
Fresh whole blood	Fresh whole blood (< 6 hours old) contains clotting factors and platelets and has a hematocrit of 35%, so it provides a balanced replacement. However, it is not available from many blood banks.
Recovered blood (cell-saver or hemofiltration blood)	Cell-saver blood is captured, filtered, rinsed with heparinized saline, and reinfused. It does not contain clotting factors or platelets and may contain minimal amounts of heparin. Blood recovered by hemofiltration from the extracorporeal circuit does retain platelets and clotting factors, but this procedure is usually not recommended.

Packed red blood cells (PRBCs)	PRBCs should be warmed to 30°C or more (optimal 37°C) to prevent hypothermia and may be reconstituted in 50–100 mL of normal saline to facilitate administration. PRBCs are necessary if blood loss is about 30% (1500–2000 mL) [hemoglobin ≤ 7]. Above 30% blood loss, whole blood may be more effective. PRBCs are most frequently used for transfusions. One unit usually contains approximately 200 mL of red blood cells, 30 mL plasma, and 100 mL of Optisol AS. One unit will usually raise the hematocrit in a 70-kg patient by 3%. PRBCs contain no clotting factors, so if multiple units are administered, then fresh frozen plasma may also be necessary.
Auto-transfusion	Mediastinal blood is reinfused through 20–40 μm filters but not washed. This procedure is associated with an increased risk of infection; if more than 500 mL is reinfused, patients may experience coagulopathy with an elevated INR, a partial thromboplastin time, and D-dimers and decreased fibrinogen.

Platelet Concentrates

Platelets may be administered to bleeding patients if the platelet count is 100,000/mm^3 or less after cardiac surgery. Since cardiopulmonary bypass renders some platelets dysfunctional, platelets may be administered even with levels 100,000/mm^3 or more. In the nonbleeding patient, platelets may not be indicated until the count reaches 20,000–30,000/mm^3. One unit increases the platelet count by 5000–10,000/mm^3. Platelet concentrates pose a risk for sensitization reactions and infectious diseases. Platelet concentrate is stored at a higher temperature (20°C–24°C) than red blood cells. This contributes to bacterial growth, so it is more prone to bacterial contamination than other blood products. An increase in temperature within 6 hours should be considered an indication of possible sepsis. Platelets should be administered through a 170 μm filter. If a patient's hematocrit is 30% or less or the patient has hypofibrinogenemia, then platelet function will be impaired; the patient may need infusion of cryoprecipitate and red blood cells to increase hematocrit. Platelets may increase filling pressures, which will lower hematocrit and precipitate fluid overload.

Fresh Frozen Plasma

Fresh Frozen Plasma (FFP) (obtained from a unit of whole blood frozen 6 hours or less after collection) includes all clotting factors and plasma proteins, so each unit administered increases clotting factors by 2–3%. FFP may be used for deficiencies of isolated factors, excess warfarin therapy, and liver disease–related coagulopathy. It may be used for patients who have received extensive blood transfusions but continue to hemorrhage. It is also helpful for those with antithrombin III deficiency. FFP should be warmed to 37°C before administration to avoid hypothermia. ABO compatibility should be observed if possible, but it is not required. Some patients may become sensitized to plasma proteins. FFP is usually not given during surgery unless partial thromboplastin time or prothrombin time is prolonged 1.5 times or more. Plasma, as with platelets, may increase filling pressures, lowering hematocrit and precipitating fluid overload.

Cryoprecipitate

Cryoprecipitate is the precipitate that forms when fresh frozen plasma (FFP) is thawed. It contains fibrinogen (150–250 mg), factor VIII-C (80–100 U), von Willebrand factor (40–50%), factor XIII, and fibronectin. One unit of FFP provides about 15 mL of cryoprecipitate, which is mixed with 15 mL plasma and pooled into 6 U of concentrate—about 200 mL. This component may be used to treat hemophilia A and hypofibrinogenemia. Cryoprecipitate may be used in patients who have recently had thrombolytic therapy. Usually 1 U is administered for every 7–10 kg. It should be administered through a 170 µm filter 4–6 hours after thawing. Formulas to calculate the required dose include:

- Blood volume = 70 mL/kg x weight in kilograms.
- Plasma volume = blood volume x (1 – hematocrit).
- Required fibrinogen (mg): 0.01 x plasma volume x (target level – current level).
- Bags of required cryoprecipitate: target milligrams of fibrinogen (250 mg/bag).

Administration of Blood Products and Jehovah Witnesses

Jehovah Witnesses have traditionally shunned transfusions and blood products as part of their religious beliefs. In 2004, the *Watchtower,* a Jehovah Witness publication presented a guide for members. When medical care indicates the need for blood transfusion or blood products and the patient or family members are practicing Jehovah Witnesses, this may present a conflict. It is important to approach the patient or family with full information and reasons for the transfusion or blood components without being judgmental, allowing them to express their feelings. In fact, studies show that while adults often refuse transfusions for themselves, they frequently allow their children to receive blood products, so one should never assume that an individual would refuse blood products based on the religion alone. Jehovah Witnesses can receive fractionated blood cells, thus allowing hemoglobin-based blood substitutes. The following guidelines are provided to church members:

Basic Blood Standards for Jehovah Witnesses	
Not acceptable	Whole blood: red cells, white cells, platelets, and plasma
Acceptable	Fractions from red cells, white cells, platelets, and plasma

Transfusion-Related Complications

Infection and Transfusion-Related Acute Lung Injury

Because there are a number of **transfusion-related complications**, transfusions are given only when necessary. Complications include the following:

- **Infection:** Bacterial contamination of blood, especially platelets, can result in severe sepsis. A number of infective agents (e.g., viral, bacterial, parasitic) can be transmitted, although increased testing of blood has decreased rates of infection markedly. Infective agents include HIV, hepatitis B and C, human T-cell lymphotropic virus, cytomegalovirus, West Nile virus, malaria, Chagas' disease, and variant Creutzfeldt-Jacob disease (from contact with meat infected with mad cow disease).
- **Transfusion-related acute lung injury (TRALI):** This respiratory distress syndrome is increasingly common and occurs in 6 hours or less. The cause is believed to be antileukocytic (anti-human leukocyte antigen) antibodies in the transfusion. It is characterized by noncardiogenic pulmonary edema (high protein level) with severe dyspnea and arterial hypoxemia. Transfusion must be stopped immediately and the blood bank notified. TRALI may result in death but usually resolves in 12–48 hours with supportive care.

Graft vs. Host Disease, Post-Transfusion Purpura, Transfusion-Related Immunosuppression, and Hypothermia

Additional **transfusion-related complications** include:

- **Graft vs. host disease:** Lymphocytes cause an immune response in immunocompromised individuals. Lymphocytes may be inactivated by irradiation, as leukocyte filters are not reliable.
- **Post-transfusion purpura:** Platelet antibodies develop and destroy the patient's platelets, so the platelet count decreases about 1 week after transfusion.
- **Transfusion-related immunosuppression:** Cell-mediated immunity is suppressed, so the patient is at increased risk of infection and, in cancer patients, transfusions may correlate with tumor recurrence. This condition relates to transfusions that include leukocytes. Red blood cells cause a less pronounced immunosuppression, suggesting a causative agent is in the plasma. Leukoreduction is becoming more common to reduce transmission of leukocyte-related viruses.
- **Hypothermia***:* This may occur if blood products are not heated. A body temperature decrease of 0.5°C–1°C increases oxygen consumption by four times.

Anticoagulants

Aspirin, Heparin, and Warfarin

Anticoagulants are used to prevent thromboemboli. All pose a risk of bleeding.

Aspirin	Often used prophylactically to prevent clots; poses less danger of bleeding than other drugs
Warfarin (Coumadin)	Blocks use of vitamin K; decreases production of clotting factors; and is used orally for patients at risk for developing blood clots, such as those with mechanical heart valves, atrial fibrillation, and clotting disorders
Heparin	The primary intravenous anticoagulant; increases the activity of antithrombin III, used for patients with myocardial infarction (MI) and those undergoing percutaneous coronary intervention (PCI) or other cardiac surgery, and monitored by activated partial thromboplastin time

Dalteparin/ Enoxaparin and Lepirudin/Bivalirudin

Anticoagulants are used to prevent thromboemboli. All pose a risk of bleeding.

Dalteparin (Fragmin) and Enoxaparin (Lovenox)	Low-molecular-weight heparins that increase activity of antithrombin III used for unstable angina, MI, and cardiac surgery
Lepirudin (Refludan) and bivalirudin (Angiomax)	Direct thrombin inhibitors used for unstable angina, PCI, and for prophylaxis and treatment for thrombosis in heparin-induced thrombocytopenia (allergic response to heparin that causes a platelet count drop of 150,000/mm^3 or less to 30–50% of baseline, usually occurring 5–14 days after beginning heparin)

Review Video: Antiplatelets and Thrombolytics
Visit mometrix.com/academy and enter code: 711284

Alternatives to Heparin

The following are alternatives to heparin:

- **Argatroban:**
  - Direct thrombin inhibitor
  - Indicated as treatment for those with heparin-induced thrombocytopenia (HIT) or at risk for HIT undergoing percutaneous coronary intervention (PCI)
  - Metabolized through the liver so used for those with renal impairment but affects INR so transition to warfarin must be done carefully
  - Starting dose: 2 µg/kg/min after effects of heparin have subsided
  - Maintenance dose: 0.5 to 1.2 µg/kg/min
  - Monitored: Partial thromboplastin time (PTT) with a goal of 1.5–3 times baseline
- **Bivalirudin:**
  - Synthetic direct thrombin inhibitor
  - Used for patients receiving aspirin with unstable angina and undergoing percutaneous transluminal angioplasty as well as for those at risk for HIT undergoing PCI; does not affect INR
  - Produces reversible thrombin binding with half-life of 25 minutes
  - Starting dose 0.15–0.2 mg/kg/hr; reduced dose given for renal impairment.
  - Maintenance dose: 0.2 mg/kg/hr (usually given with aspirin).
  - Monitored: PTT with a goal of 1.5–2.5 times baseline.
- **Desirudin:**
  - Direct thrombin inhibitor
  - Used for prevention of deep venous thrombosis (DVT), for patients at risk for heparin-induced thrombocytopenia (HIT), and for thrombosis prophylaxis for cardiac surgery; does not lead to formation of heparin antibodies
  - Effect on INR is less than with argatroban
  - Dosage: 15 mg subcutaneously twice a day; reduced dosage given for renal impairment.
  - Monitored: partial thromboplastin time (PTT) and signs of bleeding.
- **Lepirudin:**
  - Direct thrombin inhibitor
  - Usually drug of choice for those at risk for HIT.
  - Starting dose: 0.2–0.4 mg/kg bolus
  - Maintenance dose: infusion of 0.2 mg/hg/hr (continuous).
  - Monitored: PTT with a goal of 1.5–2.5 times baseline.
- **Dabigatran:**
  - Direct thrombin inhibitor
  - Used to prevent strokes with atrial fibrillation; reduced risk of stroke compared to warfarin but increased risk of gastrointestinal bleeding.
  - Withheld during invasive or surgical procedures and then restarted
  - Dosage: 150 mg orally twice daily; 75 mg given with renal impairment.
  - Monitor: activated PTT; PTT and INR are insensitive to drug, thrombin time for direct thrombin inhibitors, or Ecarin clotting time.

Managing Excess Anticoagulation with Warfarin

Excess anticoagulation with warfarin can lead to hemorrhage, so warfarin administered after cardiac surgery should be individualized with avoidance of a loading dose. Initial dosages may range from 2.5–5 mg. Management of overanticoagulation includes:

- INR 5 or less (but above therapeutic levels) without significant bleeding: Reduce or withhold one dose until INR reaches therapeutic range.
- INR 5–9 without significant bleeding: Withhold warfarin for 1–2 days until INR falls to 4 or less, OR withhold one dose of warfarin, and administer 1–2.5 mg of vitamin K orally.
- INR 9 or less without significant bleeding: Withhold warfarin for 24–48 hours (until INR reaches therapeutic range), and administer vitamin K (2.5–5 mg) orally.
- Any INR with severe bleeding: Withhold warfarin and administer vitamin K, 10 mg in 50 mL normal saline per intravenous infusion over 30 minutes, along with fresh frozen plasma (≥ 15 mL/kg). Vitamin K may be repeated every 12 hours. Prothrombin complex concentrate (25–50 units/kg) or recombinant factor VIIa (40 µg/kg if bleeding persists.

Reversal of Anticoagulation Using Protamine and Vitamin K

Protamine is used to reverse anticoagulation caused by a heparin overdose. It is administered slowly intravenously over 10 minutes and binds with heparin, eliminating its anticoagulant properties. Doses should not exceed 50 mg. It should be given undiluted but may be administered in 5% dextrose in water or normal saline. It should not be given with other drugs, as it is incompatible with some antibiotics. Each unit of protamine neutralizes about 100 USP U of heparin.

Vitamin K (phytonadione [AquaMEPHYTON]), preferably in oral form, is used to reverse anticoagulation caused by an overdose of warfarin (Coumadin) or superwarfarin (Ramik), found in rodenticides. Drug interactions can increase or decrease prothrombin times. Vitamin K requires hours to work, so packed red blood cells or fresh frozen plasma may be needed in emergency situations. Vitamin K is given only if prothrombin times are elevated, not prophylactically. Doses vary with the amount of ingestion and are given three to four times daily, usually 2–20 mg initially for warfarin and 50–150 mg for superwarfarin. Superwarfarin ingestion may require treatment for over 8 weeks.

Glycoprotein IIB/IIIA Inhibitors

Glycoprotein IIB/IIIA inhibitors are drugs that are used to inhibit platelet binding and prevent clots before and after invasive cardiac procedures, such as angioplasty and stent placement. These medications are used in combination with anticoagulant drugs, such as heparin and aspirin for the following:

- Acute coronary syndromes (ACSs), such as unstable angina or myocardial infarctions.
- Percutaneous coronary intervention (PCI), such as angioplasty and stent placement.

These medications are contraindicated in patients with a low platelet count or active bleeding.

- **Abciximab (ReoPro)** - Used with both heparin and aspirin for ACS and PCI and affects platelet binding for 48 hours after administration.
- **Eptifibatide (Integrilin)** - Used with both heparin and aspirin for ACS and PCI and affects platelet binding for 6–8 hours after administration; not used in patients with renal problems.
- **Tirofiban (Aggrastat)** - Used with heparin for PCI patients, with reduced dosage for those with renal problems, and affects platelet blinding for only 4–8 hours after administration.

Medication Used to Control Postoperative Bleeding

Recombinant Activated Factor VII

Recombinant activated factor VII (NovoSeven): This drug activates the extrinsic pathway of coagulation and stimulates production of thrombin, platelet activation, and the formation of fibrin clots, improving prothrombin time. While indicated for those with clotting disorders, factor VII is often given off-label after cardiac surgery for those with coagulopathies receiving blood products. Adverse effects include myocardial infarction, cardiac ischemia, supraventricular tachycardia, arterial thromboembolism, cerebral artery occlusion and ischemia, acute renal failure, and pulmonary emboli. Dosage varies. Patients receiving factor VII should be monitored carefully for thromboembolism and coagulation profile. Those with atherosclerotic disease, coagulopathies, or septicemia are at increased risk.

Desmopressin Acetate and Antifibrinolytic Agents

Pharmacologic agents used to control bleeding include:

- **Desmopressin acetate**: This synthetic analogue of vasopressin increases blood levels of clotting factors (VWF, FVIII, and t-PA), causes vasodilation, and shortens the clotting time (aPTT). Desmopressin acetate can prevent bleeding in patients with inherited bleeding disorders and platelet dysfunction but can also be used to control or prevent bleeding during cardiovascular surgical procedures. Because of its antidiuretic effect, desmopressin should be used with care in patients with heart failure and fluid overload.
- **Antifibrinolytic agents**: These agents, such as aprotinin, epsilon-aminocaproic acid, and tranexamic acid, inhibit the fibrinolytic pathways and decrease the risk of surgical and postoperative bleeding. Cardiovascular surgery, especially with cardiopulmonary bypass (which impairs hemostasis and increases risk of bleeding), activates the fibrinolytic system, so antifibrinolytic agents are critical to reducing the risk of bleeding and reducing the need for transfusions and are administered with anesthesia.

Aminocaproic Acid

Aminocaproic acid (Amicar): Aminocaproic acid, an antifibrinolytic agent, prevents plasminogen from binding to fibrin, interfering with the breakdown of clots. It is used in the cardiac patient with postoperative bleeding associated with fibrinolysis. Dosage is 4–5 g over 60 minutes initially and then a maintenance infusion of 1 g/hr for 8 hours or until bleeding is controlled. Adverse effects include thrombocytopenia, dysrhythmias, and thrombosis.

Neurology

Neuroprotective Strategies

Neuroprotective strategies should begin with careful screening of patients to determine those at increased risk. Patients who undergo cardiopulmonary bypass (CPB) should be screened for *N*-methyl-D-aspartate, a receptor antibody that is associated with an 18-fold increase in postoperative neurological deficit. Other neuroprotective strategies include the following: Using ultrasound or transesophageal, echocardiography to avoid atheromas, Evaluating carotid disease preoperatively, Administering statins preoperatively, Using an internal mammary artery Y graft for proximal anastomosis to reduce aortic manipulation, Using off-pump coronary artery bypass for those with severe atherosclerosis or deep hypothermic arrest for replacement of the ascending aorta, Using cell-saver to process mediastinal blood.

Using post-pump arterial filters, using single aortic cross-clamping during CPB, or avoiding cross-clamping, Providing adequate acid–base management, Flooding the surgical field with carbon dioxide to evacuate air, Controlling hyperglycemia, hypotension, and hyperthermia and managing pain, Encouraging early mobility, Providing rapid treatment of atrial fibrillation and anticoagulation, Providing early intervention and treatment for cerebral ischemia.

Peripheral Nerve Assessment of the Radial and Ulnar Nerves

The **radial nerve** branches from the brachial plexus and enervates the dorsal surface of the arm and hand, including the thumb and fingers two, three, and four. Sensation is evaluated by pricking the skin in the webbed area between the thumb and the index finger. Movement is evaluated by having the person extend the thumb, the wrist, and fingers at the metacarpal joint.

The **ulnar nerve** branches from the sciatic nerve and travels down the arm from the shoulder, traveling along the anterior forearm beside the ulna, to the palm of the hand. Sensation is evaluated by pricking the distal fat pad at the end of the small finger. Movement is evaluated by having the person extend and spread all the fingers.

Assessment and Treatment of Anoxic Encephalopathy

Assessment of anoxic encephalopathy includes the following:

- **Level of consciousness**: Verbal stimuli, shaking patient, and digital supraorbital pressure are used to elicit a response.
- **Motor activity**: Brainstem damage: flaccidity and areflexia
    - Mid-brain and upper pons damage: extensor posturing.
    - Hemispheric damage: flexor posturing.
- **Eyes**: Pupillary response and elicited eye movements if absent indicate severe damage.
    - Papilledema may occur after cardiac arrest without an increase in intracranial pressure.
    - Horizontal movement of the eyes can persist with damage to the frontal or occipital areas if the midbrain and pons are intact.
- **Imaging**: Magnetic resonance imaging provides better early information than computed tomography. Electroencephalogram shows cortical and epileptic activity.

Treatment depends on the causes, but reestablishing circulation is primary. After cardiac arrest, hypothermia (32°C–34°C) with neuromuscular blockade should be initiated quickly with rewarming after 24 hours to reduce cerebral damage.

Insertion of Lumbar Drain for Thoracic Aorta Repair

A **lumbar CSF drain** (catheter) is placed in the arachnoid space at L3-4 or L4-5 to prevent spinal ischemia and paraplegia during thoracic aortic aneurysm repair (open and endovascular procedures) for those at risk of spinal ischemia. The drain is inserted prior to surgery and should remain in place for 48 to 72 hours, increasing the pressure to 20 mm Hg after 24 postoperative hours and then clamping for 24 hours before removal. The lumbar drain allows removal of CSF to decrease pressure on the spinal cord and/or brain. The CSF pressure is decreased to less than 10 mm Hg while the aorta is cross-clamped as this helps improve spinal cord perfusion and prevent ischemia. The drain is connected to a transducer, which is leveled to the right atrium, and should be monitored for patency, volume, and color and consistency of drainage and the insertion site observed for signs of infection. Complications may include headache, hematoma, infection (meningitis), and persistent CSF leakage. Patients may complain of numbness or tingling with irritation of a nerve, and a change of position may alleviate this discomfort; if not, the drain may have to be removed.

Hepatic

LIVER FUNCTION STUDIES

Bilirubin	Determines the ability of the liver to conjugate and excrete bilirubin: direct 0.0–0.3 mg/dL, total 0.0–0.9 mg/dL, and urine 0.
Total protein	Determines if the liver is producing protein in normal amounts: 7.0–7.5 g/dL Albumin: 4.0–5.5 g/dL Globulin: 1.7–3.3 mg/dL Serum protein electrophoresis is done to determine the ratio of proteins. Albumin/globulin (A/G) ratio: 1.5:1–2.5:1. (Albumin should be greater than globulin.)
Prothrombin time (PT)	100% or clot detection in 10–13 seconds. PT is increased with liver disease. INR (PT result/normal average): INR is less than 2 for those not receiving anticoagulation and 2.0–3.0 for those receiving anticoagulation. Critical value: This is more than 3 in patients receiving anticoagulation therapy.
Alkaline phosphatase (ALP)	17–142 U/L in adults (Normal values of ALP vary with method.) Indicates biliary tract obstruction if there is no bone disease
Aspartate aminotransferase (AST) serum (SGOT)	10–40 U/L (AST increases in liver cell damage.)
Alanine aminotransferase (ALT) serum (SGPT)	5–35 U/L (ALT increases in liver cell damage.)
Gamma-glutamyltransferase (GGT) serum (SGTP)	5–55 U/L females; 5–85 U/L males (GGT increases with alcohol abuse.)
Lactate dehydrogenase (LD)	100–200 U/L (LD increases with alcohol abuse.)
Serum ammonia	150–250 U/L (Serum ammonia increases in liver failure.)
Cholesterol	Increases with bile duct obstruction and decreases with parenchymal disease

Renal

Urinalysis

Color	Pale yellow/amber, which darkens when urine is concentrated or when blood or bile are present
Appearance	Clear but may be slightly cloudy
Odor	Slight; a foul smell with a bacterial infection, depending upon the organism; some foods, such as asparagus
Specific gravity	1.015–1.025; may increase if protein levels increase or if there is fever, vomiting, or dehydration
pH	Usually ranges between 4.5–8 with an average of 5–6
Sediment	Red cell casts from acute infections, broad casts from kidney disorders, and white cell casts from pyelonephritis; leukocytes **10/mm^3** or more are present with urinary tract infections
Glucose, ketones, protein, blood, bilirubin, and nitrate	Negative; increase in urine glucose with infection (with normal blood glucose); frank blood from some parasites and diseases but also drugs, smoking, excessive exercise, and menstrual fluids; increased red blood cells from lower urinary tract infections
Urobilinogen	0.1–1.0 mg/dL

Renal Function Studies

Specific gravity	1.015-1.025; determines kidney's ability to concentrate urinary solutes
Osmolality (urine)	350–900 mOsm/kg/24 hr; shows early defects if kidney's ability to concentrate urine is impaired
Osmolality (serum)	275–295 mOsm/kg
Uric acid	Males: 4.4–7.6 mg/dL; females: 2.3–6.6 mg/dL; increased levels with renal failure
Creatinine clearance (24-hour)	Males: 85–125 mL/min/1.73 m^2; females: 75–115 mL/min/1.73 m^2 Evaluates the amount of blood cleared of creatinine in 1 minute; approximates the glomerular filtration rate
Serum creatinine	0.6–1.2 mg/dL; increases with impaired renal function, urinary tract obstruction, and nephritis; stable with normal functioning
Urine creatinine	Males: 14–26 mg/kg/24 hr; females: 11–20 mg/kg/24 hr
Blood urea nitrogen (BUN)	7–8 mg/dL (8–20 mg/dL > age 60); increases with impaired renal function, as urea is end product of protein metabolism
BUN/creatinine ratio	10:1; increases with hypovolemia; normal ratio with intrinsic kidney disease, though BUN and creatinine levels are increased

Loop Diuretics

Diuretics increase renal perfusion and filtration, thereby reducing preload and decreasing peripheral and pulmonary edema, hypertension, congestive heart failure, diabetes insipidus, and osteoporosis. There are different types of diuretics: loop, thiazide, and potassium sparing.

Loop diuretics inhibit the reabsorption of sodium and chloride (primarily) in the ascending loop of Henle. They also cause increased secretion of other electrolytes, such as calcium, magnesium, and potassium. This can result in imbalances that cause dysrhythmias. Other side effects include frequent urination, postural hypotension, increased blood sugar, and increased uric acid levels. They are short-acting so are less effective than other diuretics for control of hypertension:

- **Bumetanide (Bumex)** is given intravenously after surgery to reduce preload or orally to treat heart failure.
- **Ethacrynic acid (Edecrin)** is given intravenously after surgery to reduce preload.
- **Furosemide (Lasix)** is used to control congestive heart failure as well as renal insufficiency. It is used after surgery to decrease preload and to reduce the inflammatory response caused by cardiopulmonary bypass (postperfusion syndrome).

Thiazide Diuretics

Thiazide diuretics inhibit the reabsorption of sodium and chloride primarily in the early distal tubules, forcing more sodium and water to be excreted. Thiazide diuretics increase the secretion of potassium and bicarbonate, so they are often given with supplementary potassium or in combination with potassium-sparing diuretics. Thiazide diuretics are the first line of drugs for treatment of hypertension. They have a long duration of action (12–72 hours, depending on the drug) so they are able to maintain control of hypertension better than short-acting drugs. They may be given daily or 3–5 days a week. There are numerous thiazide diuretics, including:

- Chlorothiazide (Diuril)
- Bendroflumethiazide (Naturetin)
- Chlorthalidone (Hygroton)
- Trichlormethiazide (Naqua)

Side effects include dizziness, lightheadedness, postural hypotension, headache, blurred vision, and itching, especially during initial treatment. Thiazide diuretics cause sensitivity to sun exposure, so people should be counseled to use sunscreen.

Potassium-Sparing Diuretics

Potassium-sparing diuretics inhibit the reabsorption of sodium in the late distal tubule and collecting duct. They are weaker than thiazide or loop diuretics but do not cause a reduction in potassium levels; however, if used alone, they may cause an increase in potassium, which can cause weakness, irregular pulse, and cardiac arrest. Because potassium-sparing diuretics are less effective alone, they are often given in a combined form with a thiazide diuretic (usually chlorothiazide), which mitigates the potassium imbalance. Typical side effects include dehydration, blurred vision, nausea insomnia, and nasal congestion, especially in the first few days of treatment:

- **Spironolactone (Aldactone)** is a synthetic steroid diuretic that increases the secretion of both water and sodium and is used to treat congestive heart failure. It may be given orally or intravenously.
- **Eplerenone (Inspra)** is similar to spironolactone but has fewer side effects so it may be used with patients who cannot tolerate the other drug.

Review Video: Diuretics
Visit mometrix.com/academy and enter code: 373276

Postoperative Management of Oliguria

Oliguria may indicate acute kidney injury and should be treated aggressively to prevent further kidney damage. Measures include:

- Ensuring patency and correct positioning of a Foley catheter.
- Maintaining optimal cardiac function by treating hypovolemia, controlling cardiac arrhythmias, improving contractility, and reducing increased afterload (allowing systolic blood pressure up to 150 mm Hg).
- Providing diuretics and other medications to increase output, including intravenous furosemide, chlorothiazide, or bumetanide. Furosemide may be given with dopamine and mannitol. If filling pressures are elevated, nesiritide is indicated. Hypertension may be treated with fenoldopam.

If the initial treatments are ineffective in improving output, then fluid intake may be limited and drug doses readjusted. Potassium supplements should be avoided. A diet high in essential amino acids is indicated, and renal replacement therapy may be needed.

Intermittent Hemodialysis in Cardiac Postsurgical Patient Requiring Renal Replacement Therapy

Hemodialysis can be used intermittently to manage hyperkalemia, fluid overload, acid–base imbalances, and hypercatabolic state in patients at risk for renal failure. Blood flow through the dialysis cartridge is 300–500 mL/min. It may also be initiated with signs of uremia. Intermittent hemodialysis is contraindicated for patients who are hemodynamically unstable but should be done before signs of renal failure and a marked increase in creatinine, if possible. **Temporary intermittent hemodialysis** is performed by insertion of a catheter into the internal jugular or subclavian vein. The femoral vein is usually avoided except for short-term dialysis because of the risk of thrombosis. Treatments are usually done three times weekly for 3–4 hours. If patients are at risk for bleeding, heparin-free hemodialysis should be performed. If the patient requires long-term hemodialysis, then a fistula should be considered. Peritoneal dialysis is rarely used because it causes Abdominal distension and glucose absorption and can result in respiratory compromise and peritonitis.

CVVH and CVVHD

Continuous renal replacement therapy circulates the blood by hydrostatic pressure through a semipermeable membrane. It is used in critical care and can be instituted quickly:

- **Continuous venovenous hemofiltration (CVVH)** pumps blood through a double-lumen venous catheter to a hemofilter, which returns the blood to the patient in the same catheter. Blood flow rate is 250 mL/min. It provides continuous slow removal of fluid, is better tolerated with unstable patients, and does not require arterial access. It provides slow correction of electrolyte imbalances. CVVH has a lower risk of clotting than slow continuous ultrafiltration (SCUF). CVVH can be carried out in hypotensive or unstable patients with use of a blood pump. Electrolytes must be monitored carefully and replacement solutions provided as needed because so much fluid is removed.
- **Continuous venovenous hemodiafiltration (CVVHD)** is similar to CVVH but uses a dialysate to increase clearance of uremic toxins. CVVHD is more effective for severe electrolyte imbalance or hypercatabolic state. Blood flow rate is 150–300 mL/min. CVVHD has a lower risk of clotting than SCUF.

SCUF and CAVH

Continuous renal replacement therapy includes the following:

- **Slow continuous ultrafiltration (SCUF)** has a blood flow rate of 50–80 mL/min. It filters but provides no replacement fluid; however, it can provide a negative fluid balance of 7 L or less. There is an increased risk of clotting because of the slow filtration rate, and SCUF is ineffective for hyperkalemia or uremia.
- **Continuous arteriovenous hemofiltration (CAVH)** circulates blood from an artery (usually the femoral artery) to a hemofilter, using only arterial pressure and not a blood pump. The filtered blood is then returned to the patient's venous system, often with added fluids to offset those lost. Only the fluid is filtered. CAVH is used during cardiac surgery to remove excess fluids before cardiopulmonary bypass is discontinued. However, its use postoperatively is limited because of the need for heparinization and the need for adequate arterial pressure necessary to achieve hemofiltration.

Multisystem

Pain

Pathophysiology

The **pathophysiology of pain** comprises four steps:

1. **Transduction:** Afferent nociceptor nerve endings respond to injury (i.e., mechanical, thermal, chemical) by releasing mediators (i.e., prostaglandin, serotonin, histamine, bradykinin, substance P). These mediators activate more nociceptors. The pain impulse occurs with an action potential that results from an exchange of sodium and potassium ions at the cell membranes.
2. **Transmission:** The mediators activate the action potential and send the pain impulse from the transduction site, to the spinal cord and brain stem, and then to the thalamus and the cortical areas of higher functioning.
3. **Perception:** Once the brain perceives pain, it elicits a number of responses. The reticular response causes autonomic and motor reactions (withdrawing from a painful stimuli). The somatosensory response identifies the type, intensity, and location of pain. The limbic response provides an emotional response to pain.
4. **Modulation:** Stimuli are enhanced or inhibited by the hypothalamus, pons, and somatosensory cortex, affecting the individual response to pain.

Pain Phases

Anticipation	Patients may exhibit or overtly express anxiety about pain before cardiac surgery. Anxiety may increase the perception of pain, so patients should be provided education about what type of pain may occur and a plan for dealing with the pain. Patients with a history of substance abuse may also have concerns about addiction that must be addressed.
Presence	When pain actually occurs, strategies for managing pain can affect the patient's level of comfort and anxiety and impact recovery. Both pharmacological and nonpharmacological (e.g., massage, heat, cold, relaxation, music therapy) approaches to pain management may be used.
Aftermath	Complications may arise if pain was not managed well. Pain management should be assessed with the patient after intervention to determine if the pain management method achieved a satisfactory reduction in pain.

Nociceptive Pain

There are two primary types of pain, nociceptive and neuropathic, although some people may have a combination. **Nociceptive** or **acute pain** is the normal nerve response to a painful stimulus. Trauma that results in nociceptive pain can cause severe inflammation and damage to nerve endings. Nociceptive pain usually correlates with the extent and type of injury; that is, the greater the injury, the greater the pain. It may be procedural pain (related to wound manipulation and dressing changes) or surgical pain (related to cutting of tissue). It may also be continuous or cyclic, depending on the type of injury. Nociceptive pain is usually localized to the area of injury and resolves over time as healing takes place. Pain may be somatic, resulting from the stimulation of nerves in the skin, or visceral, from compression of abdominal/thoracic viscera. Nociceptive pain is often described as aching or throbbing, but it generally responds to analgesia. Uncontrolled, this type of pain can in time result in changes in the nervous system that lead to chronic neuropathic pain.

Neuropathic Pain

While nociceptive pain is acute, **neuropathic pain** is **chronic**. Neuropathic pain occurs when there is a primary lesion in the nervous system or a dysfunction related to damaged nerve fibers. Neuropathic pain may be associated with conditions, such as diabetes, cancer, or traumatic injury to the nervous system. This type of pain is common in chronic wounds and is more often described as burning, stabbing, electric, or shooting pains. Often the underlying pathology causing the pain is not reversible. Pain may be visceral (diffuse or cramping pain of internal organs) caused by injuries to internal organs. It is also often diffuse rather than localized. It may also be somatic pain, involving muscles, skin, bones, and joints. Neuropathic pain is often more difficult to assess than nociceptive pain because the damage may alter normal pain responses. Neuropathic pain often responds better to antidepressants and antiseizure medications than analgesics.

Review Video: Neuropathic Pain
Visit mometrix.com/academy and enter code: 780523

Pain Scale Used in Pain Assessment

Pain is subjective and may be influenced by the individual's pain threshold (the smallest stimulus that produces the sensation of pain) and pain tolerance (the maximum degree of pain that a person can tolerate). The most common current **pain assessment** tool for preteens and adolescents is the 1–10 **pain scale**:

0 = no pain.
1–2 = mild pain.
3–5 = moderate pain.
6–7 = severe pain.
8–9 = very severe pain.
10 = excruciating pain.

Review Video: Assessing Pain
Visit mometrix.com/academy and enter code: 693250

Review Video: Assessment Tools for Pain
Visit mometrix.com/academy and enter code: 634001

However, there is more to pain assessment than a number on a scale. Assessment includes information about the onset, duration, and intensity. Identifying what triggers pain and what relieves it can be very useful when developing a plan for pain management. Patients may show very different behavior when they are in pain. Some may cry and moan with minor pain, and others may exhibit little difference in behavior when truly suffering. Thus, judging pain by behavior can lead to the wrong conclusions.

PAINAD

Patients with cognitive impairment or the inability to verbalize pain may not be able to indicate the degree of pain, even by using a face scale with pictures of smiling to crying faces. The **Pain Assessment in Advanced Dementia (PAINAD)** scale may be helpful, especially for those with Alzheimer's disease. Careful observation of nonverbal behavior can indicate that the patient is in pain:

- **Respirations:** Patients often have rapid, labored breathing as pain increases with short periods of hyperventilation (Cheyne-Stokes respirations).
- **Vocalization:** Patients may remain negative in speech or speak quietly and reluctantly. They may moan or groan. As pain increases, they may call out, moan and groan loudly, or cry.
- **Facial expression:** Patients may appear sad or frightened and may frown or grimace, especially on activities that increase pain.
- **Body language:** Patients may be tense, fidgeting, pacing, and as pain increases, may become rigid, clench fists, or lie in fetal position. They may become increasingly combative.
- **Consolability:** Patients are less distractible or consolable with increased pain.

Review Video: Pediatric Pain Assessment
Visit mometrix.com/academy and enter code: 264352

WORLD HEALTH ORGANIZATION PAIN LADDER

The **World Health Organization** provides a **pain ladder** as guidance for pain management. Medications are usually given every 3–4 hours around the clock to prevent breakthrough pain.

Level 1	Mild pain	Pain management usually begins with acetaminophen or aspirin followed by nonsteroidal anti-inflammatory drugs (NSAIDs) as well as adjuvant drugs. There are a number of different NSAIDs, and people may respond differently to the different drugs; thus, patients should be monitored carefully and medications changed when indicated.
Level 2	Mild-to-moderate pain	Aspirin or acetaminophen is given with codeine and adjuvants. Medications include hydrocodone, oxycodone, and tramadol.
Level 3	Moderate-to-severe pain	Opioid drugs (e.g., morphine, fentanyl, oxycodone) are given to control this pain. Some nonopioid drugs and adjuvant drugs may also be used.

Adjuvant drugs include antianxiety medications, anticholinergics, anticonvulsants, antiemetics, antipruritics, and corticosteroids.

Adverse Systemic Effects of Pain

The **adverse systemic effects of pain** can negatively affect many body systems:

- **Cardiovascular:** Tachycardia and increased blood pressure are common responses to pain, causing increased cardiac output and systemic vascular resistance. In those with preexisting cardiovascular disease, such as compromised ventricular function, cardiac output may decrease. The increased myocardial need for oxygen may cause or worsen myocardial ischemia.
- **Respiratory:** An increased need for oxygen causes an increase in minute ventilation during splinting because pain can compromise pulmonary function. If the chest wall movement is constrained, tidal volume falls, impairing the ability to cough and clear secretions. Bed rest further compromises ventilation.
- **Gastrointestinal:** Sphincter tone increases and motility decreases, sometimes resulting in ileus. There may be increased secretion of gastric acids, which irritate the gastric lining and can cause ulcerations. Nausea, vomiting, and constipation may occur. Reflux may result in aspiration pneumonia. Abdominal distension may occur.
- **Urinary:** Increased sphincter tone and decreased motility result in urinary retention.
- **Endocrine:** Hormone levels are affected by pain. Catabolic hormones, such as catecholamine, cortisol, and glucagon, increase, and anabolic hormones, such as insulin and testosterone, decrease. Lipolysis increases along with carbohydrate intolerance. Sodium retention can occur because of increased antidiuretic hormone, aldosterone, angiotensin, and cortisol. This, in turn, causes fluid retention and a shift to extracellular space.
- **Hematologic:** There may be reduced fibrinolysis, increased adhesiveness of platelets, and increased coagulation.
- **Immune:** Leukocytosis and lymphopenia may occur, increasing the risk of infection.
- **Emotional:** Patients may become depressed, anxious, or angry; have a depressed appetite, and become sleep-deprived. These responses are most common in patients with chronic pain, who usually do not have the typical systemic responses of patients with acute pain.

Pain Control

Patient-Controlled Analgesia

Patient-controlled analgesia (PCA) allows the patient to control the administration of pain medication by pressing a button on an intravenous delivery system with a computerized pump. The device is filled with opioid (as prescribed) and must be programmed correctly and checked regularly to ensure that it is functioning properly and that controls are set. Most devices can be set to deliver a continuous infusion of opioid as well as a patient-controlled bolus. Commonly used medications after cardiac surgery include morphine sulfate, 1 g bolus and 0.3 mg/hr infusion; fentanyl, 10 μg bolus and 1 μg/kg/hr infusion; and remifentanil, 0.25–0.5 μg/kg bolus and 0.5 μg/kg/hr infusion. Each element must be set:

- **Bolus:** determines the amount of medication received when the patient delivers a dose.
- **Lockout interval:** time required between administrations of boluses.
- **Continuous infusion:** rate at which opioid is delivered per hour for continuous analgesia.
- **Limit (usually set at 4 hours):** total amount of opioid that can be delivered in the preset time limit.

Thoracic Epidural Analgesia

Thoracic epidural analgesia (TEA) provides more effective pain control after cardiac surgery than parenteral administration of opioids; it is associated with fewer pulmonary complications because the duration of mechanical ventilation is usually reduced and there are fewer cardiac dysrhythmias. Patients receiving TEA must be monitored carefully for weakness in the lower extremities as an epidural hematoma may develop at the insertion site because of heparinization. Additionally, respiratory depression may occur and delay extubation. Onset of respiratory depression is rapid with fentanyl and sufentanil and delayed with morphine; however, respiratory depression most often occurs with higher doses of drugs, such as 4 mg of morphine. Rarely, neurologic complications can occur as the result of hemorrhage or infection. Infections are uncommon, but the risk increases after 48 hours. Other adverse effects include pruritus, nausea, vomiting, and urinary retention.

Effective Pain Control for Thoracotomy

Effective pain control for thoracotomy includes the following:

- Epidural analgesia with opioids or regional local anesthetics (recommended).
- Intravenous (IV), intramuscular (IM), subcutaneous (SC), oral (PO) opioids and nonsteroidal anti-inflammatory drugs (NSAIDs), often combined as NSAIDs may reduce the amount of opioid required and decrease adverse effects. NSAIDs must be used judiciously because of the potential for adverse effects.
- Patient-controlled analgesia (PCA) with opioids.
- Cold compresses.
- Intrathecal opioids or local anesthetics.
- Transcutaneous electrical nerve stimulation.

Note: NSAIDs should be avoided if there is a risk of bleeding.

Effective Pain Control for Coronary Artery Bypass Graft

Effective pain control for coronary artery bypass graft includes the following:

- IV opioids or NSAIDs (recommended), often combined.
- IV, IM, SC, and PO opioids and NSAIDs. Oral medications include acetaminophen with oxycodone.
- Intrathecal opioids.

Note: Epidural and regional local anesthetics are rarely used.

Note: NSAIDs should be avoided with a risk of bleeding or renal hypoperfusion.

Naloxone

The opioid antagonist, **naloxone (Narcan)**, is similar in structure to agonists, but it displaces agonists at μ receptors (less so at κ or δ receptors). It reverses activity of both endogenous opioids, such as endorphins, and exogenous opioids, such as natural (morphine sulfate) and synthetic (meperidine) opioids, and narcotic antagonist analgesics, such as nalbuphine and butorphanol. It may also serve as an antagonist to the antihypertensive effect of clonidine. Naloxone is primarily used to treat known or suspected narcotic overdose or narcotic depression related to the use of narcotics during surgery. Respiratory depression caused by excessive narcotics during surgery usually resolves quickly with naloxone (1–2 minutes), and the duration is quite short (30–45 minutes) as the drug is rapidly redistributed; thus, repeated doses or a continuous drip may be needed. If opioid analgesia is abruptly reversed, sympathetic stimulation may occur with resultant tachycardia, hypertension, and pulmonary edema. Withdrawal symptoms may occur in those who are opioid dependent.

Complementary and Alternative Therapies

Complementary and alternative therapies are used as well as conventional medical treatment and should be included if this is what the patient or family wants, empowering the family to take some control. Complementary therapies vary widely and most can easily be incorporated into the plan of care. The National Center for Complementary and Alternative Medicine recognizes the following:

- Medical systems may include homeopathic, naturopathic medicine, acupuncture, and Chinese herbal medications.
- Mind–body medicine can include support groups, medication, music, art, or dance therapy.
- Biologically based practices include the use of food, vitamins, or nutrition for healing.
- Manipulative/body-based programs include massage or other types of manipulation, such as chiropractic treatment.
- Energy therapies may be biofield therapies intended to affect the aura (energy field) that some believe surrounds all living things. These therapies include therapeutic touch and Reiki.
- Bioelectromagnetic-based therapies use a variety of magnetic fields.

Prevention of Post-Operative Delirium

Methods of **prevention of delirium** in the postoperative patient include:

- Prophylaxis with atypical antipsychotics or haloperidol may be administered for those at risk.
- Frequent orientation and interactions with others to maintain alertness.
- Early and frequent ambulation to tolerance.
- Adequate hydration to decrease the risk of dehydration, which may trigger delirium.
- Avoidance of restraints, which may only increase confusion.
- Avoidance of urinary catheters, which may result in infection and resultant confusion.
- Provision of adequate pain control and prevention of severe breakthrough pain.
- Avoidance of drugs associated with delirium when possible (benzodiazepines, high-dose opioids, anticholinergics, anticonvulsants, H2 blockers, TCAs Antiarrhythmics, B-blockers, steroids, fluoroquinolones, diphenhydramine, antispasmodics).
- Adequate uninterrupted sleep: Patients should not be unnecessarily disturbed when sleeping.
- Ensuring patients are wearing their glasses and hearing aids so that they can hear and see.
- Avoidance of sleeping medications when possible.

Post-Operative Care

DVT Prophylaxis in Post-Operative Patient

Deep vein thrombosis (DVT) is usually related to poor circulation or damage to vessels and is more common in those over age 40. About 2% of cardiac post-surgical patients develop DVT. DVT is associated with inactivity and surgery. DVT prophylaxis in the post-operative patient includes:

- **Early ambulation and mobility** to improve circulation and decrease risks associated with stasis. Patients should be encouraged to exercise feet and legs while in bed.
- **Intermittent pneumatic compression devices** or *sequential compression devices* applied to distal legs while the patient is in bed to prevent stasis. These devices are generally used for all post-surgical patients or those on bedrest.

- **Compressions stockings:** Used when the patient is ambulating.
- **Anticoagulants**: Low-dose unfractionated heparin, low-molecular-weight heparin, enoxaparin, dabigatran, apixaban or rivaroxaban. Oral anticoagulants are associated with a higher risk of bleeding.
- **Anti-platelets:** High-dose ASA (>300 mg per day) although with high risk, ASA alone may be inadequate. Low-dose ASA is not adequate for prophylaxis.

Early Mobility Protocols in Post-Cardiac Surgery Patients

Early mobility protocols for the post-cardiac surgery patient are intended to prevent muscle atrophy, reduction in functional capacity, and complications, such as delirium, atelectasis, pneumonia, and DVT. Early mobilization protocols may vary, but a typical protocol includes day by day increase in activity:

- Day 1: Patient encouraged to do deep-breathing and coughing exercises and to exercise arms and legs (3 X 10 repetitions) with head of bed at 45 degree. Exercise legs on cycle ergometer for 20 minutes at 30 rpm.
- Day 2: Patient to continue exercises as for day 1 and stand upright and walk in place (3 X 1 minute).
- Day 3: Patient to continue exercises as for day 2 and begin to ambulate for short periods (7 minutes) and sit in bedside chair for 30-minute period.
- Day 4: Patient to continue exercises as for day 3 and increase ambulation to 10 minutes and sit in bedside chair for a 60-minute period.
- Day 5: Patient to continue exercises as for day 4 but increase ambulation to 15 minutes and sit in bedside chair for at least 2 hours.
- Day 6: Patient to continue exercises as for day 5 but increase ambulation to 20 minutes and begin step training (3 X continuously) with steps of 20 cm.
- Day 7 Patient to continues exercises as for day 6 but increase step training (6X continuously).

GI Prophylaxis Drugs Utilized After Cardiac Surgery

GI prophylaxis is often routinely administered after cardiac surgery to reduce the risk of stress ulcers, GI bleeding, and other GI symptoms (such as those associated with hiatal hernia) although risk factors include primarily extended intubation and mechanical ventilation of greater than 48 hours and incidence of coagulopathy:

- **H2 receptor antagonists:** Include famotidine and ranitidine. While some studies show that PPIs are more effective to reduce GI symptoms, especially bleeding, other studies indicate that H2 receptor antagonists pose less risk of postoperative infection with *Clostridium difficile* than PPIs. One advantage of H2 receptor antagonists is that they can be crushed for administration in an NG tube. H2 receptor antagonists are associated with higher risk of pneumonia.
- **Proton pump inhibitors (PPIs):** Include IV pantoprazole and PO omeprazole. PPIs are especially useful to reduce incidence of gastric hemorrhage. However, PPIs may inhibit clopidogrel. PPIs are also associated with higher risk of pneumonia.

It's important to note that low risk patients show little advantage from prolonged postoperative prophylaxis and that the risk of bleeding from stress ulcers is relatively low.

Incisional Sites

Cardiac surgery may involve a number of **incisional sites**, and all sites must be evaluated carefully.

- **Mediastinum:** The midsternal incision is used for both cardiopulmonary bypass (CPB) and some non-CPB procedures; it is usually is 6–10 inches long.
- **Chest wall:** Mini-thoracotomy incisions are usually about 2 inches in length. Procedures that require robotics or port access may result in an opening in the left chest wall (coronary artery bypass) or right chest wall (mitral repair or replacement).
- **Minimally invasive procedures:** These may result in a mini-right thoracotomy in the third intercostal space for aortic valve surgery or fourth intercostal space for mitral valve surgery. Aortic value surgery may require an upper hemisternotomy and mitral valve procedures, a lower hemisternotomy.
- **Radial artery conduit:** The incision is 2–4 inches in length.
- **Saphenous vein conduit:** In emergency situations, the incision may be 3–6 inches long, but for planned procedures, an endoscopic harvesting may result in two or three 1.5–2.5 cm incisions.

Primary Phases to Wound Healing

There are **four primary phases to wound healing**:

1. **Hemostasis** begins within minutes of incision when platelets begin to seal off the vessels and secrete substances that cause vasoconstriction. Thrombin is produced to stimulate the clotting mechanism, forming a fibrin mesh.
2. **Inflammation (lag or exudative)** occurs over days 1–4 with erythema, edema, and pain as the blood vessels release plasma, neutrophils, and polymorphonucleocytes to begin phagocytosis to remove debris and prevent infection. Neutrophils begin to fill in the incisional space.
3. **Proliferation/granulation (fibroblastic)** occurs over days 5–20 when fibroblasts produce collagen to provide support, and granulation tissue starts to form. New capillaries form. Basophils migrate to the incision and multiply. Epithelization and contracture of the wound occur.
4. **Maturation (differentiation, remodeling, plateau)** occurs after day 21. The fibroblasts leave the wound, and the collagen tightens to reduce scarring. The tissue gains tensile strength. This stage can take up to 2 years, and the wound can break down easily again during this phase.

Preventive Preoperative Measures for Surgical Site Infections

Preventive preoperative measures can reduce the incidence of postoperative infections with cardiac surgery. Measures may include:

- Identifying any infections present preoperatively and treating them before surgery.
- Applying collagen-gentamicin topically to the area of incision, especially in high-risk patients, such as diabetics and the obese (body mass index > 25).
- Avoiding shaving or using electrical clippers immediately before surgery to remove excess hair that might interfere with the procedure
- Showering before surgery (within 12 hours) and using the antimicrobial chlorhexidine gluconate in a no-rinse application the evening before surgery and the morning of surgery
- Applying topical mupirocin ointment intranasally for 1 day before surgery and 4 days after surgery.

- Providing antibiotic prophylaxis with cephalosporin alone or combined with a glycopeptide if there is a high incidence of methicillin-resistant *Staphylococcus aureus*, usually one dose before surgery and one after.

Incision Wound Complications

Risk factors before surgery are as follows:

- Diabetes, hyperglycemia.
- Obesity.
- Older adult.
- Nutritional impairment and dehydration.
- Respiratory disease (chronic obstructive pulmonary disease, emphysema).
- Anemia.
- Immunosuppression.
- Venous impairment.
- Medications (steroids, chemotherapy).
- History of smoking.

Risk factors during surgery are as follows:

- Bilateral harvesting of internal mammary arteries.
- Increased numbers of bypass grafts.
- Blood transfusions.
- Improper technique (surgical/sterile).
- Hypothermia.
- Ischemia.
- Myocardial edema.

Risk factors after surgery are as follows:

- Return to surgery.
- More than 5 U of blood or autotransfusion of mediastinal blood.
- Prolonged ventilation and prolonged cardiopulmonary resuscitation.

Surgical Site Infection Definitions Developed by the CDC/NNIS

Comparison of data requires that precise and standardized definitions be used for the descriptions of **surgical site infections.** The Centers for Disease Control (CDC)/National Nosocomial Infections Surveillance (NNIS) developed the *CDC Definitions of Nosocomial Infections* to be used in reporting to NNIS and the National Surveillance System for Healthcare Workers. The type of wound is classified according to these definitions, and then the Risk Index is applied to determine the severity of infection as well as rates of infection. Surgical site infections are identified by degree of infection among other criteria.

Category I: Superficial Incisional

The **first category** comprises **superficial incisional infection.** This occurs within 30 days of surgery and involves only skin and subcutaneous tissue of the incision; the patient has one of the following:

- Purulent drainage.
- Organisms isolated from culture of wound fluid or tissue.

- Localized signs of infection (The wound is deliberately opened by the physician, resulting in positive wound culture.).
- Diagnosis of superficial infection by surgeon or attending physician.

Category 2: Deep Incisional

The **second category** of the Centers for Disease Control/National Nosocomial Infections Surveillance **surgical site infections** may include those wounds that have both superficial and deep incisional characteristics. The definition for the second category comprises the following:

Deep incisional infection occurs within 30 days of surgery if there is no implant or within 1 year if an implant is in place. Infection appears related to the surgery and involves deep soft tissues (fascial and muscle layers) of the incision. The patient has one of following:

- Purulent drainage from an incision but not from the organ/space component of the surgical site.
- Spontaneous dehiscence of the wound or deliberately opened by surgeon when the patient has one of the following symptoms: fever (38°C), localized pain, or localized tenderness, unless the wound culture is negative.
- Abscess or other evidence of deep incision infection found on direct examination, histopathology, or radiology.
- Diagnosis of a deep incisional infection by the surgeon or attending physician.

Category 3: Organ/Space

The **third category** of the Centers for Disease Control/National Nosocomial Infections Surveillance **surgical site infection** definitions comprises the following:

- **Organ/space infection** occurs within 30 days of surgery if there is no implant or within 1 year if there is an implant in place. Infection appears related to surgery and involves any part of the body, excluding the skin incision, fascia, or muscle layers, that is opened or manipulated during the operative procedure. Specific sites are assigned to organ/space infection to identify further the location of the infection. The patient has one of the following:
- Purulent drainage from a drain that is placed through a stab wound into the organ/space.
- Organisms isolated from an aseptically obtained culture of fluid or tissue in the organ/space.
- An abscess or other evidence of infection involving the organ/space that is found on direct examination, during reoperation, or by histopathology or radiology.
- Diagnosis of an organ/space infection by a surgeon or attending physician.

Cardiac Postoperative Site Infections

Superficial

Superficial wounds (type 1) are characterized by cellulitis, with local tenderness, erythema, and serous drainage. Small areas of wound breakdown may occur with some purulent discharge. Treatment includes local wound care and antibiotics (6 weeks). Surgical exploration may be indicated if multiple areas begin to break down, suggesting a deeper infection. Wire removal or curettage of infected bone may be necessary.

Mediastinitis

Mediastinitis (type 3) is infection of the deep soft tissue (including muscle and fascia) with purulent discharge and dehiscence along with fever, chills, local tenderness, chest wall pain, and an unstable sternum. *Staphylococcus aureus* infections usually have a rapid onset, occurring within 10 days. Occult infections—common with diabetics—often have delayed symptoms with collections of purulent material but few systemic signs. The white blood cell count is almost always elevated. Treatment may include surgical exploration and antibiotics for 6 weeks. Wounds may be closed or left open. In some cases, sternotomy and vacuum-assisted closure may be indicated.

Sternal Dehiscence

Sternal wounds (type 2) are most often associated with coagulase-negative Staphy-lococcus and Staphylococcus aureus and are classified into three categories:

- Bone is sterile and viable.
- Sternal osteitis is present in the proximal two-thirds of the sternum with non-viable bone.
- Sternal osteitis is present in the distal third of the sternum with nonviable bone.

There may be significant purulent discharge. Treatment varies and can include antibiotics, surgical debridement, rewiring, and surgical repair with flap. If dehiscence occurs without infection, the goal is to retain the sternum.

Leg Graft Site Infection

Saphenous vein harvesting leads to infection in the affected leg in 10–20% of patients, especially in those with peripheral vascular disease, diabetes, or obesity. Cellulitis with breakdown of the wound, purulent discharge, tissue necrosis, hematoma, and edema may occur. Minor infections are treated with antibiotics and drainage. Deeper infections may require surgical exploration, placing of a Blake drain, and antibiotic irrigations.

Postsurgical Nosocomial Infections

About 5–10% of cardiopulmonary bypass patients develop **nosocomial infections**, usually related to respiratory infections, bacteremia from central lines, urinary infections, and surgical site infections. Most bacteremias and surgical site infections are caused by *Staphylococcus aureus*, while respiratory infections are caused by Gram-negative infections. Prophylactic antibiotics are provided within 1 hour (cephalosporins) or 2 hours (vancomycin) of surgery. Drainage should be routinely cultured. Nasal mupirocin should be given before surgery and up to 5 days postoperatively to prevent a *Staphylococcus* infection. Chlorhexidine gluconate (0.12%) oral rinse is also effective in reducing infection. Hyperglycemia must be aggressively controlled. Catheters, central lines, and ventilators should be discontinued as soon as possible. Prolonged (up to 6 weeks) treatment with antibiotics may be necessary for infections.

Bacteremia, Septicemia, and Systemic Inflammatory Response Syndrome

There are a number of terms used to refer to **severe infections** and often used interchangeably, but they are part of a continuum:

- **Bacteremia** is the presence of bacteria in the blood but without systemic infection.
- **Septicemia** is a systemic infection caused by pathogens (usually bacteria or fungi) present in the blood.
- **Systemic inflammatory response syndrome (SIRS)**, a generalized inflammatory response, affecting many organ systems, may be caused by infectious or noninfectious agents, such as trauma, burns, adrenal insufficiency, pulmonary embolism, and drug overdose. If an infectious agent is identified or suspected, SIRS is an aspect of sepsis. Infective agents include a wide range of bacteria and fungi, including *Streptococcus pneumoniae* and *Staphylococcus aureus.* SIRS include two of the following:

- Elevated (> 38°C) or subnormal rectal temperature (< 36°C).
- Tachypnea or partial pressure of carbon dioxide less than 32 mm Hg.
- Tachycardia.
- Leukocytosis (> 12,000/mm^3) or leukopenia (< 4000/mm^3).

WBC Count

White blood cell (WBC)[leukocyte] count is used as an indicator of bacterial and viral infections and leukemia:

- Normal WBC count for adults: 4,800–10,000/mm^3.
- Acute infection: 10,000+/mm^3; 30,000/mm^3 indicative of severe infection.
- Viral infection: 4,000/mm^3 and below.

White Blood Cell Differential

The white blood cell differential provides the percentage of each different type of leukocyte. An increase in the WBC count is usually related to an increase in one type of leukocyte, often immature neutrophils, known as bands; this increase is referred to as a "shift to the left," an indication of an infectious process.

Cells	Normal Values	Changes
Immature neutrophils (bands)	1-3%	Increase with infection
Segmented neutrophils (segs)	50–62%	Increase with acute, localized, or systemic bacterial infections
Eosinophils	0–3%	Decrease with stress & acute infection
Basophils	0–1%	Decrease during the acute stage of infection
Lymphocytes	25–40%	Increase in some viral and bacterial infections
Monocytes	3–7%	Increase during the recovery stage of acute infection

ETTs

Endotracheal/tracheal tubes (ETTs) are usually made of radiopaque polyvinyl chloride plastic that is pliable and able to mold to the shape of the airway. They are used to deliver anesthetic gases and oxygen directly to the trachea. ETTs are sized according to internal diameter. The tip ends are beveled, and Murphy tracheal tubes have an opening (Murphy eye) at the distal end to reduce the chance of occlusion. A large size increases airflow but can cause more trauma than small sizes. Adult ETTs usually have an inflatable cuff to affect a tracheal seal, which allows positive pressure ventilation and prevents aspiration. Cuffs may be high pressure (low volume), which can cause ischemia and mucosal trauma, and are not suitable for long anesthesia or ventilation. Low-pressure (high volume) cuffs, are used more frequently and cause less trauma, but they increase the risk of sore throat, aspiration, and spontaneous extubation.

Emergence from Anesthesia

Emergence from anesthesia must be carefully managed and varies, depending on the type of anesthetic agents used. If muscle relaxants are used to paralyze muscles during surgery, then the effects must be reversed before emergence and removal of ventilation so that the patient can breathe independently. Administration of the muscle relaxant is discontinued, and a reversing agent, such as an anticholinesterase, may be used. With general anesthesia, patients may be able to follow verbal directions soon after the anesthetic agent is discontinued, and the intubation tube can be removed unless the patient is to be continued on ventilation. In that case, the patient may be transferred to the postanesthesia unit before awakening. Patients may have some persistent difficulty thinking after emergence because of the lasting effects of some anesthetic agents. Because of respiratory depression, a common side effect of most anesthetic agents, careful monitoring of oxygen saturation and ventilation must be done during the recovery period, and supplemental oxygen is provided to improve oxygen saturation.

Delayed Emergence

Delayed emergence (failure to emerge for 30–60 minutes after anesthesia ends) is more common in the elderly because of the slowed metabolism of anesthetic agents, but it may have a variety of causes, such as drug overdose during surgery and overdose related to preinduction use of drugs or alcohol that potentiates intraoperative drugs. In this case, naloxone or flumazenil may be indicated if opioids or benzodiazepines are implicated but should be avoided unless absolutely necessary. Physostigmine may also be used to reverse the effects of some anesthetic agents. Hypothermia may also cause delay in emergence, especially core temperatures of less than 33°C and may require forced-air warming blankets to increase the temperature. Other metabolic conditions, such as hypoglycemia or hyperglycemia may also affect emergence. Patients suffering from delayed emergence must be evaluated for perioperative stroke, especially after neurological, cardiovascular, or cerebrovascular surgery. Metabolic disturbances may also delay emergence.

Transfer from Operating Room to ICU

During **transfer from the operating room to the intensive care unit (ICU)**, patients are usually ventilated with an Ambu bag during transfer, and medications are maintained with battery-powered infusion pumps. The patient must be monitored carefully for changes in hemodynamic status and electrocardiogram (ECG) tracings during transfer, and ECG and monitoring devices are transferred and checked one at a time. The endotracheal tube should be attached to the bedside ventilator, and all settings must be verified. Thoracic drainage tubes should be attached to suction. Common problems encountered include hypotension and inaccurate ECG tracings. Hypotension (systolic < 90 mm Hg or mean < 60 mm Hg) is usually associated with hypovolemia or stopping medications. All dosages of medications and infusion must be checked, and all tubes and attachments must be checked for kinks or occlusions. Chest tubes must be examined for evidence of hemorrhage. A portable chest x-ray should be done in the operating room or on admission to the ICU to evaluate the position of tubes and catheters and to note the width of the mediastinum or evidence of a pneumothorax, atelectasis, pleural effusion, or fluid overload.

Postoperative Analgesia and Sedation

Patients usually are anesthetized and intubated upon admission to the intensive care unit after surgery but may require **postoperative analgesia and sedation**. With early extubation, a short-acting agent, such as Propofol, is usually used, but patients may experience pain and require additional medication within a few hours. Before discontinuation of Propofol, nonsteroidal anti-inflammatory drugs may be administered. These include ketorolac, 30 mg intravenously (IV) [preferred because it inhibits platelet aggregation]; indomethacin, 50 mg rectally; or diclofenac, 75 mg rectally. Morphine sulfate may be given by IV infusion (0.02 mg/kg/hr for patients < 65 years of age and 0.01 mg/kg/hr for those > 65 years of age). If the patient becomes agitated with a reduction in Propofol, dexmedetomidine may improve weaning from ventilation, although Propofol and fentanyl can be used for a number of days if extubation is delayed. Breakthrough pain is controlled with boluses of morphine or ketorolac or with patient-controlled anesthesia (PCA) on the first postoperative day. Morphine, fentanyl, or remifentanil are used with PCA.

PONV

Postoperative nausea and vomiting (PONV) vary with the type of anesthetic agent used. It occurs in about 20–30% of postanesthesia patients and may be delayed up to 24 hours. Inhalational agents have a higher incidence of PONV than intravenous, and the incidence is lower with epidural or subarachnoid administration, although it may indicate the onset of hypotension. PONV correlates with the duration of surgery, with longer surgeries causing increased PONV. If high doses of narcotics, Propofol, or nitrous oxide are used, PONV is often a problem. PONV is most common in young women and also relates to menstruation. It is also increased in patients with a history of smoking or motion sickness. PONV may be associated with postoperative pain, so managing pain is an important factor in preventing PONV.

Review Video: Cancer-Related Nausea and Vomiting
Visit mometrix.com/academy and enter code: 631968

Postanesthetic Respiratory Complications

Respiratory complications are most common in the postanesthesia period, so monitoring oxygen levels is critical to preventing hypoxemia. Patients who are extubated in the operating room must be carefully monitored.

Airway obstruction may be partial or total. Partial obstruction is indicated by sonorous or wheezing respirations, and total obstruction is indicated by the absence of breath sounds. Treatment includes supplemental oxygen, airway insertion, repositioning (jaw thrust), or succinylcholine and positive-pressure ventilation for laryngospasm. If edema of the glottis is causing obstruction, intravenous corticosteroids may be used.

Hypoventilation (partial pressure of carbon dioxide > 45 mm Hg) is often mild but may cause respiratory acidosis. It is usually related to depression caused by anesthetic agents. A number of factors may slow emergence (e.g., hypothermia, overdose, metabolism) and cause hypoventilation. Hypoventilation may also be related to splinting because of pain, requiring additional pain management.

Hypoxemia (mild is a partial pressure of oxygen of 50–60 mm Hg) is usually related to hypoventilation or increased right-to-left shunting and is usually treated with supplementary oxygen (30–60%) with or without positive airway pressure.

Management of Hypotension in Immediate Postoperative Period

Inaccurate zeroing of the transducer may result in **hypotension in the immediate postoperative period**, so low blood pressure (BP) should be verified before initiating treatment. To determine if the tracing is dampened:

- Check bilateral breath sounds during manual ventilation.
- Take an auscultatory/occlusive BP reading.
- Monitor all medications and dosages, and make sure infusion rates are set properly.
- Note signs of excessive mediastinal bleeding.
- Check cardiac filling pressures, and make sure that all transducers are placed correctly and that all monitors are calibrated. (Filling pressures may be inaccurate in the immediate postoperative period.) Low-filling pressures can indicate hypovolemia, and high-filling pressures can indicate myocardial dysfunction.

- Treat confirmed hypotension with fluid resuscitation. If there is no response, administer calcium chloride, 500 mg, intravenously. Vasoactive drugs may be initiated or dosages altered.

If there is no response to previous actions and BP remains life-threateningly low, then the patient may be on the verge of cardiac arrest and may need to have resternotomy.

Blood Warmers

Rapid infusions of cold blood may cause cardiac dysrhythmias. **Blood warmers** are used to warm blood to approximately 32°C–38°C. Indications for blood warmers include the following:

- Prevention of or increase in hypothermia
- Blood flow rate of more than 100 mL/min (adult)
- Patient evidence of significant cold agglutinins
- Rapid infusion, using central lines

Blood warmers must be approved by the Food and Drug Administration. The American Association of Blood Bank standards require that blood be attached to a warmer for no more than 4 hours. Overheating blood (>42°C) may cause hemolysis, so blood warmers must have temperature controls with a visible thermometer and an online monitor that includes an audible alarm system. There are a number of different types of blood warming devices:

- Water baths
- Warming plates
- Heat exchangers with heated chambers through which blood flows in a separate chamber
- Mixing devices that combine equal volumes of normal saline (70°C) and red blood cells (4°C)

Protocols for Rewarming After Therapeutic Hypothermia

Therapeutic hypothermia is used during cardiopulmonary bypass (31° to 34° C) after non-traumatic cardiac arrest with restoration of spontaneous circulation but persistent comatose state and (32° to 34° C) to protect the brain and myocardium from ischemia. The risk of arrhythmias increases if the body core temperature falls to less than 30°C. **Rewarming procedures** generally begin about 15 minutes prior to releasing the aortic cross-clamp and restoring circulation. Peripheral vasoconstriction is often used postoperatively after CPB to provide core warming. Heated intravenous fluid and humidifiers in the ventilator circuits may be used for hypothermia but are usually not effective for increasing core temperatures. Heated blankets may be applied. Following CPB, the patient should be warmed at the rate of ≤ 0.5° C/min to about 36°C before leaving the operating room. Because brain temperature may be higher than measurable core temperature, raising the temperature to 37° C may impair neurocognitive functioning. The temperature gradient between the arterial blood outlet and the venous inlet should be a maximum of 10° C for rewarming to avoid too rapid rewarming and outgassing.

Postoperative Mediastinal Bleeding

Excessive **postoperative mediastinal bleeding** occurs in 3–14% of cardiac patients. Changing the patient's position may cause increased chest tube drainage because of pooling of blood. Acute onset of bleeding is characterized by bright red blood and continuous steady discharge. Dark red blood suggests older blood rather than active bleeding, especially if discharge slows after an initial increase. Bleeding may be surgical (bleeding from vessel or sutures) or nonsurgical (related to coagulopathy). Chest tube drainage should not exceed 200 mL in 2–6 hours. Excessive bleeding may require coagulation studies, a repeat chest x-ray to evaluate the width of the mediastinum, and transesophageal echocardiogram if cardiac tamponade is suspected. Indications for emergent surgical exploration include the following situations:

- Blood loss of more than 400 mL/hr for 4 hours.
- Blood loss of 300 mL/hr for 3 hours.
- Blood loss of 400 mL/hr for 2 hours.
- Blood loss of 500 mL/hr for 1 hour.

Treatment for coagulopathy may include fresh frozen plasma, platelets, cryoprecipitate, packed red blood cells, desmopressin to improve platelet function, aminocaproic acid to prevent fibrinolysis, and factor VIIa to help achieve hemostasis.

RISK FACTORS

Mediastinal bleeding that is directly associated with the surgery with a normal coagulation profile is classified as surgical bleeding, while bleeding associated with coagulopathies is classified as medical bleeding. When bleeding occurs, identifying and treating the underlying cause is critical. Causes can include a residual or rebound heparin effect, excessive protamine, thrombocytopenia or platelet dysfunction, deficiency in clotting factor, and fibrinolysis. A number of **risk factors** may increase the risk of postsurgical mediastinal bleeding:

- Older age and patients with small body surface area (especially females).
- History of anemia and advanced cardiac disease, especially with left ventricular dysfunction.
- History of kidney or liver disease, diabetes, peripheral vascular disease, and coagulopathies.
- Medications (preoperative), including high-dose aspirin, low-molecular-weight heparin ($\leq$ 18 hours), fondaparinux ($\leq$ 48 hours), clopidogrel, prasugrel, IIb/IIIA inhibitors, thrombolytic treatment before emergent surgery, and an incomplete INR reversal for patients on warfarin.
- Complex, emergent, or repeat operations and use of an internal thoracic artery graft.

TREATMENT OPTIONS FOR MEDIASTINAL BLEEDING ASSOCIATED WITH COAGULOPATHIES

Treatment for **mediastinal bleeding associated with coagulopathies** varies, depending on the underlying problem. Routine point-of-care testing of coagulation is indicated after cardiac surgery to help determine the cause of bleeding:

- Increased activated clotting time more than 130 seconds and increased partial thromboplastin time more than 1.5 x normal: protamine, 2550 mg, initially although reinfusing cell-saver blood may reintroduce heparin and result in heparin-rebound effect, so may need continuous infusion at low dose or repeat doses.
- Thrombocytopenia less than 100,000/mm^3 or platelet dysfunction (common in patients who are markedly anemic or have undergone cardiopulmonary bypass): administration of platelet transfusions; without bleeding, platelet transfusions not indicated until the level falls to 20,000–30,000/mm^3 (although most patients bleed at 50,000–60,000/mm^3).
- INR over 1.5: administration of fresh frozen plasma.
- Fibrinogen less than 100 mg/dL: administration of cryoprecipitate.
- Increased prothrombin time: fresh frozen plasma, cryoprecipitate, or both.

NPWT

Application of **negative pressure wound therapy (NPWT)** is done after a wound is determined to be appropriate for this treatment and debridement is completed, leaving the wound tissue exposed. There are a number of different electrical suction NPWT systems, such as the vacuum-assisted closure system and the Versatile I. Several layers of paraffin or petroleum jelly (Vaseline) gauze may be placed over the heart to help prevent right ventricular rupture, but this covering is not rigid, and rupture can occur. Application steps include:

1. Apply nonadherent porous foam cut to fit and completely cover the wound.
2. Polyurethane (hydrophobic, repelling moisture) is used for all wounds EXCEPT those that are painful, have tunneling or sinus tracts, deep trauma wounds, and wounds needing controlled growth of granulation.
3. Polyvinyl (hydrophilic) is used for all wounds EXCEPT deep wounds with moderate granulation, deep pressure ulcers, and flaps.
4. Secure foam occlusive transparent film.
5. Cut opening to accommodate the drainage tube in the dressing, and attach drainage tube.
6. Attach tube to suction canister, creating a closed system.
7. Set pressure as indicated.
8. Change dressings two to three times a week.

Monitoring and Diagnostics

Hemodynamic Monitoring

Cardiac Output

Cardiac output is the amount of blood pumped through the ventricles during a specified period. Normal cardiac output is about 5 L/min (normal values: 4–8 L/min) at rest for an adult. With exercise or stress, this volume may multiply three or four times with concomitant changes in the heart rate and stroke volume. The basic formulation for calculating cardiac output is the heart rate per minute multiplied by measurement of the stroke volume, which is the amount of blood pumped through the ventricles with each contraction. The stroke volume is controlled by preload, afterload, and contractility.

- Cardiac output = heart rate x stroke volume.

The heart rate is controlled by the autonomic nervous system. Normally, if the heart rate decreases, stroke rate increases to compensate, but with cardiomyopathies, this may not occur, so bradycardia results in a sharp decline in cardiac output. Cardiac index evaluates the cardiac output in terms of the body surface area (BSA):

- Cardiac index = cardiac output/BSA.
- The normal values are 2.2–4.0 L/min/m^2.

Preload and Afterload

Preload refers to the amount of elasticity in the myocardium at the end of diastole when the ventricles are filled to their maximum volume and the stretch on the muscle fibers is the greatest. The preload value is based on the volume in the ventricles. The amount of preload (stretch) affects stroke volume because as stretch increases, the resultant contraction also increases (Frank-Starling Law). Preload may decrease because of dehydration, diuresis, or vasodilation. Preload may increase because of increased venous return, controlling fluid loss, transfusion, or intravenous fluids.

Afterload refers to the amount of systemic vascular resistance to left ventricular ejection of blood and pulmonary vascular resistance to right ventricular ejection of blood. Determinants of afterload include the size and elasticity of the great vessels and the functioning of the pulmonic and aortic valves. Afterload increases with hypertension, stenotic valves, and vasoconstriction.

Perfusion Pressure, Pulse Pressure, and MAP

The **perfusion pressure**, measured by the **mean arterial pressure (MAP)** that is necessary, may vary with different conditions and circumstances. The **pulse pressure** is the difference between systolic and diastolic pressures, and this can be an important indicator. For example, with a decrease in cardiac output, vasoconstriction takes place in the body's attempt to maintain the blood pressure. In this case, the MAP may remain unchanged, but the pulse pressure narrows. Necessary values for MAP include the following:

- More than 60 mm Hg to perfuse coronary arteries.
- Approximately 70–90 mm Hg to perfuse the brain and other organs, such as the kidneys, and to maintain cardiac patients and decrease the workload of the left ventricle.
- Approximately 90–110 mm Hg to increase cerebral perfusion after neurosurgical procedures, such as carotid endarterectomy.

Patients should be assessed for changes in pulse pressure that may be precipitated by medications, such as diuretics that alter fluid volume.

Cardiac Index

Cardiac index is the cardiac output divided by the body surface area (BSA). This is essentially a measure of cardiac output tailored to the individual, based on height and weight, measured in liters/min per square meter of BSA:

- Normal values are: 2.2–4.0 L/min/m^2.
- Formula: Cardiac index = cardiac output/BSA.

Stroke Volume

Stroke volume is the amount of blood pumped through the left ventricle with each contraction, minus any blood remaining inside the ventricle at the end of systole:

- Normal values are: 60–100 mL/beat (1 mL/kg/beat).
- Formula: Stroke volume = cardiac index in L/min) x (heart rate per minute) x (1000).

MAP

Mean arterial pressure (MAP) is the average arterial blood pressure and can be calculated with the diastolic pressure (DP) and systolic pressure (SP):

- Normal values are: 70–100 mm Hg.
- Formula: MAP = DP + SP – DP/3.

SVR

Systemic vascular resistance (SVR) is the resistance to blood flow in all vessels except pulmonary vessels:

- Normal values are: 800–1200 dynes/cm^5.
- Formula: SVR = MAP – central venous pressure/cardiac
- output x 80.

PVR

Pulmonary vascular resistance (PVR) is the resistance in the pulmonary arteries and arterioles against which the right ventricle has to pump during contraction. It is the mean pressure in the pulmonary vascular bed divided by blood flow. If PVR increases, stroke volume decreases.

- Normal values are: 50–250 dynes/cm^5.
- Formula: PVR = pulmonary artery pressure – pulmonary capillary wedge pressure/cardiac output x 80.

Stroke Volume Index

Stroke volume index is the stroke volume tailored to the individual:

- Normal values are: 33–47 mL/beat/m2.
- Formula: Stroke volume index = stroke volume/BSA.

Left Ventricular Stroke Work Index

Left ventricular stroke work index measures the contractility of the left ventricle:

- Normal values are: 45–75 g/M/m2/beat.
- Formula: Left ventricular stroke work index = stroke volume index x (mean arterial pressure – pulmonary capillary wedge pressure) x 0.0136.

Pulmonary Capillary Wedge Pressure

Pulmonary capillary wedge pressure/pulmonary artery wedge pressure/pulmonary artery occlusion pressure is an indirect measurement of preload or filling pressure of the left ventricle.

- Normal values are: 8–12 mm Hg.

Hemodynamic Monitoring

Hemodynamic monitoring is the monitoring of blood flow pressures. For effective postoperative cardiac functioning, the correct relationship between high and low pressures must be maintained. During surgery, catheters are placed; the most common sites are the left atrium, right atrium, pulmonary artery, or superior vena cava.

CVP

Central venous pressure (CVP), the pressure in the right atrium or vena cava, is used to assess function of the right ventricles, preload, and flow of venous blood to the heart. Normal pressure ranges from 2–6 mm Hg but may be elevated after surgery to 6–8 mm Hg. Incorrect catheter placement or malfunctioning can affect readings.

- **Increased CVP** is related to overload of intravascular volume caused by decreased function, hypertrophy, or failure of the right ventricle; increased right ventricular afterload, tricuspid valve stenosis, regurgitation, or thrombus obstruction; or a shunt from the left ventricle to the right atrium. It can also be caused by arrhythmias or cardiac tamponade.
- **Decreased CVP** is related to low intravascular volume, decreased preload, or vasodilation.

CVC Complications

Central venous catheters (CVCs) are used for hemodynamic monitoring; obtaining blood samples; and administering blood, fluids, or medication. CVCs are usually secured with a suture or staple and covered with a protective dressing. CVCs must have heparin flushes to prevent thrombus formation. Placement of a CVC may result in a number of complications, so the catheter must be monitored carefully. **Complications** include the following:

- Pneumothorax (usually during initial catheter placement) or hemothorax.
- Perforation of vessels near the catheter, arterial puncture, or superior vena cava puncture.
- Air embolism from negative intrathoracic pressure.
- Thrombus formation, thrombophlebitis, or emboli.
- Perforation of the pericardium.
- Hemorrhage or formation of a hematoma (most often associated with placement of a CVC in the jugular vein).
- Cardiac arrhythmias from contact with the endocardium during placement.
- Extravasation of fluids.
- Local inflammation.
- Central line–associated bloodstream infections primarily related to *Staphylococcus aureus* or *S. epidermidis.*

Oxygen Saturation

Hemodynamic monitoring includes monitoring **oxygen saturation** levels, which must be maintained for proper cardiac function. Changes in the oxygen saturation levels can indicate complications in the postsurgical patient. The central venous catheter often has an oxygen sensor at the tip to monitor oxygen saturation in the right atrium. If the catheter tip is located near the renal veins, this can cause an increase in right atrial oxygen saturation and a decrease near the coronary sinus. Increased oxygen saturation may result from the left atrial shunt to the right atrial shunt, abnormal pulmonary venous return, increased delivery of oxygen, or a decrease in oxygen extraction. Decreased oxygen saturation may be related to low-cardiac output with an increase in oxygen extraction or a decrease in arterial oxygen saturation with normal differences in the atrial and ventricular oxygen saturation.

MVG

Mixed venous gases (MVG), especially venous oxygen saturation (SvO_2), are monitored for indications of respiratory failure, reduced oxygenation, anemia, and changes in cardiac output. MVG refers to venous blood that has returned to the heart from the superior and inferior vena cava and the coronary sinus. A sample from the right atrium may reflect primarily blood from the superior vena cava, which usually has a lower saturation (70%) than blood from the inferior vena cava (80%) or the coronary sinus (56%). The blood in the right ventricle and pulmonary artery is completely "mixed," and the saturation averaged. MVG is usually measured by sampling through a pulmonary artery catheter. Normal values include the following:

- **$PvCO_2$:** 41–51 mm Hg (partial pressure of carbon dioxide in venous blood).
- **PvO_2:** 35–49 mm Hg (partial pressure of oxygen in venous blood).
- **SvO_2:** 60–80% (oxygen saturation in venous blood).

If there is a decrease in SvO_2, then the oxygenation is not sufficient for tissue needs.

PAP and PAM

Pulmonary artery pressure (PAP) is measured by a pulmonary artery catheter that is usually fed through the right ventricle to the main pulmonary artery; it is measured with the patient in the supine position (45° elevation or less).

- **Normal values** are 10–20 mm Hg (mean PAP: 15 mm Hg). Postoperative rates should be less than 25 mm Hg. PAP is usually about 25–34% of the systemic blood pressure rate. Oxygen saturation is usually about 80%.
- **Increased pressure** may indicate pulmonary obstruction or embolus, left-to-right shunt, left ventricular failure, pulmonary hypertension, mitral stenosis, pneumothorax, lung/alveolar hypoplasia, hyperviscosity of blood, or increased left atrial pressure.
- **Decreased pressure** may indicate a decrease in intravascular volume or cardiac output or obstruction of pulmonary blood flow.

Pulmonary Artery Mean (PAM) provides the average pressure in the pulmonary artery during one cardiac cycle as PAP increases with contraction of the right ventricle and then decreases until the next contraction (mean PAM: 15 mm Hg).

PAC

The **pulmonary artery catheter (PAC)** can provide information about cardiac output, cardiac index, and intracardiac pressures and allows for earlier identification of left ventricular (LV) function than a central venous pressure line, which is associated with longer intubation and increased morbidity. Pressures include the following:

- **Pulmonary artery systolic (PAS) pressure** indicates pressure from the tricuspid valve to the mitral valve and provides a good indication of pulmonary artery pressures (PAP). PAS increases with pulmonary hypertension.
- **Pulmonary artery diastolic (PAD) pressure** indicates pressure between the pulmonic and aortic valves and provides a good indication of LV function (if there is no obstruction). PAD is usually slightly higher than pulmonary artery occlusive pressure (PAOP) and pulmonary artery wedge pressure (PAWP) [≤ 5 mm Hg].
- **PAOP and PAWP** indicate pressure between the distal end of the PAC and the aortic valve when the PAC balloon is inflated, providing better information about LV function than PAD. It is used to assess LV preload. Normal values are 4–12 mm Hg. Increased pressure may indicate left ventricular failure, mitral insufficiency, or mitral stenosis. The balloon should be inflated slowly and left deflated after reading.

Left Atrial Pressure

Left atrial pressure may be monitored in the postsurgical period by way of a catheter inserted during surgery into the left atrium from the right superior pulmonary vein or through the left atrial appendage. Oxygen saturation of blood in the left atrium should be 100%. Left atrial pressures should be as follows:

- **Normal values** are 1–2 mm Hg higher than right atrial pressure (4–12 mm Hg). Pressures above 12–14 mm Hg postsurgically are cause for concern.
- **Increased pressure** may indicate an increase in end-diastolic pressure of the left ventricle, a decrease in function, hypertrophy, heart failure, or an increase in left ventricular afterload. An increase may also indicate mitral valve stenosis, backflow, or thrombus obstruction, a significant right-to-left shunt, excessive intravascular volume, tachycardia with arrhythmias, or cardiac tamponade.
- **Decreased pressure** may indicate a decrease in intravascular fluid or insufficient preload.

Aortic Blood Flow

Aortic blood flow is assessed with esophageal Doppler monitoring (EDM) for evaluation of hypoperfusion (hypovolemia or septic shock), major organ dysfunction (renal or liver failure), hypotension, heart failure, cardiogenic shock, ruptures within the heart, mitral regurgitation, or tamponade. EDM may be used before, during, or after cardiac surgery. An esophageal probe is inserted through the patient's mouth while the patient is sedated, and Doppler ultrasound technology is used to monitor both the function of the left ventricle and the patient's fluid status. The probe may be left in place if the patient can tolerate it, but the patient should be monitored carefully for mucosal irritation. EDM can show the flow time, peak velocity, and minute distance, while stroke volume and cardiac output are calculated. Normal ranges include the following:

- Corrected flow time: 330–360 msec

Peak velocities are listed below:

- 20 years: 90–120 cm/sec
- 40 years: 80–110 cm/sec
- 60 years: 60–90 cm/sec
- 80 years: 40–70 cm/sec

Intra-Arterial Blood Pressure Monitoring and MAP

Intra-arterial blood pressure monitoring is done for systolic, diastolic, and **mean arterial pressure (MAP)** for conditions that decrease cardiac output, tissue perfusion, or fluid volume. A catheter is inserted into an artery, such as the radial (most frequently used), dorsalis pedis, femoral, or axillary, percutaneously or through a cut-down. Before catheter insertion, collateral circulation must be assessed by Doppler or the Allen test (used for the hand). In the Allen test, both the radial and ulnar arteries are compressed, and the patient is asked to clench the hand repeatedly until it blanches; then one artery is released, and the tissue on that side should flush. Then the test is repeated again, releasing the other artery. The MAP is most commonly used to evaluate perfusion as it shows pressure throughout the cardiac cycle. Systole is one-third and diastole two-thirds of the normal cardiac cycle. The MAP for a blood pressure of 120/60 mm Hg (normal range 70–100 mm Hg) is as follows:

[(Diastole x 2) + (systole x 1)]/3 = MAP.

(60 x 2 = 120) + (120) = 240/3 = MAP of 80.

Noninvasive Hemodynamic Monitoring Through Thoracic Electrical Bioimpedance Monitoring

Thoracic electrical bioimpedance monitoring is a noninvasive method of monitoring hemodynamics (e.g., cardiac output, blood flow, contractibility, pre- and after-load, pulmonary artery pressure). Electrodes placed on the thorax measure changes in electrical output associated with the volume of blood through the aorta and its velocity. The monitor to which the electrodes are attached converts the signals to waveforms. The heart rate is shown on an electrocardiogram (ECG) monitor. The equipment calculates the cardiac output based on the heart rate and fluid volume. A typical bioimpedence monitor has four sets of bioimpedance electrodes and three ECG electrodes. Height, weight, and length of the thorax are entered into the machine. Two sets of bioimpedance electrodes are placed at the base on the neck bilaterally and then two sets on each side of the chest. The distance between the neck electrodes and the chest electrodes (on the same side) must be entered into the machine. ECG leads are placed where they consistently monitor the QRS signal; they may need to be moved to achieve this.

LCOS

Low-cardiac output syndrome (LCOS) is a common complication of cardiac surgery, especially aortic valve surgery. LCOS results in an imbalance between the supply of oxygen and body needs, leading to metabolic acidosis. LCOS incidence relates to left ventricular ejection fraction (LVEF).

- 6% with a LVEF of more than 40%.
- 12% with a LVEF of 20–40%.
- 23% with a LVEF of less than 20%.

Causes include left ventricular dysfunction resulting in a transient decrease in perfusion, cardiac arrest from cardioplegia and myocardial stunning, decreased preload, increased afterload, dysrhythmias, and myocardial infarction. Indications include a decrease in pulmonary venous oxygen saturation (< 70%) and mean arterial pressure, confusion/altered mental status, hypotension, narrow pulse pressure, poor peripheral perfusion, reduced or absent urinary output, and need for inotropic support for more than 30 minutes or intra-aortic balloon pump (IABP) therapy. Treatment depends on the underlying cause but can include fluids, vasopressors, and inotropic agents. Epinephrine, norepinephrine, dopamine, or dobutamine is indicated for ejection fractions 20% below baseline. Vasopressors include phenylephrine, vasopressin, or epinephrine. Nitroprusside and IABP therapy are used for increased afterload.

Management of Postoperative Preload Alterations

Preload refers to the volume of blood returning to the right or left heart at diastole (end of filling) as measured by central venous pressure, which measures the right filling pressure and pulmonary artery occlusion pressure, which reflects the left ventricular (LV) end-diastolic pressure. Adequate preload is essential for tissue perfusion. A decrease in preload after surgery may result from excessive diuresis, hypothermia, vasodilation related to warming, fluid resuscitation (volume may leave the vasculature for the interstitium with capillary leak), bleeding, vasodilators, and decreased LV compliance. Fluid resuscitation is determined by the type of fluid loss and hematocrit and the presence of coagulopathies. Fluid resuscitation should aim for a mean arterial pressure of 70–80 mm Hg. With bleeding or coagulopathy, blood products and coagulation factors may be needed. If there is no bleeding, then crystalloids or colloid may increase preload to a pulmonary artery occlusion pressure of 18–20 mm Hg. Even with decreased preload, inotropic agents should be avoided.

Management of Postoperative Increased Afterload and SVR

Alterations in **systemic vascular resistance (SVR)** may occur after surgery, as indicated by afterload. Right-sided afterload is reflected by pulmonary vascular resistance (PVR) and left-sided, by SVR. Left-sided **afterload increase** is of most concern. Systolic blood pressure has the most pronounced effect on SVR. Cardiac output improves with reduction in afterload, but SVR often increases to compensate for low cardiac output. About 60% of postsurgical patients exhibit hypertension, usually because of vasoconstriction, which may relate to an inflammatory response to cardiopulmonary bypass or metabolic acidosis. Other causes of increased afterload include hypovolemia, hypothermia, hypercarbia, volume overload, cardiogenic shock, anxiety, and pain. Treatment includes vasodilators (e.g., sodium nitroprusside, nitroglycerin, milrinone), which often require administration of fluids to balance the decrease in preload and maintain intravascular fluid volume. Blood pressure must be monitored frequently with nitroprusside as it may cause a precipitous drop. An intra-aortic balloon pump may be required in severe cases.

Other Monitoring

Capnography

Capnography measures exhaled carbon dioxide and may include a capnometer, which provides a numeric CO2 measure, or a capnogram, which provides a visual waveform. End tidal CO2 (ETCO2 or PETCO2) is the partial pressure of CO2 at the end of expiration. The normal ETCO2 is 35 to 45 mm Hg, and the waveforms should be consistent. Hypercarbia (level >45 mm Hg) occurs with hypoventilation (overdose, sedation, post-seizures, head trauma, stroke), and hypocarbia (level <35 mm Hg) with hyperventilation (anxiety, bronchospasm, pulmonary edema, decreased cardiac output). Capnography is more sensitive than pulse oximetry, which changes more slowly in the presence of apnea. Capnography is used initially to confirm correct placement of an ETT. Once intubated, patients should be monitored with continuous waveform capnography. Capnography should be monitored during position change and transfers to ensure that the ETT is not dislodged. ETCO2 levels are less accurate with sidestream measurement used for nasal cannula and facemask than with the mainstream sensor used with an ETT, so it's important to keep the sensor close to the mouth and secured.

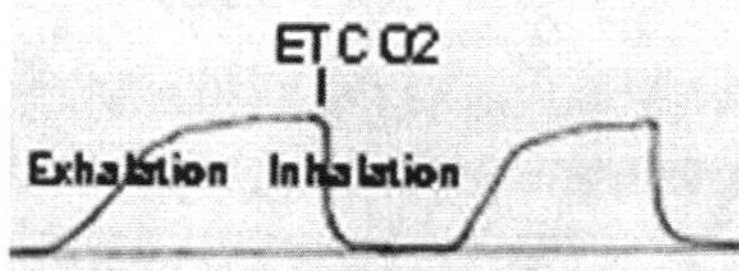

Assessment of Heart Sounds

Auscultation of **heart sounds** can help to diagnose different cardiac disorders. Areas to auscultate include the aortic area, pulmonary area, Erb's point, tricuspid area, and the apical area. The normal heart sounds represent closing of the valves:

- The **first heart sound (S_1)**, "lub," is closure of the mitral and tricuspid valves (heard at apex/left ventricular area of the heart).
- The **second heart sound (S_2)**, "dub," is closure of the aortic and pulmonic valves (heard at the base of the heart). There may be a slight splitting of the S_2.

The time between S_1 and S_2 is systole, and the time between S_2 and the next S_1 is diastole. Systole and diastole should be silent, although ventricular disease can cause gallops, snaps, or clicks, and stenosis of the valves or failure of the valves to close can cause murmurs. Pericarditis may cause a friction rub.

Additional Heart Sounds

Additional heart sounds include:

- **Gallop rhythms**: The third heart sound (S3) occurs after the second heart sound (S2) in children and young adults but may indicate heart failure or left ventricular failure in older adults (heard with patient lying on left side). The fourth heart sound (S4) occurs before the first heart sound (S1) and occurs with ventricular hypertrophy, such as from coronary artery disease, hypertension, or aortic valve stenosis.
- **Opening snap**: Opening snap is an unusual high-pitched sound, occurring after S2 with stenosis of the mitral valve from rheumatic heart disease.
- **Ejection click**: Ejection click is a brief high-pitched sound, occurring immediately after S1 with stenosis of the aortic valve.
- **Friction rub**: Friction rub is a harsh, grating sound heard in systole and diastole with pericarditis
- **Murmur**: Murmurs are caused by turbulent blood flow from stenotic or malfunctioning valves, congenital defects, or increased blood flow. Murmurs are characterized by location, timing in the cardiac cycle, intensity (rated from grade I to grade VI), pitch (low-to-high pitched), quality (rumbling, whistling, blowing), and radiation to the carotids, axilla, neck, shoulder, or back.

Postoperative Monitoring Using Pulse Oximetry

Pulse oximetry, continuous or intermittent, uses an external oximeter that attaches to the patient's finger or earlobe to measure arterial oxygen saturation (SpO_2), the percentage of hemoglobin that is saturated with oxygen. The oximeter also usually attaches to a machine that emits a beep with each heartbeat and indicates the current heart rate. Blood pressure monitoring is also necessary. The oximeter uses light waves to determine SpO_2. In patients with pronounced vasoconstriction, the earlobe may provide more accurate readings than the finger. It is important to maintain SpO_2 at

95% or more, although some patients with chronic respiratory disorders, such as chronic obstructive pulmonary disease may have a low SpO_2. If SpO_2 falls, the oximeter should be repositioned, as incorrect position is a common cause of inaccurate readings. Oximetry is often used postoperatively to assess peripheral circulation and when patients are on mechanical ventilation. Oximeters do not provide information about carbon dioxide levels, so they cannot monitor carbon dioxide retention. Oximeters cannot differentiate between different forms of hemoglobin, so if hemoglobin has picked up carbon dioxide, the oximeter will not recognize that.

TRAIN-OF-FOUR METHOD FOR NEUROMUSCULAR MONITORING OF A PATIENT AFTER GENERAL ANESTHESIA

The **train-of-four** (four sequential electrical impulses) is a peripheral nerve stimulator that is used to evaluate nerve function in patients who have received neuromuscular blocking agents (NMBAs). A baseline recording (usually of the ulnar or facial nerve) should be made prior to administration of the NMBA to determine the lowest level of electrical stimulation required to stimulate the nerves so that the nerve causes full twitching four out of four (4X4) times (TOF ratio of 1.0 or 100%). Train-of-four monitoring allows one to maintain the correct dosage of the NMBA in the patient's system if the patient is to be maintained on the drug, to assess the effectiveness of reversal agents, and to monitor recovery after the NMBA has been discontinued. Fade (decreasing stimulation) occurs with administration of the NMBA. The TOF ratio is determined by dividing the magnitude of the first of four stimulations by the fourth. Recovery is TOF ratio equal to or greater than 0.9.

Diagnostics

ABGs

Arterial blood gases (ABGs) are monitored to assess effectiveness of oxygenation, ventilation, and acid-base status, and to determine oxygen flow rates. Partial pressure of a gas is that exerted by each gas in a mixture of gases, proportional to its concentration, based on total atmospheric pressure of 760 mm Hg at sea level. Normal values include:

- **Acidity/alkalinity (pH):** 7.35–7.45. The critical value of serum pH is 7.20 or less, the point at which adverse effects occur. Patients who are heavily sedated and not compensating with respirations may develop decreased serum bicarbonate (HCO_3) and acidemic pH.
- Partial pressure of carbon dioxide ($PaCO_2$): 35–45 mm Hg.
- Partial pressure of oxygen (PaO_2): 80 mm Hg or more.
- HCO_3^- concentration: 22–26 mEq/L.
- Oxygen saturation: 95% or more.

The relationship between these elements, particularly the $PaCO_2$ and the PaO_2, indicates respiratory status. For example, a $PaCO_2$ over 55 mm Hg and a PaO_2 less than 60 mm Hg in a patient previously in good health indicates respiratory failure. There are many issues to consider. Ventilator management may require a higher $PaCO_2$ to prevent barotrauma and a lower PaO_2 to reduce oxygen toxicity.

Review Video: Blood Gases
Visit mometrix.com/academy and enter code: 611909

DRAWING AND HANDLING SAMPLES

An **arterial blood gas sample** should be drawn, using a heparinized and vented syringe. This allows for the sample to rise in the syringe by the arterial pressure. Heparin is critical to prevent coagulation of the sample both while in the syringe and while moving through the blood gas analyzer. Pressure must be applied to the artery for 5 minutes after drawing a sample. If a collected sample remains at room temperature for more than 15 minutes, changes will occur in the partial pressures of oxygen (PaO_2) and carbon dioxide ($PaCO_2$) and pH. These changes are from natural metabolism occurring within the blood. The best way to slow down the metabolism for delayed analysis is to decrease the temperature of a sample collected in a glass syringe by placing it in an ice bath. Blood gas samples obtained in plastic syringes should not be placed in ice baths because after 15 minutes the PaO_2 can rise as much as 20 mm Hg, and this artificial reading can affect treatment. Ice baths may alter electrolyte readings.

Assessing Acid–Base Balance

The following are the steps to assessing acid–base balance with ABGs:

1. Assess on which side of the normal range the pH falls and determine if it is acidemia, alkalemia, or normal.
2. Look at the partial pressure of carbon dioxide ($PaCO_2$) and determine if it is normal, high (acidemia), or low (alkalemia). The $PaCO_2$ indicates involvement of the respiratory system and can be altered by the respiratory rate of the patient.
3. Assess the metabolic component of the blood gas values by looking at the serum bicarbonate (HCO_3^-). If it is high, it is showing more base than if it is low and more acidic in nature.
4. Determine if either the $PaCO_2$ or the HCO_3^- can explain the pH. If the pH is normal when the other values are not, then the pH is being compensated.

Advantages of Point of Care Units to Analyze Samples

Point-of-care units used to analyze arterial blood gas (ABG) samples are small and portable, making them ideal for use at the patient bedside. ABG analysis can be taken out of the lab and placed directly into the field where the patient need is greatest. Some point of care units are attached to arterial lines, and lab results can be obtained in 60 seconds or less. Their use drastically shortens the time required for critical results to be delivered to the physician and eases demands on the laboratory. Since the units are compact, they use disposable electrode cassettes, which are tested before each use. Calibration and quality control are included in the electrode cassette. However, the equipment is expensive so it is most cost-effective when multiple readings are required.

Respiratory Acidosis

Respiratory acidosis is precipitated by inadequate ventilation of alveoli, interfering with gaseous exchange so that carbon dioxide increases and oxygen decreases, causing excess carbonic acid (H_2CO_3) levels. The body maintains a normal pH by balancing bicarbonate (HCO_3^-) [renal] with partial pressure of carbon dioxide ($PaCO_2$) [pulmonary] in a 20:1 ratio. If the pH alters, the system (renal or pulmonary) that is not causing the problem compensates. Respiratory acidosis after cardiac surgery is commonly related to central respiratory depression related to cardiac arrest, obesity, drugs (e.g., opiates, sedatives, anesthesia, neuromuscular blocking agents), pulmonary issues (e.g., pulmonary edema or embolism, acute respiratory distress syndrome, aspiration, airway obstruction, pneumothorax, atelectasis, restrictive lung disease, asthma, bronchospasm), increased production of carbon dioxide from shivering or sepsis, hypoventilation, inadequate mechanical ventilation, or ventilation/perfusion ratio.

- **Acute**: Increased $PaCO_2$ with decreased pH caused by sudden decrease in ventilation.
- **Chronic:** Increased $PaCO_2$ with normal pH and serum HCO_3^- over 30 mm Hg with renal compensation.

Arterial blood gas values in respiratory acidosis are as follows:

- pH less than 7.35; $PaCO_2$ more than 42 mm Hg; Increased H_2CO_3.

Symptoms and Treatment of Acute Respiratory Acidosis

Symptoms include the following:

- Acute respiratory acidosis:
- Increased heart rate
- Tachypnea
- Hypertension
- Confusion and pressure in head related to cerebrovascular vasodilation, especially if partial pressure of carbon dioxide (PaCO2 more than 60 mm Hg
- Increased intracranial pressure with papilledema
- Ventricular fibrillation
- Hyperkalemia

Treatment includes:

- Improving ventilation; careful use of mechanical ventilation
- Medications as indicated (depending on cause): bronchodilators, anticoagulation therapy, diuretics, and antibiotics
- Pulmonary hygiene

Symptoms and Treatment of Chronic Respiratory Acidosis

Symptoms:

- Chronic respiratory acidosis: Symptoms may be subtler with chronic respiratory acidosis because of the compensatory mechanisms. If the PaCO2 remains over 50 mm Hg for long periods, the respiratory center becomes increasingly insensitive to the carbon dioxide as a respiratory stimulus, replaced by hypoxemia, so supplemental oxygen administration should be monitored carefully to ensure that respirations are not depressed.

Treatment includes:

- Improving ventilation; careful use of mechanical ventilation
- Medications as indicated (depending on cause): bronchodilators, anticoagulation therapy, diuretics, and antibiotics
- Pulmonary hygiene

Respiratory Alkalosis

Respiratory alkalosis results from hyperventilation, during which extra carbon dioxide is excreted, causing a decrease in carbonic acid (H_2CO_3) concentration in the plasma. In the cardiac surgery patient, acute respiratory alkalosis may be triggered by hypoventilation related to anxiety or pain; increased demand for oxygen with fever, bacteremia (especially Gram-negative), and sepsis; pulmonary disorders, such as pneumonia, pulmonary edema or embolism; and ventilation/perfusion mismatch. Other causes include incorrect ventilator settings and respiratory stimulants. Chronic respiratory alkalosis may result from chronic hepatic insufficiency, cerebral tumors, and chronic hypocapnia.

Symptoms, Treatment, and Arterial Blood Gas Values

Characteristics	Decreased partial pressure of carbon dioxide ($PaCO_2$). Normal or decreased serum bicarbonate (HCO_3^-) as kidneys conserve hydrogen and excrete HCO_3^-. Increased pH.
Symptoms	Vasoconstriction with decreased cerebral blood flow, resulting in lightheadedness, alterations in mentation, and unconsciousness Numbness and tingling Tinnitus Tachycardia and dysrhythmias
Treatment	Identifying and treating underlying cause. If respiratory alkalosis is related to anxiety, breathing in a paper bag may increase carbon dioxide level. Some people may require sedation. Arterial blood gas values in respiratory alkalosis: pH over 7.45 $PaCO_2$ less than 38 mm Hg Decreased H_2CO_3

Metabolic Acidosis

Metabolic acidosis is a deficit in base bicarbonate (HCO_3^-) and occurs when an acid other than carbonic acid (e.g., ketoacid from diabetic ketoacidosis [DKA], lactic acid from shock) builds up in the body or with loss of HCO_3^- from body (diarrhea) fluids. The compensatory mechanism is increased carbon dioxide excretion through the lungs with Kussmaul respirations and increased renal excretion. Metabolic acidosis in cardiac surgery patients is associated with decreased cardiac output and cardiac function, inadequate systemic and peripheral perfusion, hypotension, hypovolemia, and vasoconstriction (related to hypothermia). Other causes include sepsis, renal failure, renal tubular acidosis, DKA, ischemia, and anaerobic metabolism. Symptoms include drowsiness, confusion, headache, coma, hypotension, arrhythmias (related to compensatory hyperkalemia), peripheral vasodilation, nausea, vomiting, diarrhea, and deep, rapid respirations. Arterial blood gas values are as follows:

- Increased anion gap (most common).
- Carbonic acid less than 22 mEq/L (decrease a cardinal sign).
- pH less than 7.35.
- Decreased partial pressure of carbon dioxide.

Treatment includes eliminating excess chloride, HCO_3^- if pH is less than 7.1, and serum HCO_3^- is less than 10 mEq/L. Serum potassium must be monitored during treatment as hypokalemia may occur.

Metabolic Alkalosis

Metabolic alkalosis occurs with either a loss of base acid (e.g., from vomiting or nasogastric [NG] tube) or a gain in bicarbonate (HCO_3^-). As a compensatory mechanism, the respiratory rate decreases to increase partial pressure of carbon dioxide ($PaCO_2$), and renal excretion of HCO_3^- increases. In cardiac surgery patients, hypokalemia, hypochloremia, excess diuretics (especially thiazides), adrenal disorders, NG suctioning, vomiting, and multiple transfusions of citrated blood products are seen. Hypokalemia and hypocalcemia are commonly found with metabolic alkalosis and must be treated. Symptoms predominately relate to hypocalcemia and can include tingling, hypertonic muscles, and dizziness. Other symptoms include depressed respirations, atrial tachycardia, and ventricular dysrhythmias. Skin turgor is often poor. Arterial blood gas values are as follows:

- pH over 7.45
- Carbonic acid more than 26 mEq/L
- Increased $PaCO_2$

Treatment includes restoring fluid balance and identifying and treating the underlying cause. Potassium chloride or sodium chloride is the primary treatment, depending on the potassium level. Proton pump inhibitors are given with NG suctioning, and doses of loop diuretics and thiazides are reduced. In patients with marked diuresis and loss of potassium, acetazolamide or hydrochloric acid may be administered.

Use of Atrial Electrograms Post-Operatively for the Diagnosis of Cardiac Dysrhythmias

Atrial electrograms are ECGs recorded from epicardial pacing wires that are attached to the atrial myocardium during cardiovascular surgery and connected to a monitoring lead in the event that postoperative pacing support is required. P-waves on the atrial electrogram are amplified over those of standard ECGs, so arrhythmias whose P-waves are difficult to visualize (VT and AV blocks) are more easily detectable. Atrial arteriograms also increase the ability to detect SV arrhythmias (AFib/AFl, AT, junctional arrhythmias). Generally, atrial leads exit at the upper chest or upper abdomen (right side for atrial and left for ventricular wires). The atrial electrogram can be recorded with a bedside monitor and should be recorded for any evidence of arrhythmia as a supplement to external ECG. Complications related to the wires include post-operative infection, perforation, cardiac tamponade, and ventricular arrhythmias. The epicardial leads are intended for use of 7 days or less and may be less reliable if used for extended periods. The wires are removed by applying gentle traction.

Chest X-Ray Interpretation

Chest x-rays are used to **confirm placement** of medical devices:

- **Central line**: Correct position of the tip of the central line is in the superior vena cava (SVC) or at the cavoatrial junction (where the right lateral border of the SVC meets the superior border of the RA).
- **Nasogastric tube**: Correct position of the tip is equal to or greater than 10 cm distal to the gastro-esophageal junction.
- **Intra-aortic balloon pump** (IABP): The location of the balloon should be in the proximal descending aorta below the where the left subclavian artery originates. The balloon should extend to just superior to the splanchnic vessels.
- **Endotracheal tube**: The position of the ETT varies according to neck position. If the neck is flexed, the tube tip should be at 3 cm (± 2) above the carina; if neutral 5 cm (± 2) above; and if extended 7 cm (± 2) above. The x-ray should include the mandible to help to ascertain neck position. If the carina is not visible on the film, then the tip should be positioned with the neck in neutral position at T2-T4.

The **chest x-ray** is an important tool in diagnosing pulmonary abnormalities:

- **Pneumothorax**: A white band of gas (visceral-pleural line) is seen between the parietal pleura, which lines the chest wall, and the visceral pleura, which covers the outside of the lungs. Air is seen without lung markings in the part of the chest that is least dependent. For example, if the film is taken with the patient upright, air collects at the apex. Pneumothorax is most difficult to diagnose with the patient in supine position.
- **Pulmonary edema**: Pulmonary vasculature may be redistributed with blurring of vasculature, interstitial markings may be increased at the lung base (horizontal Kerley B lines of <2 cm), and the heart may appear enlarged or within normal parameters, depending on whether the pulmonary edema is associated with heart failure. Perihilar shadowing (Butterfly/Batwing distribution of alveolar edema) may be evident.

RBC Tests to Evaluate Bleeding

Red Blood Cell (RBC) Tests are as follows:

- **Total RBCs:**
    - Males over 18 years: 4.5–5.5 million/mm3
    - Females over 18 years: 4.0–5.0 million/mm3
- **Hemoglobin**: Carries oxygen and is decreased in anemia and increased in polycythemia. Normal values:
    - Males over 18 years: 14.0–17.46 g/dL
    - Females over 18 years: 12.0–16.0 g/dL
- **Hematocrit**: Indicates the proportion of RBCs in a liter of blood (usually about three times the hemoglobin number). Normal values:
    - Males over 18 years: 45–52%.
    - Females over 18 years: 36–48%
- **Mean corpuscular volume (MCV)**: Indicates the size of RBCs and can differentiate types of anemia. For adults, a MCV of less than 80 μm3 is microcytic and over 100 μm3 is macrocytic. Normal values:
    - Males over 18 years: 84–96 μm3
    - Females over 18 years: 76–96 μm3
- **Mean corpuscular hemoglobin concentration (MCHC)**: Indicates the average concentration of hemoglobin in each cell (Hb/RBC = MCHC).
    - Normal values: Males and females over 18 years: 30–35 g/dL and 30–35%.
- **Reticulocyte count**: Measures marrow production and should rise with anemia.
    - Normal values: 0.5–1.5% of total RBCs

Coagulation Profile

The **coagulation profile** measures clotting mechanisms, identifies clotting disorders, screens preoperative patients, and diagnoses excessive bruising and bleeding. Values vary depending on the laboratory.

Prothrombin time (PT)	10–14 seconds	PT increases with anticoagulation therapy, vitamin K deficiency, decreased prothrombin, disseminated intravascular coagulation (DIC), liver disease, and malignant neoplasm. Some drugs many shorten time.
Partial thromboplastin time (PTT)	30–45 seconds	PTT increases with hemophilia A and B, von Willebrand's, vitamin deficiency, lupus, DIC, and liver disease.
Activated partial thromboplastin time (aPTT)	21–35 seconds	This is similar to PTT but decreases in extensive cancer, early DIC, and after acute hemorrhage; aPTT is used to monitor heparin dosage.
Thrombin clotting time (TCT) or thrombin time (TT)	7–12 seconds (< 21)	TT is used most often to determine the dosage of heparin; prolonged with multiple myeloma, abnormal fibrinogen, uremia, and liver disease.
Bleeding time	2–9.5 minutes	Using the Ivy method on the forearm, bleeding time increases with DIC, leukemia, renal failure, aplastic anemia, von Willebrand's, some drugs, and alcohol.
Platelet count	150–400,000/mm³	There will be increased bleeding with fewer than 50,000/mm³ platelets and increased clotting with more than 750,000/mm³.

Review Video: Coagulation Profile
Visit mometrix.com/academy and enter code: 423595

DIC Panel

Disseminated intravascular coagulation (DIC) panel includes a number of tests. Generally, test results that measure materials needed for clotting are decreased and those that measure clotting times are increased. Typical findings that indicate DIC include the following:

Activated partial thromboplastin time (aPTT)	Increased time
Prothrombin time	Findings vary, including increased time (in 75%), normal time (in 25%), or shortened time (in 25%)
Partial thromboplastin time	Increased time (in 50–60%)
Thrombin time	Increased
D-dimer	D-dimer, a specific polymer that results when fibrin breaks down, giving a marker to indicate the degree of fibrinolysis, increased (usually more reliable than FSP)
Fibrinogen	Decreased
Platelets	Less than 100,000/mm³

Fibrin split products (FSP)	Increased (in 75–100%). FSPs occur as more clots form and more breakdown of fibrinogen and fibrin occur, interfering with blood coagulation by coating platelets, disrupting thrombin, and attaching to fibrinogen so stable clots cannot form.
Clotting factor assays (V, VI, VII, X, XIII)	Decreased
Antithrombin III	Decreased (in 90%)

QT Interval Monitoring

Continuous QT interval monitoring measures from the QRS complex (depolarization) to the end of the T wave (repolarization). Indications (AHA recommendations) include patients:

- Newly diagnosed with bradyarrhythmia.
- Receiving anti-arrhythmic drugs or other drugs associated with torsade de pointes (a life-threatening dysrhythmia).
- Overdosing on agents or receiving antipsychotics or drugs that may cause arrhythmias.
- With electrolyte imbalances (hypokalemia, hypomagnesemia) that may cause arrhythmias.
- With acute neurological events, such as stroke.

The normal QT interval is greater than 460 ms in females and greater than 440 ms in male. QT interval value greater than 500 ms increases risk of torsades de pointes. If the QT interval extends greater than half the RR, it is prolonged. Long QT syndrome occurs when depolarization and repolarization is prolonged between beats and can result in torsades de points or VT. Long QT syndrome may be a genetic condition or may be acquired and associated with electrolyte imbalances, some medications (antidepressants, diuretics, antibiotics), and some conditions (anorexia nervosa).

ST Segment Monitoring

Continuous ST segment monitoring is indicated to assess transient myocardial ischemia for patients with:

- Acute coronary syndrome.
- Unstable angina.
- Myocardial infarction.

ST segment elevation is found when ischemia is transmural, often indicating a myocardial infarction. ST elevation generally indicates the need for immediate intervention to improve blood flow to the heart. ST depression, on the other hand, is found with myocardial ischemia that is subendocardial and usually associated with coronary artery insufficiency. With ST depression, the oxygen supply to the heart is inadequate for needs, such as may occur when patients exercise or experience tachycardia. If the ST change is ≥2mm for 15 minutes, a 12-lead ECG should be taken to confirm elevation or depression. If ST segment changes are noted, the nurse should make sure that the patient is correctly positioned (supine, <45° head elevation) and that leads are in intact and positioned correctly to ensure that readings are accurate. In addition to ischemia, ST changes may be caused by intermittent RBBB, LBBB, dysrhythmias, pericarditis, digoxin (depression) myocardial contusion, and ventricular paced rhythms.

Serum Lactate Monitoring in Post-Operative Cardiac Patient

Lactic acid is a product of anaerobic metabolism, which occurs when oxygen supply to the tissues in inadequate. Therefore, serum lactate may be monitored to assess hypoxia, which is indicated by levels >2 mmol/L. Levels >4 mmol/L often indicate organ failure and if levels >2 mmol/L persist for 4 hours, the patient is at increased risk of death, Lactate acid is cleared by the liver, so lactate tends to accumulate faster in the presence of liver impairment. With a normally functioning liver, hypoxia may be present even if serum lactate stays within normal limits. Additionally, localized hypoperfusion may not raise serum lactate levels, so serum lactate is often a late sign of hypoperfusion. Another factor is that with septic shock, lactate levels may increase even with adequate perfusion. When used to monitor treatment, a decrease of 5% to 10% per hour indicates an adequate response, but if the level remains unchanged or increases, the patient is at risk of hypoxia.

ECG

The **electrocardiogram (ECG)** records and shows a graphic display of the electrical activity of the heart through a number of different waveforms, complexes, and intervals:

- **P wave.** The P wave is the start of an electrical impulse in the sinus node that spreads through the atria, initiating muscle depolarization.
- **QRS complex.** The QRS complex represents ventricular muscle depolarization and atrial repolarization.
- **T wave.** The T wave represents ventricular muscle repolarization (resting state) as cells regain negative charge.
- **U wave.** The U wave represents repolarization of the Purkinje fibers.

A modified 2-lead ECG is often used to monitor basic heart rhythms and dysrhythmias.

Typical placement of leads for a 2-lead ECG is 3–5 centimeters inferior to the right clavicle and left lower ribcage. Typical placement for a 3-lead ECG is the right arm near the shoulder, the V_5 position over fifth intercostal space, and the left upper leg near the groin.

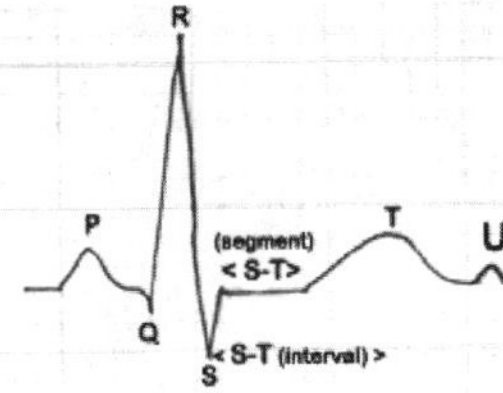

ADMINISTRATION OF 12-LEAD ECG

The **12-lead electrocardiogram** provides a graphic representation of the electrical activity of the heart. It is indicated for chest pain, dyspnea, syncope, acute coronary syndrome, pulmonary embolism, and possible myocardial infarction. It gives a picture of electrical activity from twelve perspectives through the placement of ten body leads:

Four limb leads are placed distally on the wrists and ankles (but may be placed more proximally if necessary).

Precordial leads:

- V_1: right sternal border at fourth intercostal space
- V_2: left sternal border at fourth intercostal space
- V_3: midway between V_2 and V_4
- V_4: left midclavicular line at fifth intercostal space

- V_5: horizontal to V_4 at left anterior axillary line
- V_6: horizontal to V_5 at left midaxillary line

Right-sided leads, which are not always needed, are placed on the right in a mirror image of the left leads, usually to diagnose right ventricular infarction through ST elevation.

TEE

Transesophageal echocardiography (TEE) is commonly used for monitoring during cardiac surgery, providing information about cardiac function and anatomy. TEE uses ultrasound waves from a piezoelectric crystal. These waves penetrate tissue and bounce back, creating a display. Multiple views can be obtained from different areas of the esophagus. M-mode gives a one-dimensional view and is useful for velocity. B-mode is two-dimensional and provides a cross section that shows cardiac performance. Live three-dimensional echocardiography displays images in vector format and allows better visualization and assessment. Pulsed-wave Doppler and continuous-wave Doppler measure velocity. TEE is used most commonly to assess ventricular function, myocardial ischemia, stroke volume (ejection fraction), function of valves (aortic and mitral), residual intracardiac air, fluid volume, cardiac structures, and abnormalities (tamponade and pericarditis). TEE helps to monitor the effects of anesthesia on cardiac function and may be used postoperatively to evaluate potential problems, such as low cardiac output, marked hypotension, or cardiac tamponade.

CSC Practice Test

Want to take this practice test in an online interactive format?
Check out the bonus page, which includes interactive practice questions and much more: **mometrix.com/bonus948/csc**

1. A patient with a history of congestive heart failure and hypertension has been admitted to the ICU following a CABG procedure. The patient remains intubated. Physical exam and assessment finding data are as follows:

BP: 85/44 mmHg
HR: 111 bpm; pulses are weak and thready
RR: 32 breaths/min
CI: 1.5 L/min/m^2
Oxygen saturation: 95% on 50% FiO_2
Urine output: 35 mL since arrival to the unit 3 hr ago
Chest tube drainage: 90 mL since arrival to the unit 3 hr ago
Surgical dressing: clean, dry, and intact
Hgb: 14.7 g/dL

The nurse recognizes that which one of the following is the most likely cause?

a. Retroperitoneal bleeding
b. Fat embolism
c. Compartment syndrome
d. Cardiogenic shock

2. A patient is in the CVICU in the immediate postoperative period following a CABG for triple vessel coronary artery disease. The patient is intubated and sedated on a propofol infusion. The patient is shivering with a temperature of 35.2 °C. The patient's blood pressure is 145/85 mmHg, and the heart rate is 101 bpm. The nurse applies warm blankets. What additional order would the nurse anticipate?

a. Administer labetalol IV push.
b. Administer vecuronium IV push.
c. Administer flumazenil IV push.
d. Administer acetaminophen IV.

3. A patient is admitted to the ICU after sustaining a stab wound to the chest. The patient's chest x-ray from the emergency room showed that the patient had a mild pericardial effusion. The patient begins to complain of worsening chest pain, dyspnea, restlessness, and dizziness. Which of the following is the most likely cause of the patient's symptoms?

a. Cardiac tamponade
b. Endocarditis
c. Pulmonary hypertension
d. Pulmonary embolism

4. A patient is in the ICU post transthoracic valve replacement. The patient begins to experience chest pain, nausea, and diaphoresis. The 12-lead electrocardiogram (ECG) shows ST elevation in leads V_3 and V_4. The nurse recognizes that the patient may be having an ST elevation MI affecting which one of the following aspects of the heart?

a. Low lateral wall
b. Inferior wall
c. Septum
d. Anterior wall

5. A patient in the ICU is day 2 post transthoracic aortic repair. The patient has a history of pulmonary hypertension and begins to complain of shortness of breath. The nurse recognizes that all of the following are signs or symptoms of pulmonary hypertension except:

a. A loud P2 heart sound
b. Ascites
c. A loud S1 heart sound
d. Left-sided pansystolic murmur

6. A patient has been admitted to the CVICU post CABG procedure. The patient is hypotensive with the following assessment findings:

BP: 90/42 mmHg
HR: 105 bpm
CI: 2.6 L/min/m^2
SVR: 890 dyne/s/cm^{-5}
CVP: 14 mmHg
SvO_2: 73%
Urine output: 65–100 mL/hr, clear yellow
Lactate: 2.1 mmol/L

The nurse would anticipate which one of the following orders?

a. Initiate a dobutamine infusion.
b. Initiate a norepinephrine infusion.
c. Initiate a dopamine infusion.
d. Initiate a nitroglycerine infusion.

7. A nursing preceptor in the ICU is training a nurse new to the unit on continuous renal replacement therapy (CRRT). The preceptor should intervene when the trainee makes which statement?

a. "Calcium levels should be monitored closely when using heparin as an anticoagulant."
b. "Right internal jugular access placement is preferred over left internal jugular access placement."
c. "Citrate anticoagulation can contribute to electrolyte imbalances."
d. "CRRT can remove fluid and clear solutes from the body."

8. The nurse is caring for a patient in the ICU 1 hour status post carotid endarterectomy. Which one of the following findings should be the most concerning to the nurse?

a. High-pitched, musical sound when breathing
b. Numbness in the neck and shoulder after intraoperative nerve block
c. Systolic blood pressure of 155 mmHg
d. Headache pain rated at 5/10

9. A patient in the CVICU is scheduled for a CT angiogram of the heart in order to evaluate the patient's valvular heart disease. What information should the nurse include when educating the patient on the procedure?

a. A beta-blocker may be given before the procedure.
b. The CT cannot be done on patients with permanent pacemakers.
c. A cold flush may be felt when the contrast is injected.
d. The procedure cannot be done on patients with reduced kidney function.

10. A patient in the ICU is day 1 postsurgical valve replacement. The patient has a 15-year history of heroin use and begins to experience symptoms of opioid withdrawal. The nurse is most concerned about which one of the following findings?

a. Restlessness
b. Diarrhea
c. Insomnia
d. Muscle spasms

11. A patient is in the ICU after a surgical tricuspid valve repair. The patient has an order for ketorolac 30 mg IVP q6 hr prn for pain. Which one of the following lab results is most important to monitor?

a. Blood urea nitrogen (BUN)
b. PT/PTT
c. Hemoglobin
d. Alanine transaminase

12. A patient in the ICU is awaiting surgery for a dissecting aortic aneurysm. The patient is complaining of back pain 8/10, has a blood pressure of 170/95 mmHg, heart rate of 115 bpm, temperature of 38.4 °C, and oxygen saturation of 92% on 2 L of oxygen by nasal cannula. Which one of the following orders should the nurse prioritize?

a. Labetalol 10 mg IVP q30 min prn SBP >140 mmHg
b. Acetaminophen 650 mg suppository now
c. Oxygen titration prn to maintain the oxygen saturation at >94%
d. Hydromorphone 0.5 mg IVP q2 hr prn for pain levels of 6–10

13. Sustained hypertension after a CABG procedure is associated with all of the following EXCEPT:

a. Reduced afterload
b. Increased SVR
c. Reduced cardiac output
d. Increased afterload

14. The nurse is caring for a patient admitted to the ICU 1 hour following an on-pump CABG procedure. The nurse is most concerned about which one of the following findings?

a. Blood pressure (BP): 170/101 mmHg
b. Capillary blood glucose: 385 mg/dL
c. Patient can be aroused only with repeated tactile stimulation
d. Central venous pressure (CVP): 10 mmHg

15. A patient is in the ICU waiting to go to surgery for a valve replacement. The nurse finds the patient to be anxious. The patient tells the nurse, "I am so scared, and I don't think I want to go through with this surgery." The most appropriate response from the nurse is:

a. "Can you tell me what it is about the surgery that makes you afraid?"
b. "This surgery is very important and necessary for you to live."
c. "I will ask the surgeon to come and talk to you."
d. "Would you like me to give you something to help you calm down?"

16. A patient arrives in the CVICU post transcatheter valve replacement. The patient has a right brachial arterial line, a right subclavian triple lumen catheter, and a right groin incision. The patient is drowsy but is oriented to person, place, and time. The nurse assesses the patient and finds the patient complaining of pain and numbness to the right arm. The patient's arm is pale and cold. What is the most likely cause of the patient's assessment findings?

a. Arterial thrombosis
b. Retroperitoneal bleeding
c. Arterial air embolus
d. Compartment syndrome

17. A patient is in the CVICU post CABG procedure. The nurse is concerned because the patient remains hypotensive and slightly tachycardic. Assessment findings are as follows:

BP: 91/46 mmHg
HR: 105 bpm
CVP: 2 mmHg
CI: 2.4 L/min
Intake and output balance: +2.5 L
Hgb: 12.1 g/dL

Which order is most appropriate?

a. Infuse one unit of packed red blood cells.
b. Initiate a dobutamine infusion.
c. Initiate a nitroprusside infusion.
d. Infuse Hespan 500 mL IV.

18. The nurse is caring for a patient in the ICU with a diagnosis of dilated cardiomyopathy. The patient's ejection fraction is 10% based on the results of the transthoracic echocardiogram, and the central venous pressure (CVP) reading is 24 with jugular venous distension present upon assessment. The patient is in atrial fibrillation with a heart rate of 80–110 bpm. Which one of the following orders should the nurse question?

a. Furosemide 40 mg IVP two times a day
b. Amiodarone 400 mg PO two times a day
c. Warfarin 5 mg PO daily
d. Verapamil 80 mg PO three times a day

19. A patient in the CVICU has been admitted following a CABG procedure. The patient has a history of pulmonary hypertension, has a PaO_2 of 55, and remains intubated. The physician has ordered epoprostenol sodium (Flolan). The nurse recognizes that which one of the following is correct regarding the administration of this medication for pulmonary hypertension?

a. The medication must be administered via inhalation therapy.
b. The medication should be titrated down in increments of 20 ng/kg/min every 5 minutes as the PaO_2 level improves.
c. The nurse should monitor the patient for hypertension during medication administration.
d. The medication increases the risk for bleeding.

20. A patient in the CVICU day 3 post Cox maze procedure is requiring high-flow nasal cannula therapy. The nurse understands that which one of the following is correct regarding this device?

a. The high-flow nasal cannula reduces the positive end expiratory pressure effect.
b. The high-flow nasal cannula accelerates the removal of respiratory secretions.
c. The FiO_2 should be titrated up before the flow rate in the event of oxygen desaturation.
d. The high-flow nasal cannula reduces the risk of viral transmission.

21. A patient is admitted to the CVICU post thoracoabdominal aneurysm repair with a lumbar drain. The nurse understands that which one of the following is the purpose of the drain during and after cardiac surgery?

a. The lumbar drain prevents damage to the phrenic nerve.
b. The lumbar drain increases spinal cord perfusion.
c. The lumbar drain prevents postoperative bleeding.
d. The lumbar drain prevents thrombolytic stroke.

22. The nurse is caring for a patient in the CVICU day 3 post CABG. The patient has a surgical sternal incision and surgical incision to the right lower extremity. The patient is on 4 L of oxygen by nasal cannula and is hemodynamically stable. Which intervention should the nurse include in the plan of care?

a. Maintain bed rest.
b. Apply sequential compression devices to the bilateral lower extremities.
c. Apply anti-itch ointment for wound itching.
d. Teach the patient to clean the incision sites with mild, fragrance-free soap and water.

23. A patient has been admitted to the CVICU post transcatheter valve replacement surgery. The nurse was told in report that the patient has a history of congestive heart failure and was in rate-controlled atrial fibrillation before the procedure. The patient is now in atrial fibrillation with a rapid ventricular response. The patient's heart rate ranges from 130 to 170 bpm, the blood pressure is 90/55 mmHg, and the patient is complaining of dizziness. The nurse would anticipate which one of the following?

a. Bedside cardioversion
b. Amiodarone by mouth
c. An 0.9% sodium chloride bolus of 1,000 mL
d. Administer digoxin IVP

24. A patient has been admitted to the ICU after being found unresponsive at home. Upon arrival at the ICU, the patient again becomes unresponsive and goes into ventricular fibrillation. Cardiopulmonary resuscitation is initiated, and a return of spontaneous circulation is obtained. The team inserts a Swan-Ganz catheter and an arterial line. The initial findings are as follows:

BP: 88/44 mmHg
MAP: 58
CVP: 22 mmHg
CI: 1.8 L/min
CO: 2.5 L/min
PAWP: 52

Which one of the following orders should the nurse question?

a. Dobutamine infusion at 2 mcg/kg/min
b. A 0.9% sodium chloride 1 L bolus
c. Norepinephrine infusion to maintain the MAP at >65
d. Furosemide 40 mg intravenous push (IVP) stat

25. The nurse is educating the patient and family in the CVICU about the ordered cryoprecipitate infusion. What information would the nurse include in the teaching?

a. The blood product does not require Rh or blood typing compatibility.
b. Cryoprecipitate is used to increase platelets.
c. Cryoprecipitate is always from a single donor.
d. The bag of cryoprecipitate will take 6 hours to infuse.

26. A patient is in the ICU in the immediate postoperative period following CABG for an MI. The patient experienced bleeding perioperatively, and the hemoglobin decreased to 7.1 g/dL from 11.9 g/dL preoperatively. The physician has ordered two units of packed red blood cells. Which intervention is most appropriate to prevent transfusion-associated circulatory overload (TACO)?

a. Monitor the CVP.
b. Titrate fluids to keep intake and output net zero.
c. Transfuse each unit of blood over the course of 3–4 hr.
d. Transfuse only leukoreduced blood.

27. A patient has been extubated 6 hours after CABG. The patient has since become progressively more confused and tachycardic. The doctor orders a stat arterial blood gas. The results are as follows:

pH: 7.25
$PaCO_2$: 36
HCO_3: 15
PaO_2: 70

The nurse would expect what other finding?

a. Cheyne-Stokes respirations
b. Kussmaul's respirations
c. Pulsus paradoxus
d. Wheezing

28. All of the following are correct regarding transcatheter aortic valve replacement (TAVR) procedures EXCEPT:

a. TAVRs are indicated for patients with aortic stenosis at high risk for surgical complications.
b. A computed tomography (CT) angiogram of the chest, abdomen, and pelvis is performed to determine the correct valve size.
c. General anesthesia is the required method of sedation during TAVR procedures.
d. Rapid ventricular pacing is done during TAVR procedures to aid in appropriate valve placement.

29. The nurse is caring for a patient 12 hours after a Cox maze III procedure. The patient is experiencing muscle rigidity and has a temperature spike to 40.3 °C. The nurse suspects malignant hyperthermia. The nurse understands that which one of the following agents, if used during anesthesia, places the patient at risk for malignant hyperthermia?

a. Propofol
b. Nitrous oxide
c. Succinylcholine
d. Etomidate

30. A patient is in the ICU after having an ischemic stroke on day 4 post CABG. The patient was agitated and combative after the stroke, causing increased intracranial pressure. The patient is intubated and sedated on propofol 10 mcg/kg/min and fentanyl 50 mcg/hr to reduce agitation. The patient is restless but falls asleep when unstimulated. The nurse's assessment reveals a bispectral index score of 90. Which action should the nurse take?

a. Decrease the fentanyl dose.
b. Contact the doctor for an order to obtain a stat CT of the head for the patient.
c. Increase the propofol dose.
d. Complete a neurological assessment.

31. A patient has been in the ICU for 5 days after an open aortic dissection repair. The patient's recovery has been complicated by the development of acute renal failure requiring continuous renal replacement therapy (CRRT), pulmonary edema, and prolonged ventilation. The team implements the ABCDEF bundle to prevent delirium and optimize the patient's outcomes. The nurse understands that all of the following are components of the ABCDEF bundle EXCEPT:

a. Early mobilization
b. Spontaneous awakening trials
c. Fluid administration
d. Pain management

32. A patient in the CVICU post Cox maze IV procedure has reverted back to atrial fibrillation with rapid ventricular response, and the team has ordered bedside electrical cardioversion. The nurse recognizes that all of the following are correct regarding cardioversion EXCEPT:

a. Sync will need to be selected on the monitor for the procedure.
b. The patient should be given analgesics for pain.
c. The electrical charge will be synchronized with the T wave.
d. The patient will be shocked initially at 100 joules.

33. The nurse is caring for a patient in the rewarming phase of targeted temperature management post cardiac arrest. Which one of the following nursing actions is appropriate during the rewarming phase?

a. Rewarm the patient to 38 °C.
b. Check the patient's blood sugar q6 hr.
c. Discontinue IV fluids containing potassium.
d. Anticipate and prepare for hypertension.

34. A senior nurse is orienting a novice nurse on cardiac advanced life support (CALS). The nurse would teach that all of the following are components of CALS EXCEPT:

a. Epinephrine should be administered first.
b. If a defibrillator is available, defibrillation is first for the patient in ventricular fibrillation.
c. Attempt to pace the patient in asystole.
d. Turn off the pacer in pulseless electrical activity to determine if ventricular fibrillation is the underlying rhythm.

35. The nurse received a report on a patient arriving to the CVICU post Cox maze procedure. The nurse has been told in report that the patient received a dose of desmopressin to prevent postoperative bleeding. The nurse should monitor the patient for which one of the following?

a. Hyponatremia
b. Hypernatremia
c. Hyperglycemia
d. Weight loss

36. The nurse is caring for a patient day 1 post CABG that has been extubated at the start of the shift. What intervention should be included in the plan of care to prevent a pulmonary embolism?

a. Incentive spirometry 10 times q1 hr while awake.
b. Bilateral sequential compression devices.
c. Continuous capnography.
d. Continuous positive airway pressure at night.

37. A patient is in the CVICU after experiencing a hemorrhagic stroke following treatment for atrial fibrillation. The physician orders cerebral oximetry monitoring. The nurse understands that which one of the following is the indication for cerebral oximetry monitoring?

a. Assess for cerebral vasospasms.
b. Monitor continuous intracranial pressure.
c. Identify cerebral ischemia early.
d. Record seizure activity.

38. A patient is experiencing bleeding and cardiac tamponade post CABG procedure. The patient remains intubated and sedated with 10 mL of serous drainage from the mediastinal drain since arriving at the CVICU 90 minutes prior. Assessment data are as follows:

BP: 90/57 mmHg
CO: 2.5 L/min
HR: 135 bpm
Hgb: 5.9 g/dL
INR: 1.3

The nurse would anticipate which one of the following interventions?

a. Vitamin K 10 mg PO stat
b. Lopressor 5 mg IVP stat
c. Stat echocardiogram
d. Emergent resternotomy

39. A patient is in the CVICU day 1 post CABG. The nurse will administer hydromorphone to prevent which complication?

a. Hypertension
b. Atelectasis
c. Pneumomediastinum
d. Dysrhythmias

40. The nurse is discharging a patient from the CVICU following a CABG procedure. The nurse has educated the patient on the newly prescribed medication, atorvastatin. What statement, if made by the patient, indicates the need for additional teaching?

a. "I should not take this medication with grapefruit juice."
b. "My medication works better when I take it at night."
c. "I will need to have blood testing periodically to monitor my liver function."
d. "A yellowish discoloring of my skin is normal when taking this medicine."

41. The nurse is caring for a venovenous ECMO patient who is sedated on ketamine and paralyzed with cisatracurium. The order received is to titrate the infusions to a train of four of two out of four twitches. The nurse receives report that the patient has been sedated with two out of four twitches over the past 4 hours, but the patient now has four out of four twitches and is breathing over the ventilator. Which action is most appropriate for the nurse to take next?

a. Reduce the patient's ketamine.
b. Increase the patient's ketamine.
c. Increase the patient's cisatracurium.
d. Decrease the amplitude on the device, and recheck the train of four.

42. A patient in the ICU is day 1 status post open aortic aneurysm dissection repair. The 1-hour postoperative findings are as follows:

Urine output: 75–100 mL/hr
Lactate: 9 mmol/L
Creatinine: 1.5 mg/dL
Hemoglobin: 8.1 g/dL

The nurse would be concerned about which one of the following findings 1 day postoperatively?

a. Urine output of 35–45 mL/hr
b. Lactate of 5 mmol/L
c. Creatinine of 2.3 mg/dL
d. Hemoglobin of 8 g/dL

43. The nurse is caring for a patient in the ICU with a diagnosis of severe mitral valve disease. The patient is scheduled for an open heart surgical valve replacement using a biological valve the next day. What information should the nurse include when providing preoperative education to the patient and family?

a. The patient will require lifelong anticoagulation.
b. The patient will need to lie flat for 6 hours after the surgery.
c. The patient may hear a clicking sound when the valve closes.
d. The biological valve may need to be replaced due to degradation.

44. The nurse is caring for a patient in the CVICU day 5 post CABG who has developed severe left ventricular heart failure. The patient has an ejection fraction of 15%, and the patient's mean arterial pressure (MAP) has been between 50 and 55 mmHg. The patient is on a dobutamine infusion. The patient is in remission after treatment for breast cancer in situ 5 years ago. She was diagnosed with hepatitis C 13 years ago and is currently homeless. The patient is being evaluated for left ventricular assist device (LVAD) placement. Which one of the following is likely to rule the patient out for LVAD placement?

a. History of breast cancer
b. Homelessness
c. MAP <60
d. Diagnosis of hepatitis C

45. A patient in the ICU is 3 hours post open mitral valve replacement with a biological valve. The patient experienced bleeding intraoperatively and required four units of packed red blood cells for stabilization. The patient remains intubated and develops hypotension and hypoxia with a PaO_2 reading of 65 per the arterial blood gas results. The patient has copious pink frothy secretions and auscultated bilateral crackles. Cardiac pressures are as follows:

CI: 3 L/min/m^2
CO: 4.9 L/min
Right atrial pressure (RAP): 8 mmHg
Pulmonary artery systolic (PAS) pressure: 22 mmHg
Pulmonary artery diastolic (PAD) pressure: 10 mmHg
PCWP: 12 mmHg
SV: 70 mL

Based on these findings, what is the most likely cause of the patient's condition?

a. Transfusion-related acute lung injury
b. Pulmonary hypertension
c. Endocarditis
d. Pneumothorax

46. A patient is in the ICU following a CABG procedure with the following assessment findings:

BP: 115/75 mmHg
HR: 108 bpm
CVP: 10 mmHg
CI: 2.1 L/min
CO: 3.8 L/min
PCWP: 24 mmHg
SVR: 965 dynes/sec/cm^{-5}

The nurse would anticipate orders to administer which one of the following treatments?

a. Dobutamine
b. 0.9% sodium chloride
c. Nitroprusside
d. Norepinephrine

47. The nurse is monitoring a patient in the ICU when the patient's pulse oximetry begins to alarm with a reading of 80%. The patient is alert and awake on 4 L of oxygen via nasal cannula. Which action should the nurse take next?

a. Verify accuracy by correlating the heart rate on the pulse oximeter with the ECG rate.
b. Contact the physician for a stat arterial blood gas order.
c. Place the patient on a 100% nonrebreather mask.
d. Ask the patient if they are experiencing shortness of breath.

48. The nurse is performing a preoperative assessment on a patient in preparation for a CABG procedure following an MI. The nurse hears a pericardial friction rub at the left sternal border during auscultation. What is the most likely cause of the assessment findings?

a. Cardiac tamponade
b. Pleural effusion
c. Pericarditis
d. Pulmonary hypertension

49. A patient has been admitted to the ICU after sustaining a gunshot wound to the left upper chest. The patient's assessment data reveal the following:

BP: 85/49 mmHg
HR: 130 bpm
RR: 30 breaths/min
Temperature: 99.8 °F
Oxygen saturation: 93% on 50% FiO_2 via Venturi mask
Breath sounds: Bilateral rales
Heart sounds: Muffled
Mental status: Alert and oriented ×4 and restless
Other: Jugular venous distension present

The nurse should anticipate which one of the following procedures?

a. Pericardial window
b. Resuscitative thoracotomy
c. Emergent intubation and mechanical ventilation
d. Arterial blood gas

50. An ICU patient is on day 3 post open valve repair. The physician is preparing to remove the epicardial pacing wires. The nurse should anticipate an order for which one of the following?

a. Perform a 12-lead ECG stat after removal.
b. Initiate continuous heparin infusion before removal.
c. Obtain INR with results before removal.
d. Hold any aspirin.

51. The nurse is caring for a patient in the 12 hours after a thoracic endovascular aortic repair. The patient has developed back pain and weakness of the lower extremities. The surgeon has diagnosed the patient with spinal cord ischemia. What intervention would be most effective for preventing additional spinal complications?

a. Check bladder pressure q4 hr.
b. Perform neurological checks q1 hr.
c. Induce mild hyperthermia to maintain a body temperature of 37.2–37.8 °C.
d. Maintain MAP >80.

52. A patient is in the immediate postoperative period following a CABG procedure and begins to experience hemodynamic deterioration. The patient is hypotensive, has muffled heart sounds, and is experiencing pulsus paradoxus. The patient has <10 mL output in the chest tube. What is the most likely cause of the patient's deterioration?

a. Pneumomediastinum
b. Protamine reaction
c. Cardiac tamponade
d. Retroperitoneal bleeding

53. A patient admitted to the ICU following a transcatheter aortic valve replacement has a hematoma to the incision site that has increased in size since admission. The patient rates sudden back pain at 8 out of 10, and the patient's blood pressure is 85/42 mmHg. Which one of the following orders should the nurse implement first?

a. Administer a 1 L bolus of 0.9% sodium chloride.
b. Start a norepinephrine infusion to maintain a MAP goal of >65.
c. Collect a stat complete blood count.
d. Administer hydromorphone 0.5 mg IV push (IVP) stat.

54. A patient is in the ICU post surgical repair of an aortic aneurysm dissection. The patient is experiencing heart failure with a cardiac index of 2 L/min. Another clinical finding of decreased cardiac output includes which one of the following?

a. Creatinine of 1 mg/dL
b. Lactate of 12 mmol/L
c. SvO_2 of 80%
d. Wide pulse pressure

55. The nurse who is caring for patients in the ICU understands that all of the following are interventions for the prevention of postoperative sternal infections in CABG patients EXCEPT:

a. Postoperative antibiotics
b. Mediastinal chest tubes
c. Continuous insulin infusion
d. Chest stabilization vest

56. Reversible impaired contractility after the reperfusion of viable cardiac tissue with CABG is known as:

a. Cardiogenic shock
b. Myocardial stunning
c. Right-sided heart failure
d. Myocardial hibernation

57. The nurse is caring for a patient in the CVICU post CABG procedure who is intubated and sedated on dexmedetomidine (Precedex). The patient is receiving 0.9% sodium chloride at 75 mL/hr with urine output of 45–55 mL/hr. The patient's vital signs are as follows:

HR: 59 bpm
CVP: 12 mmHg
BP: 155/89 mmHg
Respirations: 14 per min
Oxygen saturation: 95% on 50% FiO_2
Temperature: 37.7 °C

The nurse would anticipate which one of the following orders?

a. Increase the 0.9% sodium chloride rate.
b. Stop the Precedex infusion.
c. Administer acetaminophen.
d. Administer atropine.

58. Heparin is used during CABG procedures to prevent which complication?

a. Dysrhythmias
b. Stroke
c. Bleeding
d. Hypotension

59. The nurse is caring for a patient in the ICU with a left pleural chest tube in place. The patient has had a mental status change, and an order for a stat CT scan of the head has been placed. During the transfer to the CT table, the drainage system broke and became disconnected from the chest tube. Which action should the nurse take next?

a. Clamp the chest tube until arrival back at the ICU.
b. Place the end opening of the chest tube in a container of sterile water.
c. Notify the physician.
d. Place Vaseline gauze over the end of the chest tube.

60. A patient is admitted to the ICU following a CABG procedure. The patient is connected to the monitor, and the below rhythm is displayed. The nurse recognizes the rhythm as which one of the following?

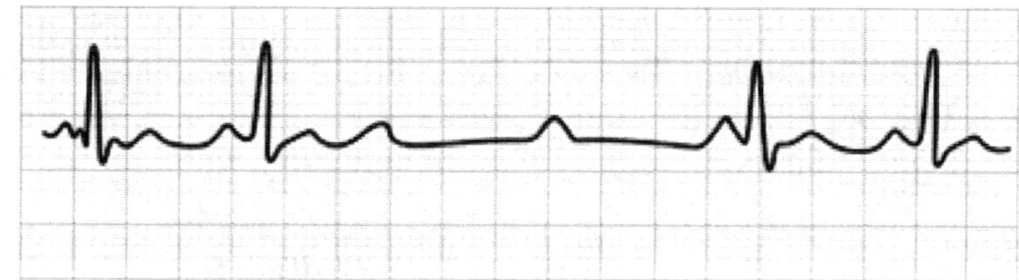

a. Idioventricular rhythm
b. Third-degree heart block
c. Normal sinus rhythm with couplets
d. Second-degree heart block Mobitz type 2

61. A patient in the ICU develops sudden-onset abdominal pain, vomiting, and diarrhea 12 hours post on-pump CABG. An epigastric bruit is auscultated during the physical assessment, and mesenteric ischemia is suspected. Which one of the following would provide the most definitive diagnosis of mesenteric ischemia?

a. CT angiography of the abdomen
b. Lactate levels
c. Abdominal x-ray
d. Exploratory laparotomy

62. A patient has been admitted to the CVICU on venoarterial (VA) extracorporeal membrane oxygenation (ECMO) therapy. The patient had a CABG procedure but was unable to be weaned from the cardiopulmonary bypass machine. The nurse understands that which one of the following is correct regarding VA ECMO?

a. Chattering of the ECMO circuit occurs when retrograde flow causes deoxygenated blood to circulate.
b. North-south syndrome occurs when the venous cannula is occluded.
c. The sweep gas setting determines the CO_2 levels.
d. A decrease in afterload will inhibit flow.

63. A patient is in the ICU day 1 status post open repair of a dissected abdominal aortic aneurysm. The patient has a wound vacuum-assisted closure machine attached to the abdominal surgical site and is intubated and sedated on propofol. The nurse would be most concerned about which one of the following findings?

a. Bladder pressure of 10 mmHg
b. Change in pupillary response to unequal, 5, and fixed in the right eye
c. Serosanguinous drainage of 200 mL to wound vacuum-assisted closure machine over the past 4 hr
d. Temperature of 100.2 °F

64. A senior nurse is precepting a novice nurse in the ICU. When educating the novice nurse about capnography, what information should the nurse include?

a. The end-tidal CO_2 should be the same as the $PaCO_2$.
b. Reduced end-tidal CO_2 is a characteristic of increased pulmonary blood flow.
c. Mainstream capnography measures the CO_2 via a sensor in the ventilator.
d. Sidestream capnography can only be used in intubated patients.

65. A patient arrived at the ICU with an open chest from the operating room following a CABG procedure. The patient is in cardiac arrest, and the physician states he will internally defibrillate the patient. The nurse understands that all of the following are correct regarding internal defibrillation EXCEPT:

a. The sync must be turned off on the monitor.
b. The patient should be shocked using 200 joules.
c. The paddles should be placed over the right and left ventricles.
d. Internal cardiac massage can be done immediately following defibrillation.

66. The nurse is educating a patient in the ICU about his upcoming Cox maze procedure. The nurse tells the patient that the left atrial appendage will be closed in an effort to:

a. Prevent postoperative bleeding
b. Prevent stroke
c. Prevent heart failure
d. Prevent valve disease

67. The nurse is orienting a novice nurse in the ICU that is caring for a patient status post off-bypass CABG procedure. The nurse should provide additional education when the novice nurse makes which one of the following statements?

a. "Heparin is not used during off-pump CABG procedures."
b. "Off-pump CABG procedures are done on a beating heart."
c. "Off-pump CABG procedures are associated with a lower risk of kidney injury versus on-pump CABG procedures."
d. "Off-pump CABG procedures are associated with a higher risk of reocclusion versus on-pump CABG procedures."

68. A patient is in the ICU 36 hours post CABG procedure after having an MI. The patient experienced myocardial reperfusion edema and has an open chest with a transparent sterile dressing in place. The previous day's lab results are as follows:

WBCs: 9.5 billion/L
High-sensitivity troponin: 21 ng/L
Hemoglobin: 9.5 g/dL
Potassium: 3.6 mEq/L

The nurse is most concerned about which one of the following current lab results?

a. WBCs: 11.9 billion/L
b. High-sensitivity troponin: 18 ng/L
c. Hemoglobin: 6.8 g/dL
d. Potassium: 3.3 mEq/L

69. A patient is in the ICU day 1 post CABG. The patient develops dependent edema, ascites, and jugular venous distension. Which one of the following is most likely the cause of the assessment findings?

a. Left-sided heart failure
b. Right-sided heart failure
c. Pulmonary edema
d. Acute renal failure

70. A patient in the ICU has been receiving furosemide twice a day following a mitral valve replacement surgery. The patient complains of dizziness and is tachycardic with a heart rate in the 110s. The nurse suspects hypovolemia. Which assessment finding should the nurse expect?

a. Decreased urine output
b. Presence of S3 heart sound
c. Hyponatremia
d. Hepatojugular reflux

71. What is the rationale for maintaining mild hypothermia in patients undergoing coronary artery bypass graft (CABG) procedures?

a. To increase the cellular metabolism
b. To reduce the oxygen demand
c. To reduce the systemic vascular resistance (SVR)
d. To prevent microemboli formation

72. The nurse is caring for a patient in the CVICU with an intra-aortic balloon pump (IABP) that was inserted using a right femoral approach. Which one of the following findings indicates that the IABP is improving the patient's cardiac function?

a. Increased afterload
b. Increased pulmonary capillary wedge pressure
c. Increased V waves on ECG
d. Decreased pulmonary capillary wedge pressure

73. The nurse is analyzing an arterial blood gas result and recognizes that which one of the following is associated with metabolic acidosis?

a. Base excess: –8 mmol/L
b. pH: 7.62
c. HCO_3: 29 mEq/L
d. $PaCO_2$: 56 mmHg

74. The nurse is caring for a 56-year-old female patient in the immediate postoperative period following a Cox maze procedure. When analyzing the ECG strip, the nurse finds that the patient has a QTc of 510 msec. Which electrolyte imbalance is consistent with this finding?

a. Hyperkalemia
b. Hypokalemia
c. Hypocalcemia
d. Hypercalcemia

75. A patient is in the CVICU day 2 post CABG. The patient's assessment findings are as follows:

BP: 95/45 mmHg
HR: 112 bpm
CVP: 3 mmHg
CO: 4 L/min
Urine output: 25–30 mL/hr

The nurse would anticipate which one of the following orders?

a. An 0.9% sodium chloride bolus
b. Norepinephrine infusion
c. Furosemide IVP
d. Labetalol IVP

76. A patient is in the ICU 1 day post CABG. The nurse notifies the physician that the patient has had 20–25 mL/hr of urine output from the indwelling Foley catheter over the past 2 hours. The nurse confirms that there were no kinks or other issues with the indwelling Foley catheter. The patient's assessment findings are as follows:

BP: 149/76 mmHg
HR: 81 bpm
CVP: 16 mmHg
CI: 3.1 L/min/m^2
SvO_2: 75%

Which order would the nurse anticipate?

a. Discontinue the indwelling Foley catheter.
b. Administer a 500 mL 0.9% sodium chloride bolus.
c. Administer furosemide 20 mg IVP.
d. Perform a stat bladder scan.

77. Patients undergoing CABG procedures usually receive protamine sulfate. The nurse recognizes that its administration places the patient at risk for which one of the following?

a. Bleeding
b. Thrombosis
c. Pulmonary vasodilation
d. Systemic hypertension

78. A patient is in the ICU 1 day after an open surgical repair of the tricuspid valve. The nurse assesses the patient at the start of the shift. The nurse finds that the patient has new-onset right-sided facial droop and slurred speech. The nurse recognizes which one of the following as the most likely cause of the patient's symptoms?

a. Anxiety
b. Bell's palsy
c. Ischemic stroke
d. Hemorrhagic stroke

79. A patient is in the CVICU day 1 post thoracic aneurysm repair. The patient's systolic blood pressure decreases to <100 mmHg, and the respirations become rapid and shallow while on the pressure mode on the ventilator. The patient writes, "I feel like I can't breathe" on a sheet of paper. An arterial blood gas analysis is ordered, and the results are as follows:

pH: 7.30
$PaCO_2$: 52
HCO_3: 36
PaO_2: 68

Which order should the nurse complete first?

a. Attach and monitor the patient using an end-tidal CO_2 detector.
b. Initiate a norepinephrine infusion.
c. Administer a 250 mL 0.9% sodium chloride bolus.
d. Change the ventilator mode to assist control.

80. A patient is in the ICU 2 days following a CABG procedure. The patient has been on NPO status since the surgery due to nausea and vomiting. The patient is now confused, delirious, and restless but has vital signs within normal limits and an oxygen saturation level of 98% on 2L of oxygen by nasal cannula. What is the mostly likely cause of the patient's symptoms?

a. Hypernatremia
b. Hyperkalemia
c. Hyperglycemia
d. Hypercapnia

81. A patient in the ICU is scheduled for an elective endovascular repair of the aorta. The patient's orders state that they are on nothing-by-mouth (NPO) status except for medications. The patient has a history of diabetes mellitus type 2, chronic kidney disease stage 3, chronic back pain treated with oxycodone 5 mg as needed (prn) four times a day, and hypertension. Which medication order should the nurse question?

a. Metoprolol 25 mg PO
b. Oxycodone 5 mg PO
c. Metformin 500 mg PO
d. Amlodipine 10 mg PO

82. Which one of the following would be the most reliable indicator of poor perfusion in a patient after an open surgical valve replacement?

a. Blood pressure of 90/55 mmHg
b. Extremities being cool to the touch
c. Lactate level of 10 mmol/L
d. Heart rate of 125 bpm

83. The nurse is caring for a patient in the CVICU 1 week post open repair of a dissected aortic aneurysm. The patient is intubated and has the following assessment findings:

Alanine aminotransferase (ALT): 85 U/L
Aspartate aminotransferase (AST): 155 U/L
Creatinine: 2.6 mg/dL
Potassium: 5.7 mEq/L
Total bilirubin: 2.7 mg/dL
GFR: 40 mL/min
PaO_2/FiO_2 ratio: 120 mmHg
Platelets: 160,000/mL
Glasgow Coma Scale score: 6
Ascites
Generalized +3 edema

The most likely cause of these assessment findings is

a. Heparin-induced thrombocytopenia (HIT)
b. Acute renal failure
c. Cerebrovascular accident
d. Multiorgan dysfunction syndrome

84. A patient in the CVICU has the following hemodynamic profile day 1 post CABG procedure:

CVP: 8 mmHg
SvO_2: 38%
SVR: 1,320 dyne/s/cm^{-5}
MAP: 65 mmHg

Which result would be most concerning to the nurse?

a. CVP
b. SvO_2
c. SVR
d. MAP

85. Which one of the following is correct regarding minimally invasive cardiac surgery?

a. It requires the use of cardiopulmonary bypass.
b. It requires a median sternotomy.
c. General anesthesia is required for minimally invasive cardiovascular surgery.
d. It can use robotic assistance during procedures.

86. A patient in the ICU has been diagnosed with an acquired ventral septal rupture secondary to myocardial infarction (MI). The patient received a vasodilator, had an intra-aortic balloon pump (IABP) placed, and is preparing to go to surgery for a ventral septal defect repair. What is the primary rationale for the vasodilator and IABP placement in the patient?

a. Increase afterload
b. Decrease afterload
c. Increase contractility
d. Decrease contractility

87. A patient is in the CVICU requiring prolonged mechanical ventilation following an open valve replacement. The ICU team is initiating tube feedings in order to provide nutritional support. Which order could place the patient at risk for aspiration?

a. Bolus of Glucerna 200 mL given q8 hr
b. Blood sugar level checks q6 hr with sliding scale coverage for results >150 mg/dL
c. Insertion of a nasoduodenal feeding tube
d. Free water flush 25 mL q4 hr

88. A patient in the CVICU is scheduled for a transthoracic echocardiogram at 0800 the next morning. What information should the nurse include when educating this patient about the procedure?

a. A probe will be placed down the esophagus.
b. The patient will be on NPO status after midnight.
c. A Foley catheter will be placed.
d. The patient will need to lie on the left side.

89. A nurse in orientation is learning about heparin-induced thrombocytopenia (HIT) type II. Which statement made by the nurse orientee indicates the need for additional teaching?

a. "The greatest risk to patients with HIT type II is thromboembolic events."
b. "HIT type II is caused by an immune response."
c. "Heparin will be discontinued in patients with HIT type II."
d. "There is no medication available for the treatment of HIT type II."

90. The nurse is preparing to assist with the extubation of a patient in the ICU post CABG procedure. Which one of the following is indicated for the prevention of postextubation complications?

a. Give sips of water to check the patient's swallowing ability 30 minutes after extubation.
b. Place the patient on 6 L of humidified oxygen via face mask when extubated.
c. Maintain bed rest for 24 hr.
d. Obtain a stat chest x-ray.

Answer Key and Explanations

1. D: Cardiogenic shock occurs when the heart fails to pump effectively resulting in decreased organ and tissue perfusion. The patient's hypotension, low cardiac index, and low urine output are signs of cardiogenic shock and the resultant poor organ perfusion. The patient's tachycardia is an attempted compensatory mechanism of the body to increase perfusion. The patient's hemoglobin is within normal limits and not indicative of bleeding, and there is no evidence of excessive bleeding from the chest tube or surgical incision. The patient's tachypnea is a result of pulmonary congestion secondary to cardiogenic shock. A fat embolism is more likely to occur following a traumatic injury to a large bone. Compartment syndrome causes reduced blood flow to the CABG donor site, and the complication would not cause hypotension, low cardiac output, or low urine output.

2. B: Hypothermia and shivering post CABG procedure can contribute to complications by increasing myocardial oxygen consumption, causing vasoconstriction, and increasing cardiac filling pressures. Vecuronium is a neuromuscular blockade that can be administered to the intubated and sedated patient to stop shivering. Sedation is required because vecuronium induces paralysis, but it does not have a sedative effect. The patient does not need labetalol because the cause of the hypertension is likely the patient's shivering. In addition, the rewarming of the patient causes vasodilation, which will also lower the blood pressure. Flumazenil is used for the reversal of benzodiazepines and is not indicated for this patient. IV acetaminophen is used for fever and pain and is not indicated for this patient.

3. A. Based on the patient's admitting diagnosis and the symptoms described, the patient's pericardial effusion has likely worsened and caused cardiac tamponade. Cardiac tamponade is a buildup of blood or fluid around the heart limiting its ability to contract effectively. Endocarditis, pulmonary hypertension, and pulmonary embolism can cause the symptoms described by the patient but they are not the likely diagnosis based on the patient's background information and diagnosis.

4. D: ST segment elevation in leads V_3 and V_4 is associated with an anterior wall injury; in leads V_5 and V_6, it is associated with injury to the low lateral wall; in leads II, III, and aVF, it is associated with injury to the inferior wall; and in leads V_1 and V_2, it is associated with injury to the septum.

5. C: Pulmonary hypertension is characterized by a rise in the pulmonary artery pressure. The S1 heart sound may be muffled in pulmonary hypertension due to the increased volume in the right side of the heart. Forceful closure of the pulmonary valves due to elevated pulmonary pressures causes a loud P2 heart sound. Ascites is caused as the right side of the heart fails and can no longer accommodate blood circulation, resulting in liver congestion. The pansystolic murmur is caused by damage to the tricuspid valve resulting from increased pressure within the right ventricle.

6. B: Norepinephrine is an alpha agonist and a potent vasoconstrictor. It is indicated for the treatment of hypotension in patients with low SVR and normal cardiac output. Dobutamine is an inotropic agent indicated for the treatment of low cardiac output and elevated SVR. Dopamine is an α, β_1, β_2, and DA_1 agonist depending on the dosage. It will increase the heart rate and increase or decrease the SVR depending on the dose. It is not appropriate for the patient because it will further elevate the heart rate, which will increase myocardial oxygen demand. It could also lower the patient's already reduced SVR.

7. A: Heparin can be used as an anticoagulant during CRRT, but there is no need to monitor calcium levels secondary to heparin use. Citrate is the anticoagulant used during CRRT that can reduce calcium levels. The right internal jugular location is preferred for access because it offers a straighter route to the atrium. Citrate can contribute to electrolyte disturbances by reducing calcium levels via chelating, when hypertonic citrate solutions are used, and by causing metabolic alkalosis from increasing bicarbonate. CRRT can remove fluid and clear solutes like traditional hemodialysis.

8. A: The high-pitched, musical breathing sound describes stridor, which is indicative of narrowing of the airway. This must be treated emergently in patients that are post endarterectomy because it indicates swelling that could occlude the airway. The nerve block would not be expected to wear off for at least 6 hours; therefore, numbness is expected. The blood pressure is elevated, but it does not require emergent intervention. A headache of 5/10 severity can occur and should be treated with acetaminophen. If pain medication is not effective in treating the headache, then the physician should be notified.

9. A: A CT angiogram of the heart is a CT scan that is done with radiation and contrast dye to visualize cardiac vessels. A beta-blocker may be given before the procedure to slow the heart for better visualization. Pacemakers are CT scan safe. Magnetic resonance imaging cannot be done on patients with permanent pacemakers because the live magnet can cause significant tissue damage. A warm flush may be felt when the contrast dye is injected. Patients with reduced kidney function can have a CT angiogram, but additional interventions such as increased fluid intake before and after the procedure may be prescribed.

10. B: Diarrhea would be the most concerning symptoms because it can contribute to dehydration and electrolyte disturbances in a patient who is already at risk due to the vulnerable state of the heart following valve replacement surgery. Restlessness, insomnia, and muscle spasms are uncomfortable for the patient, but they are not life-threatening.

11. C: Ketorolac is classified as a nonsteroidal anti-inflammatory drug and is used for the treatment of pain. The patient's hemoglobin should be monitored because ketorolac increases the risk for bleeding. The patient had a recent surgery, which also increases the risk for bleeding. The PT/PTT is a lab test that assesses for bleeding times, and it can be used to assess for coagulopathies, but it does not reflect active bleeding. Blood urea nitrogen (BUN) is a waste product removed by the kidneys. Increased BUN levels can indicate that the kidneys are not working properly, but this is not specific because increased BUN levels can also be caused by dehydration and heart failure. The alanine transaminase level can evaluate liver function. Ketorolac is more detrimental to the liver in patients with already reduced liver function.

12. A: An aortic dissection occurs when there is a tear in the inner lining of the aorta. It is imperative to control the blood pressure to prevent extending the dissection and causing hemorrhage. Fever, oxygenation, and pain should all be addressed, but the assessment data indicate that the patient's other symptoms are not life-threatening.

13. A: Hypertension is not associated with reduced afterload. It is associated with increased afterload and increased SVR, which may contribute to reduced cardiac output in postoperative CABG patients with hypertension.

14. A: Elevated blood pressure after a CABG procedure can contribute to life-threatening bleeding. The elevated capillary blood glucose is a concern, but it can be treated with insulin and does not require emergent intervention. The patient is likely to be drowsy and recovering from anesthesia 1 hour after surgery, requiring repeated tactile stimulation to arouse. A central venous pressure (CVP) of 10 mmHg is indicative of adequate volume status.

15. A: Response A is most appropriate because assessment is the first step in the nursing process. The nurse asked a question specific enough for the patient to provide more details that will contribute to the development of patient-centered interventions. Response B is dismissive of the patient's fears and eliminates the opportunity to provide additional information that may be helpful to the patient. Responses C and D are interventions that are developed prematurely because they are not preceded by assessment questions.

16. A: Patients with brachial arterial lines are at risk for complications such as pseudoaneurysm, thrombus, and infection. The patient's symptoms are indicative of the presence of an occlusion resulting from an arterial clot. The patient is at risk for retroperitoneal bleeding due to the femoral access site, but the symptoms for this complication are leg pain, abdominal pain, and bruising to the affected area. An arterial air embolism is the result of introduction of air into the arterial circulation. Signs and symptoms could include shortness of breath, chest pain, and/or mental status change. Compartment syndrome occurs when the pressure increases in a muscular compartment. Compartment syndrome does cause an alteration in perfusion to the affected extremity, but it is usually the result of trauma or severe tissue damage.

17. D: Hespan is a hetastarch in 0.9% sodium chloride. It is appropriate in this patient because, despite adequate cardiac output and a positive fluid balance, the patient remains hypotensive with low filling pressures. Packed red blood cells are not indicated because the patient's hemoglobin is sufficient. Dobutamine is not indicated because the patient's cardiac index indicates adequate cardiac output. Nitroprusside would be contraindicated for this patient because it would cause the blood pressure and CVP to continue to decline and worsen the hemodynamic instability.

18. D: Dilated cardiomyopathy can lead to heart failure as a result of ventricular dilation without cardiac muscle wall thickening. Verapamil should be questioned because it is a calcium channel blocker with negative inotropic effects, which can worsen heart failure. The patient has increased preload evidenced by a CVP measurement of 24 and jugular venous distension. Furosemide is used to reduce preload. Amiodarone is an antiarrhythmic drug used to treat the patient's atrial fibrillation. Warfarin is an anticoagulant used to prevent thrombi (i.e., blood clots).

19. D: Flolan is a medication used to treat pulmonary hypertension by causing pulmonary and systemic vasodilation. Flolan inhibits platelet aggregation and increases the risk for bleeding. The medication can be administered via continuous IV infusion. It can also be administered via inhalation in ventilated patients. Down titration by 20 ng/kg/min every 5 minutes can cause rebound pulmonary and systemic hypertension due to the rapid decrease in the drug. It is recommended to titrate down by 1–2 ng/kg/min every 15 min. Flolan causes vasodilation, and the nurse should monitor for hypotension during its administration.

20. B: The high-flow nasal cannula is an oxygen delivery device that can deliver 21–100% FiO_2 at up to 60 liters per minute via nasal cannula. The device uses humidification, which moistens the mucosa and increases the drainage of respiratory secretions. The high-flow nasal cannula increases the positive end expiratory pressure effect by raising the airway pressure at the end of expiration, thereby increasing oxygenation. The flow rate should be titrated before the FiO_2 because flow rates are more effective at oxygen delivery and increasing tidal volume. The high-flow nasal cannula increases the risk of viral transmission due to the increased number of particles released by the high flow rates.

21. B: Patients undergoing thoracoabdominal aneurysm surgery are at risk for paraplegia resulting from spinal cord ischemia. The lumbar drain reduces cerebrospinal fluid pressure, thereby increasing spinal cord perfusion. Phrenic nerve damage during cardiac surgery usually occurs due to dissection, which cannot be prevented or treated with a lumbar drain. The lumbar drain reduces cerebrospinal fluid pressure but does not prevent postoperative bleeding or thrombolytic stroke.

22. D: The sternal incision and saphenous graft site incision will require cleaning with mild, fragrance-free soap and water to prevent infection. The patient should ambulate as soon as hemodynamically stable. Sequential compression devices are contraindicated because they can contribute to postoperative wound complications. Itching as wounds heal in post-CABG patients is an expected finding. The patient should not apply creams, lotions, or ointments to the itching site.

23. D: Digoxin is a cardiac glycoside used to treat atrial fibrillation with a rapid ventricular rate by slowing the heart, increasing cardiac contractions, and slowing the conduction through the AV node. Bedside cardioversion is not indicated because the patient came into the hospital with atrial fibrillation. The amount of time during which the patient has been in atrial fibrillation is unknown. A patient undergoing cardioversion after being in sustained atrial fibrillation >48–72 hours is at a much higher risk for a thrombotic event. Amiodarone IV can be used in patients with atrial fibrillation with a rapid ventricular rate; however, in the hospital, an IV bolus followed by a continuous drip is administered. Amiodarone PO will have a delayed onset of action, and it would be used when weaning off the amiodarone IV drip. The patient has a history of heart failure, and, although the blood pressure is low, it is likely due to reduced cardiac output associated with the atrial fibrillation with a rapid ventricular rate.

24. B: The patient's pulmonary artery catheter (aka Swan-Ganz catheter) readings reveal a diagnosis of congestive heart failure. A fluid bolus will worsen the cardiac pressures by increasing the preload and the pulmonary arterial wedge pressure. Dobutamine is given to increase the contractility of the heart, furosemide to reduce preload, and norepinephrine to increase the blood pressure.

25. A: Cryoprecipitate is a blood product made from fresh frozen plasma that contains clotting factors. It does not require Rh or ABO compatibility. Cryoprecipitate is not used to increase platelets. It is used to increase clotting factors such as fibrinogen, factor VIII, and von Willebrand factor. Cryoprecipitate may be from a single donor or may be pooled from multiple donors. Cryoprecipitate should be infused within 4 hours of pooling over 30–60 minutes.

26. C: The patient had an MI and may be at risk for circulatory overload due to myocardial injury and CABG. Transfusing the blood at a slower rate will reduce the amount of volume that the heart has to pump, thereby decreasing the chance of vascular congestion. Monitoring the CVP is an appropriate intervention, but it will not prevent transfusion-associated circulatory overload (TACO). Titrating fluids to keep intake and output at net zero may not be sufficient if the patient has decreased heart function.

27. B: The arterial blood gas results indicated that the patient is experiencing metabolic acidosis. Kussmaul's respirations is a compensatory mechanism that involves deep, rapid breathing and hyperventilation that occurs in an effort to reduce carbon dioxide (CO_2) and rid the body of excess acid. Cheyne-Stokes respirations involves periods of apnea and hyperventilation and is usually associated with stroke and heart disease. Pulsus paradoxus is a decrease in the systolic blood pressure with inspiration. It is usually associated with cardiac tamponade or other conditions that interfere with the mechanical action of the heart. Wheezing is a whistling sound heard when the airways are narrowed. It is usually associated with asthma and other airway-restricting diseases.

28. C: During the transcatheter aortic valve replacement (TAVR) procedure (aka transcatheter aortic valve implantation), a new valve is placed via minimally invasive means using a catheter without removing the old valve. Patients undergoing TAVRs may receive conscious sedation or general anesthesia. TAVR procedures are indicated for patients with aortic stenosis at high risk for surgical complications, and a CT angiogram of the chest, abdomen, and pelvis is done prior to determine the appropriate size for the new valve. Rapid ventricular pacing allows for better visualization to aid in appropriate valve placement.

29. C: Malignant hyperthermia is a genetic condition that when triggered can cause electrolyte disturbances, rhabdomyolysis, and death if left untreated. Succinylcholine is a depolarizing muscle relaxing agent used during anesthesia that can trigger malignant hyperthermia. Propofol, nitrous oxide, and etomidate are safe to use in patients with the genetic predisposition because these drugs do not trigger a response.

30. C: Bispectral index monitoring is a device used to assess sedation levels. The patient's bispectral index score is 90, which is indicative of a patient who is awake and responding to voices. The propofol infusion should be increased to achieve the appropriate levels of sedation necessary for the prevention of increased intracranial pressure. Decreasing the fentanyl dose will reduce sedation levels and may cause an increase in intracranial pressure. The patient has not had any significant neurological changes that require a stat CT scan of the head. Conducting a complete neurological assessment will not prevent increased intracranial pressure.

31. C: The ABCDEF bundle is also known as the ICU liberation bundle; it is a set of evidence-based recommendations used to holistically treat the patient by addressing pain, delirium, mobility, and sleep disturbances in the ICU. Fluid management is not a component of the ABCDEF bundle. The F stands for family involvement, which can decrease anxiety and depression in ICU patients. Early mobilization, spontaneous awakening trials, and pain management are all components of the ABCDEF ICU liberation bundle.

32. C: Electrical cardioversion is the conversion of the heart back to a normal sinus rhythm using electrical shocks that are synchronized with the R wave in the electrical conduction cycle. The mode of the monitor used for cardioversion must be changed from defibrillation to sync to ensure that the shocks are synchronized with the R wave and not on the T wave. An asynchronous shock can convert the patient to ventricular fibrillation. The shocking of the patient is painful, and opioid analgesics are usually administered. Cardioversion for atrial fibrillation usually starts at 100 joules.

33. C: Targeted temperature management is the intentional cooling of patients who remain comatose after cardiac arrest and return of spontaneous circulation. Targeted temperature management causes a shift in potassium when cooling the patient; potassium supplementation for hypokalemia is usually required. Potassium supplementation should be discontinued during rewarming to prevent rebound hyperkalemia. The goal for rewarming is 37 °C. The patient's blood sugar levels should be monitored every 1–2 hours for hyperglycemia and hypoglycemia due to changes in insulin sensitivity. Rewarming will cause vasodilation, which is most likely to cause hypotension.

34. A: Epinephrine should only be administered in CALS under the direction of a cardiothoracic surgeon. It is not routinely used in CALS because it can damage newly sutured vessels and grafts by causing rebound hypertension. Defibrillation is recommended first if available as opposed to chest compressions, which may damage the myocardium and may not be sufficient to obtain adequate cardiac output. Generation of an electrical current via pacing can stimulate the heart and convert the patient to a viable or shockable rhythm. Ventricular fibrillation is a shockable rhythm. Identification of a shockable rhythm versus the unshockable pulseless electrical activity rhythm will delineate whether defibrillation is appropriate.

35. A: Desmopressin is a synthetic version of antidiuretic hormone. Desmopressin increases water retention and urine concentration, which can lead to dilutional hyponatremia. Desmopressin is more likely to cause hyponatremia versus hypernatremia. Desmopressin may be used to treat diabetes insipidus, and it does not cause hyperglycemia. Due to water retention, desmopressin is more likely to cause weight gain versus weight loss.

36. B: Sequential compression devices are used to prevent the development of lower extremity clots, thereby inhibiting blood clot migration into the pulmonary vasculature. Incentive spirometry is used to expand the lungs and prevent atelectasis and pneumonia. Continuous capnography is used to detect end-tidal CO_2. Continuous positive airway pressure is used to keep the airways open in people with sleep apnea.

37. C: Cerebral oximetry monitoring uses spectrometry to measure regional oxygen saturation. It is a continuous and noninvasive method for early detection of cerebral desaturation and ischemia. Transcranial Doppler ultrasound is used to assess for cerebral vasospasms. The intracranial bolt or ventriculostomy can be inserted to monitor intracranial pressure. The electroencephalogram is used to record seizure activity.

38. D: The patient is experiencing bleeding that is severe enough to limit adequate myocardial contraction and cardiac output. The assessment data are indicative of severe bleeding, and an emergent resternotomy will be done to open the chest, locate and stabilize the bleeding, and relieve the cardiac tamponade.

39. B: Atelectasis is lung collapse resulting from alveolar deflation. Patients can be at risk for atelectasis after a CABG procedure due to pain-related shallow breathing. Hydromorphone is an opioid analgesic that can be given postoperatively for pain management. A side effect of hydromorphone is reduced blood pressure, but it is not indicated for the treatment of hypertension. Antihypertensive agents are indicated for post-CABG hypertension. Pneumomediastinum is characterized by escaped air from the lungs migrating to the mediastinum; it can occur during or after CABG, but it cannot be prevented with hydromorphone. Dysrhythmias after CABG are prevented with antiarrhythmic drugs and/or transcutaneous pacing.

40. D: A yellowing discoloration of the skin may be indicative of liver damage, a particular risk in patients taking atorvastatin. The patient should be educated to notify the physician of this development. Atorvastatin should not be taken with grapefruit juice because it can increase the patient's risk for muscle damage and kidney injury. The medication should be taken at night because the cholesterol-generating enzyme is more active at night. Blood will need to be drawn periodically to monitor the liver function.

41. B: Train of four is a device that monitors the patient for appropriate levels of paralytic medications based on the physician's orders. This patient requires an increase in ketamine because patients receiving a paralytic should remain sedated. Titrate the sedation up and the paralytic down first to prevent the patient from being paralyzed and awake. Reducing the patient's ketamine while increasing the cisatracurium will further awaken the patient and cause him or her to experience paralysis while awake. The nurse should assess the patient's train of four using the same amplitude in order to prevent the premature weaning of medications.

42. C: Creatinine is a measure of kidney function. The patient's creatinine in the immediate postoperative period was abnormally elevated and continues to increase significantly 1 day postoperatively indicating an acute kidney injury and the need for intervention. The urine output decreased from the previous day, but it is adequate and would need to be monitored. The lactate level may be elevated due to impaired perfusion resulting from the aortic dissection and surgery. The lactate level continues to decline, indicating improvement. The hemoglobin level is low, but it is stable and would need to be monitored.

43. D: Biological replacement valves are made of tissue from humans or animals that can degrade over time; they usually require replacement sooner than mechanical valves. The patient with a mechanical valve will require lifelong anticoagulation, whereas those with a biological valve generally do not require long-term anticoagulation unless they have concurring conditions requiring it. The patient is having open heart surgery as opposed to a procedure with femoral artery access; therefore, the patient will not need to lie flat to immobilize an extremity. Mechanical valves cause a clicking sound when they close.

44. B: Homelessness may rule the patient out for LVAD placement because the patient requires extensive device maintenance, medications, and social support. The MAP is an indication of low cardiac output, and LVADs are used for patients in heart failure, so this is an expected finding. The patient's hepatitis C is a chronic disease and is not a contraindication for LVAD placement.

45. A: Transfusion-related acute lung injury is caused by an abnormal immune response after transfusion leading to damage to the lung endothelial cells and subsequent leaking of fluid into the lungs. The patient received four units of packed red blood cells and now has hallmark signs of transfusion-related acute lung injury—pulmonary edema as evidenced by pink frothy secretions, crackles, and hypoxia. Pulmonary hypertension causes elevation of pulmonary artery pressure readings. The PAS and PAD pressures for this patient are within normal limits. Endocarditis is an infection of the heart lining having symptoms of fever, chills, and cough. The patient is experiencing pulmonary complications not indicative of endocarditis. A pneumothorax occurs when the lung collapses and air is found in the chest cavity. The patient has crackles, but the lung sounds are auscultated bilaterally. A hallmark sign of a pneumothorax is diminished or absent lung sounds on the affected side.

46. A: The patient's hemodynamic alteration demonstrates low cardiac output with heart failure. Dobutamine is a positive inotrope used to increase stroke volume, contractility, and cardiac output. The patient's CVP and blood pressure are not indicative of hypovolemia. Nitroprusside is a vasodilator, which is not indicated because the patient's SVR and blood pressure are within normal limits. Norepinephrine is a vasoconstrictor used to increase blood pressure. It is not indicated because the patient's blood pressure is within normal limits and vasoconstriction would worsen the cardiac output.

47. D: The first step in the nursing process is assessment of the patient. Before checking the monitor or implementing interventions, the patient should be assessed. Contacting the physician for an arterial blood gas and placing the patient on a nonrebreather mask are interventions that should not be completed before completion of the assessment.

48. C: Pericarditis is the inflammation of the pericardium resulting from the patient's MI. A pericardial friction rub is produced when there is friction between the dry pericardium and the heart. Cardiac tamponade and pleural effusion occur when there is excess fluid around the heart, which produces muffled or distant heart sounds. Pulmonary hypertension is elevated pressure within the pulmonary vasculature. The forceful closure of the pulmonic valves results in a loud P2 heart sound.

49. A: Beck's triad is present (hypotension, jugular venous distension, and muffled heart sounds), which is indicative of cardiac tamponade. Cardiac tamponade is an increase in fluid in the pericardial sac, which can lead to decreased cardiac output and shock. A pericardial window is performed to drain the excess pericardial fluid. A resuscitative thoracotomy involves opening the chest emergently to access major cardiac vessels in patients with life-threatening hemorrhage. The patient is oriented with 93% oxygen saturation and is not requiring intubation or arterial blood gases.

50. C: Removal of pacing wires from the epicardium can cause bleeding and tamponade. The INR should be less than 2.5–3 before removal. A 12-lead ECG may be requested by the physician before removal to assess for arrhythmias, and continuous ECG monitoring is required during and after removal. The patient can continue low-molecular-weight heparin, but a continuous heparin infusion will increase bleeding time and increase the risk for bleeding. Aspirin can continue prior to and after removal of the pacing wires.

51. D: Spinal cord ischemia can occur after a thoracic endovascular aortic repair as a result of reduced blood flow during the procedure and/or reperfusion inflammation causing spinal cord edema. Maintaining the mean arterial pressure (MAP) at >80 promotes spinal cord infusion and can improve symptoms. Abdominal compartment syndrome is most commonly associated with abdominal aneurysm, and monitoring bladder pressures is indicated for identifying abdominal compartment syndrome. Hyperthermia will promote vasodilation, which will likely decrease the blood pressure. This will cause a decrease in the MAP and a subsequent decrease in spinal perfusion. Mild hypothermia can provide protection for the spinal cord and prevent ischemia via decreased metabolism and inflammation.

52. C: Cardiac tamponade is the accumulation of blood or other fluid in the pericardial sac surrounding the heart resulting in impaired cardiac contractility. A pneumomediastinum is the presence of air in the chest cavity, between the lungs. The patient may present with subcutaneous emphysema and chest pain that worsens with breathing. Protamine is given during CABG to reverse the effects of heparin. A protamine reaction is characterized by an anaphylactic reaction with hypotension, and/or pulmonary vasoconstriction after the administration of protamine. Retroperitoneal bleeding is caused by bleeding into the posterior abdominal peritoneum. Signs and symptoms may include flank pain, abdominal pain, and a palpable mass in the area.

53. A: The patient is likely experiencing a retroperitoneal bleed. It is most important to replace the patient's fluid volume loss until a blood transfusion can be given, if indicated. Replacing the fluid volume loss can also help raise the blood pressure. Norepinephrine can be indicated for hypotension, but less so in the context of hypotension secondary to hypovolemia. Collecting blood for a complete blood count and administering pain medication should follow the bolus because it is more important to first stabilize the patient by replacing the lost fluid volume.

54. B: Elevated lactate levels are a sign of poor tissue perfusion resulting from the inability of the body to clear the substance. The creatinine level and SvO_2 are within normal limits and are not indicative of decreased cardiac output. A narrow pulse pressure is indicative of poor cardiac output.

55. B: Mediastinal chest tubes are indicated after a CABG procedure to prevent blood accumulation in the pericardial space and tamponade. Postoperative antibiotics may be administered prophylactically to prevent sternal infections. Continuous insulin infusions prevent hyperglycemia, which slows wound healing. Chest stabilization vests can help prevent wound dehiscence.

56. B: Myocardial stunning occurs when viable cardiac tissue is reperfused after CABG-induced ischemia, resulting in transiently impaired contractility in the postoperative period. Cardiogenic shock is failure of the heart to provide forward blood flow and tissue perfusion. Cardiogenic shock is a medical emergency that cannot be reversed without intervention. Right-sided heart failure is the inability of the right ventricle to pump effectively. Reversibility of the condition depends on the etiology. Myocardial hibernation is the impairment of blood flow and contractility.

57. B: Precedex is an alpha$_2$-adrenergic receptor agonist used as a sedative with analgesic, hypnotic, and anxiolytic effects. Precedex can cause bradycardia and hypertension as a result of norepinephrine release and the stimulation of alpha receptors. Discontinuing the patient's Precedex infusion will likely correct the bradycardia and hypertension and prevent symptomatic bradycardia. The patient's CVP is elevated, which indicates adequate volume status. Acetaminophen is not indicated because patients may experience a low-grade fever after surgery as a result of the body's inflammatory response. Atropine is not indicated because the patient's bradycardia is not affecting the cardiac output. Discontinuing the Precedex will likely correct the bradycardia.

58. B: Heparin thins the blood during on- and off-pump CABG procedures to prevent embolic events such as stroke. Heparin does not prevent dysrhythmias. Prevention strategies for dysrhythmias include a preoperative assessment for risk factors for dysrhythmias with treatment and epicardial pacing postoperatively. Heparin increases the risk for bleeding; therefore, the patient must be monitored for this complication. Heparin does not prevent hypotension. Maintaining adequate volume status reduces the risk for hypotension.

59. B: Placing the chest tube into a container of sterile water creates a water seal until the nurse can obtain a replacement for the chest tube drainage system. Clamping the chest tube prevents the release of air and can result in the development of a tension pneumothorax. Placing a Vaseline gauze over the end of the chest tube can prevent the release of air and can also result in a tension pneumothorax. There is no need to notify the physician first because the nurse can take the necessary actions to replace the drainage system.

60. D: The second-degree heart block Mobitz type 2 is caused by a block below the AV node that periodically interrupts conductions. It differs from second-degree heart block type 1 in that, in Mobitz type 2, the PR interval is consistent with a random drop of the QRS. Mobitz type 1 (Wenckebach) has a progressively longer PR interval until a QRS is dropped. An idioventricular rhythm is the result of the cardiac impulse originating in the ventricles. It is characterized by wide and bizarre QRS complexes, no P waves, and a rate of less than 60. A third-degree heart block is the absence of electrical conduction between the atrial and ventricles. It is characterized by a heart rate of less than 50, wide QRS complexes, and independent P waves and QRS complexes. Normal sinus rhythm is characterized by a P wave, QRS, and T wave in every complex.

61. A: Mesenteric ischemia is caused by a loss of blood flow to the intestines. Mesenteric ischemia can occur after a CABG procedure due to hypotension or a clot lodging in the mesenteric vessels. CT angiography would provide the most definitive diagnosis because the vasculature in the abdomen is visualized in order to detect ischemia during the procedure. Although lactate levels may be elevated in patients with mesenteric ischemia, increased lactate levels may also be present in other serious conditions. Abdominal x-rays do not enable the direct visualization of clots in the mesenteric vessels. An exploratory laparotomy could be done to explore the bowels and remove any ischemic bowel sections. However, CT angiography is a less invasive diagnostic procedure that can include an angioplasty to remove any occlusions found.

62. C: VA ECMO is a form of circulatory and gas exchange support. Sweep is the flow of gas through the oxygenator that facilitates CO_2 removal. Chattering of the ECMO circuit is noise that occurs when the cannula is occluded. North-south syndrome occurs when the retrograde flow causes deoxygenated blood to be ejected from the heart. An increase in afterload will inhibit flow by increasing resistance.

63. B: Neurological complications are the most common complication following aneurysm repair due to the dislodgement of atherosclerotic emboli and air embolisms. Unequal, nonreactive pupils are late indicators of neurological injury. The bladder pressure is within normal limits for ICU patients. Approximately 50 mL per hour of serosanguinous drainage is not excessive and would not lead to hemodynamic instability in the patient. The patient's temperature may be slightly elevated following surgery due to the inflammatory response.

64. C: Capnography devices measure exhaled carbon dioxide (CO_2). Mainstream capnography devices are inserted into the exhalation port on the ventilator measuring the end-tidal CO_2 via sensor. The end-tidal CO_2 should be 1–5 mmHg less than the $PaCO_2$ levels. Reduced end-tidal CO_2 is a characteristic of decreased pulmonary blood flow. Sidestream and microstream capnography can be used for nonintubated patients.

65. B: Internal defibrillation is used in patients with an open chest who are in ventricular fibrillation or pulseless ventricular tachycardia. Internal defibrillation can be accomplished with 5-50 joules because the paddles come into direct contact with the heart. Sync must be turned off because it is used in cardioversion, not defibrillation. There is no rate to sync the defibrillation to patients in ventricular fibrillation or pulseless ventricular tachycardia. The paddles should be placed firmly over the left and right ventricles to prevent damage to cardiac structures or the anastomosis. An internal cardiac massage can be done in conjunction with internal defibrillation in an effort to decompress the heart immediately before and after defibrillation.

66. B: The Cox maze procedure uses incisions or radiofrequency to create scar tissue in the atria in an effort to stop atrial fibrillation. During the procedure, the surgeon may close the left atrial appendage to prevent clot formations that can lead to stroke. Removal of the left atrial appendage does not prevent postoperative bleeding, heart failure, or valve disease.

67. A: Off-pump CABG procedures bypass one or more blocked coronary arteries without a cardiopulmonary bypass machine. The procedure is done on the beating heart, and heparin is used during on- and off-pump CABG procedures to reduce thromboembolic complications. The heart remains beating during off-pump CABG procedures. The inflammatory response, nonpulsatile blood flow, hypoperfusion, and possible embolic events resulting from right atrial and aortic cannulation place the patient on pump at greater risk for kidney injury during CABG procedures. Off-pump CABG procedures are associated with higher rates of reocclusion.

68. C: Hemoglobin is responsible for carrying oxygen to the tissues. The hemoglobin levels shown above are less than the normal ranges of 14–18 g/dL for males and 12–16 g/dL for females. The large drop in hemoglobin could indicate postoperative surgical bleeding, which would require emergent intervention. After an MI, white blood cells increase as a result of the inflammatory response to cardiac injury. The potassium level has decreased to below the normal range, but it would not require emergent intervention.

69. B: Right-sided heart failure may occur after a CABG procedure secondary to intraoperative cardiac injury, reperfusion injury, or left-sided dysfunction that overstresses the right side of the heart to the point of failure. The signs and symptoms of right-sided heart failure are the result of inadequate circulation through the right side of the heart leading to venous congestion. Symptoms of left-sided heart failure are shortness of breath resulting from congestion in the pulmonary vasculature and decreased cardiac output. Symptoms of pulmonary edema are predominantly respiratory in nature and include crackles and shortness of breath. Acute renal failure could lead to edema, but the combined findings here are indicative of cardiac involvement. Right-sided heart failure leads to ascites and venous congestion within the liver.

70. A: Decreased urine output could be present in patients with hypovolemia due to reduced perfusion to the kidneys. The S3 heart sound is indicative of pressure on the ventricles, and it may be seen in hypervolemia resulting from heart failure. Hyponatremia usually occurs when the patient's sodium concentration is low. With hypovolemia, the sodium concentration is usually high, resulting in hypernatremia. Hepatojugular reflux occurs when the jugular veins become engorged as a result of firm palpation of the liver. Heart failure-induced hypervolemia is usually the cause.

71. B: Mild hypothermia reduces oxygen demand and can reduce cardiac damage during CABG procedures. Additionally, hypothermia reduces the cellular metabolism and would likely increase the systemic vascular resistance (SVR). Heparin is used to prevent emboli formation.

72. D: The pulmonary capillary wedge pressure should decrease when the IABP is effective because it will reduce pulmonary congestion as a result of increased left ventricular blood flow, contractility, and cardiac output. The IABP will also decrease afterload, thereby reducing the resistance that the left ventricle must overcome. The pulmonary capillary wedge pressure will decrease in an effective IABP. V waves are characteristic findings in patients with ischemic mitral regurgitation. V waves should decrease or disappear when an IABP is effective.

73. A: Base excess is an indication of the amount of bicarbonate required to normalize the patient's pH. The patient has a base deficit, which is indicative of more acid and less bicarbonate. A pH level of 7.62 is indicative of alkalosis. An elevated bicarbonate level is indicative of respiratory acidosis or metabolic alkalosis. The increased $PaCO_2$ level is indicative of respiratory acidosis or metabolic alkalosis.

74. C: A female patient's QTc should be <450 msec. The patient's QTc is a symptom of hypocalcemia, which causes long QTc. Hyperkalemia can result in tall peaked T waves on ECG. Hypokalemia can result in premature ventricular contraction on ECG. Hypercalcemia can result in a shortened QTc on ECG.

75. A: The patient's blood pressure, CVP, and urine output are reduced and are indicative of hypovolemia requiring additional IV fluid administration. Norepinephrine will likely decrease renal perfusion in the patient who is hypotensive and hypovolemic, which will worsen oliguria Furosemide will further reduce preload, which can cause a reduction in the cardiac output and perfusion. Labetalol will vasodilate the patient and result in the blood pressure further declining.

76. C: The patient's assessment data are indicative of adequate volume and cardiac output. The patient's CVP and blood pressure are elevated, which could indicate hypervolemia and the patient could be experiencing postoperative urinary retention. General anesthetic agents can cause decreased bladder tone and contractility. Furosemide is a loop diuretic and should be given to reduce the blood pressure, reduce the CVP, and stimulate urine output. The indwelling Foley catheter should not be discontinued because the urine output will need to be closely monitored. The patient's filling pressures are adequate, and a fluid challenge is not indicated. A bladder scan is done to assess the volume in the bladder and perform an in/out catheterization if indicated. The patient already has an indwelling Foley catheter in place.

77. B: Protamine sulfate is used during CABG procedures to reverse the anticoagulation effects of perioperative heparin administration. The resultant coagulation can then cause thrombus formation. Protamine sulfate is used to reverse heparin in order to prevent postoperative bleeding;

therefore, bleeding is not a complication. Protamine sulfate administration can cause pulmonary vasoconstriction as opposed to vasodilation, it is thought, as a result of complement activation. Systemic hypotension is expected with protamine administration when the drug is administered too rapidly as a result of histamine activation.

78. C: Patients undergoing valve surgeries are at risk for embolic events as a result of the dislodgement of materials from the valve during surgical manipulation. Slurred speech and facial droop are symptoms of stroke. This stroke is likely ischemic (rather than hemorrhagic) in nature secondary to the embolic event resulting in altered blood flow to the brain. Anxiety does not cause right-sided weakness or facial droop. Although Bell's palsy can result in the symptoms described, it is caused by dysfunction of facial nerves.

79. D: The assist control ventilator mode delivers a set rate and volume. The patient's arterial blood gas results reveal partially compensated respiratory acidosis; therefore, changing the patient's vent mode is the priority intervention for stabilizing the patient's respiratory status. The end-tidal CO_2 detector will be beneficial for monitoring CO_2 levels, but that is not a priority. Norepinephrine and the 0.9% sodium chloride bolus would help to stabilize the blood pressure, but stabilization of the patient's respiratory status is a priority to prevent the patient from rapidly deteriorating.

80. A: Hypernatremia can be caused by dehydration because water loss is greater than sodium loss, thereby creating a higher ratio of sodium to water. The patient's nausea and vomiting place him at risk for dehydration. Hypokalemia is more likely to result from dehydration. The patient's NPO status is more likely to result in hypoglycemia, which results in fatigue, vision changes, and frequent urination. Hypercapnia is when the CO_2 is abnormally elevated. Hypercapnia may cause respiratory deterioration, but this patient is stable with 98% oxygen saturation on only 2L oxygen by nasal cannula.

81. C: Metformin should be questioned because the patient has stage 3 kidney disease and its use in combination with the contrast dye used during the procedure can worsen the patient's condition. Oxycodone should be given to prevent opioid withdrawal and anxiety. Metoprolol and amlodipine are antihypertensive drugs, which should be given preoperatively to prevent cardiac complications and hypertension.

82. C: Increased production of lactate results from decreased oxygen and diminished clearance by the hypoperfused liver and kidney. A low blood pressure reading may be the cause of low perfusion, but it is not always indicative of poor perfusion. A patient's extremities may be cool to the touch in the postsurgical period due to anesthesia-related impaired temperature regulation and/or the temperature of the patient's environment. Tachycardia may be a compensatory mechanism for poor perfusion, but there can be other postoperative causes of tachycardia such as pain or anxiety.

83. D: Multiorgan dysfunction syndrome is characterized by the dysfunction of two or more organs resulting from severe infection, inflammation, and/or tissue hypoxia. The elevated ALT, AST, AST/ALT ratio, total bilirubin, and ascites are indicative of liver dysfunction. The low GFR and elevated creatinine and potassium are indicative of renal dysfunction. The low PaO_2/FiO_2 ratio is indicative of respiratory failure. The patient's altered mental status is indicative of neurological dysfunction. HIT leads to a platelet count of <150,000/mL. The patient does have a low Glasgow Coma Scale score, but the assessment findings do not include any additional signs/symptoms of stroke.

84. B: The SvO_2 is the mixed venous oxygen saturation, and it represents the amount of oxygen present in the blood returning to the heart after tissue perfusion. An SvO_2 level of 38% is extremely low and represents severely reduced oxygenation and perfusion. This condition requires emergent intervention. The CVP is on the low side of normal, and it is indicative of low filling pressure. The SVR is on the higher side of normal and represents afterload. The MAP is low, and it is indicative of low blood pressure.

85. D: Minimally invasive cardiac surgery can use robotic assistance and involves small cuts in the chest as opposed to median sternotomy. The benefits of minimally invasive cardiac surgery are that it does not require cardiopulmonary bypass and it avoids the median sternotomy approach. Minimally invasive cardiovascular surgery can be performed with sedation ranging from regional anesthesia to general anesthesia.

86. B: Decreasing afterload is the primary role of vasodilators and an IABP in the context of ventral septal rupture secondary to an MI, and it will help stabilize the patient before surgery by reducing the amount of blood shunting to the right side of the heart, thereby increasing the amount of blood to the body. Increasing afterload would make it more difficult for the blood to be pumped to the body. Increasing or decreasing contractility is not a function of the IABP. It increases the stroke volume, thereby improving cardiac output.

87. A: Administering a 200 mL bolus tube feeding can place the patient at risk for aspiration because he or she may not be able to accommodate a volume of 200 mL at one time, thereby increasing the risk for regurgitation and aspiration into the lungs. Elevated blood sugar levels can reduce gastric motility and increase the risk of aspiration resulting from the regurgitation of undigested food. Inserting a nasoduodenal feeding tube can reduce the risk of aspiration because it is postpyloric, as opposed to the insertion of a nasogastric tube. Flushing the tube with 25 mL of free water every 4 hours will help maintain tube patency and will not increase the risk of aspiration.

88. D: A transthoracic echocardiogram is done to visualize the structure of the heart and assess cardiac function using ultrasound. The transthoracic echocardiogram is noninvasive, and the patient will be placed on their left side to optimize visualization of the heart. The transthoracic echocardiogram is noninvasive; however, the other type of echocardiogram, the transesophageal echocardiogram, requires placement of the probe down the esophagus. The patient is awake during the procedure and will not require sedation; therefore, there is no need for the patient to be NPO after midnight. There is no indication for Foley catheterization for this procedure.

89. D: Argatroban is a US Food and Drug Administration (USDA)-approved medication used to treat HIT. Although patients with HIT are at risk for bleeding, thromboembolic events are the greatest risk. HIT is caused by an immune response that triggers the release of heparin antibodies, which results in the clumping of platelets. Heparin will need to be discontinued with HIT type II, but it does not need to be discontinued with HIT type I.

90. B: The patient will need to be extubated to a face mask with humidified oxygen and then weaned down to a nasal cannula, and then to room air as tolerated to ensure adequate respiratory support. The patient should be kept on NPO status for at least 4 hours to make sure that any throat irritation and vocal cord swelling are resolved. The patient should ambulate as soon as they are hemodynamically stable. There is no indication for a stat chest x-ray post extubation.

How to Overcome Test Anxiety

Just the thought of taking a test is enough to make most people a little nervous. A test is an important event that can have a long-term impact on your future, so it's important to take it seriously and it's natural to feel anxious about performing well. But just because anxiety is normal, that doesn't mean that it's helpful in test taking, or that you should simply accept it as part of your life. Anxiety can have a variety of effects. These effects can be mild, like making you feel slightly nervous, or severe, like blocking your ability to focus or remember even a simple detail.

If you experience test anxiety—whether severe or mild—it's important to know how to beat it. To discover this, first you need to understand what causes test anxiety.

Causes of Test Anxiety

While we often think of anxiety as an uncontrollable emotional state, it can actually be caused by simple, practical things. One of the most common causes of test anxiety is that a person does not feel adequately prepared for their test. This feeling can be the result of many different issues such as poor study habits or lack of organization, but the most common culprit is time management. Starting to study too late, failing to organize your study time to cover all of the material, or being distracted while you study will mean that you're not well prepared for the test. This may lead to cramming the night before, which will cause you to be physically and mentally exhausted for the test. Poor time management also contributes to feelings of stress, fear, and hopelessness as you realize you are not well prepared but don't know what to do about it.

Other times, test anxiety is not related to your preparation for the test but comes from unresolved fear. This may be a past failure on a test, or poor performance on tests in general. It may come from comparing yourself to others who seem to be performing better or from the stress of living up to expectations. Anxiety may be driven by fears of the future—how failure on this test would affect your educational and career goals. These fears are often completely irrational, but they can still negatively impact your test performance.

Elements of Test Anxiety

As mentioned earlier, test anxiety is considered to be an emotional state, but it has physical and mental components as well. Sometimes you may not even realize that you are suffering from test anxiety until you notice the physical symptoms. These can include trembling hands, rapid heartbeat, sweating, nausea, and tense muscles. Extreme anxiety may lead to fainting or vomiting. Obviously, any of these symptoms can have a negative impact on testing. It is important to recognize them as soon as they begin to occur so that you can address the problem before it damages your performance.

The mental components of test anxiety include trouble focusing and inability to remember learned information. During a test, your mind is on high alert, which can help you recall information and stay focused for an extended period of time. However, anxiety interferes with your mind's natural processes, causing you to blank out, even on the questions you know well. The strain of testing during anxiety makes it difficult to stay focused, especially on a test that may take several hours. Extreme anxiety can take a huge mental toll, making it difficult not only to recall test information but even to understand the test questions or pull your thoughts together.

Effects of Test Anxiety

Test anxiety is like a disease—if left untreated, it will get progressively worse. Anxiety leads to poor performance, and this reinforces the feelings of fear and failure, which in turn lead to poor performances on subsequent tests. It can grow from a mild nervousness to a crippling condition. If allowed to progress, test anxiety can have a big impact on your schooling, and consequently on your future.

Test anxiety can spread to other parts of your life. Anxiety on tests can become anxiety in any stressful situation, and blanking on a test can turn into panicking in a job situation. But fortunately, you don't have to let anxiety rule your testing and determine your grades. There are a number of relatively simple steps you can take to move past anxiety and function normally on a test and in the rest of life.

Physical Steps for Beating Test Anxiety

While test anxiety is a serious problem, the good news is that it can be overcome. It doesn't have to control your ability to think and remember information. While it may take time, you can begin taking steps today to beat anxiety.

Just as your first hint that you may be struggling with anxiety comes from the physical symptoms, the first step to treating it is also physical. Rest is crucial for having a clear, strong mind. If you are tired, it is much easier to give in to anxiety. But if you establish good sleep habits, your body and mind will be ready to perform optimally, without the strain of exhaustion. Additionally, sleeping well helps you to retain information better, so you're more likely to recall the answers when you see the test questions.

Getting good sleep means more than going to bed on time. It's important to allow your brain time to relax. Take study breaks from time to time so it doesn't get overworked, and don't study right before bed. Take time to rest your mind before trying to rest your body, or you may find it difficult to fall asleep.

Along with sleep, other aspects of physical health are important in preparing for a test. Good nutrition is vital for good brain function. Sugary foods and drinks may give a burst of energy but this burst is followed by a crash, both physically and emotionally. Instead, fuel your body with protein and vitamin-rich foods.

Also, drink plenty of water. Dehydration can lead to headaches and exhaustion, especially if your brain is already under stress from the rigors of the test. Particularly if your test is a long one, drink water during the breaks. And if possible, take an energy-boosting snack to eat between sections.

Along with sleep and diet, a third important part of physical health is exercise. Maintaining a steady workout schedule is helpful, but even taking 5-minute study breaks to walk can help get your blood pumping faster and clear your head. Exercise also releases endorphins, which contribute to a positive feeling and can help combat test anxiety.

When you nurture your physical health, you are also contributing to your mental health. If your body is healthy, your mind is much more likely to be healthy as well. So take time to rest, nourish your body with healthy food and water, and get moving as much as possible. Taking these physical steps will make you stronger and more able to take the mental steps necessary to overcome test anxiety.

Mental Steps for Beating Test Anxiety

Working on the mental side of test anxiety can be more challenging, but as with the physical side, there are clear steps you can take to overcome it. As mentioned earlier, test anxiety often stems from lack of preparation, so the obvious solution is to prepare for the test. Effective studying may be the most important weapon you have for beating test anxiety, but you can and should employ several other mental tools to combat fear.

First, boost your confidence by reminding yourself of past success—tests or projects that you aced. If you're putting as much effort into preparing for this test as you did for those, there's no reason you should expect to fail here. Work hard to prepare; then trust your preparation.

Second, surround yourself with encouraging people. It can be helpful to find a study group, but be sure that the people you're around will encourage a positive attitude. If you spend time with others who are anxious or cynical, this will only contribute to your own anxiety. Look for others who are motivated to study hard from a desire to succeed, not from a fear of failure.

Third, reward yourself. A test is physically and mentally tiring, even without anxiety, and it can be helpful to have something to look forward to. Plan an activity following the test, regardless of the outcome, such as going to a movie or getting ice cream.

When you are taking the test, if you find yourself beginning to feel anxious, remind yourself that you know the material. Visualize successfully completing the test. Then take a few deep, relaxing breaths and return to it. Work through the questions carefully but with confidence, knowing that you are capable of succeeding.

Developing a healthy mental approach to test taking will also aid in other areas of life. Test anxiety affects more than just the actual test—it can be damaging to your mental health and even contribute to depression. It's important to beat test anxiety before it becomes a problem for more than testing.

Study Strategy

Being prepared for the test is necessary to combat anxiety, but what does being prepared look like? You may study for hours on end and still not feel prepared. What you need is a strategy for test prep. The next few pages outline our recommended steps to help you plan out and conquer the challenge of preparation.

Step 1: Scope Out the Test

Learn everything you can about the format (multiple choice, essay, etc.) and what will be on the test. Gather any study materials, course outlines, or sample exams that may be available. Not only will this help you to prepare, but knowing what to expect can help to alleviate test anxiety.

Step 2: Map Out the Material

Look through the textbook or study guide and make note of how many chapters or sections it has. Then divide these over the time you have. For example, if a book has 15 chapters and you have five days to study, you need to cover three chapters each day. Even better, if you have the time, leave an extra day at the end for overall review after you have gone through the material in depth.

If time is limited, you may need to prioritize the material. Look through it and make note of which sections you think you already have a good grasp on, and which need review. While you are studying, skim quickly through the familiar sections and take more time on the challenging parts.

Write out your plan so you don't get lost as you go. Having a written plan also helps you feel more in control of the study, so anxiety is less likely to arise from feeling overwhelmed at the amount to cover.

Step 3: Gather Your Tools

Decide what study method works best for you. Do you prefer to highlight in the book as you study and then go back over the highlighted portions? Or do you type out notes of the important information? Or is it helpful to make flashcards that you can carry with you? Assemble the pens, index cards, highlighters, post-it notes, and any other materials you may need so you won't be distracted by getting up to find things while you study.

If you're having a hard time retaining the information or organizing your notes, experiment with different methods. For example, try color-coding by subject with colored pens, highlighters, or post-it notes. If you learn better by hearing, try recording yourself reading your notes so you can listen while in the car, working out, or simply sitting at your desk. Ask a friend to quiz you from your flashcards, or try teaching someone the material to solidify it in your mind.

Step 4: Create Your Environment

It's important to avoid distractions while you study. This includes both the obvious distractions like visitors and the subtle distractions like an uncomfortable chair (or a too-comfortable couch that makes you want to fall asleep). Set up the best study environment possible: good lighting and a comfortable work area. If background music helps you focus, you may want to turn it on, but otherwise keep the room quiet. If you are using a computer to take notes, be sure you don't have any other windows open, especially applications like social media, games, or anything else that could distract you. Silence your phone and turn off notifications. Be sure to keep water close by so you stay hydrated while you study (but avoid unhealthy drinks and snacks).

Also, take into account the best time of day to study. Are you freshest first thing in the morning? Try to set aside some time then to work through the material. Is your mind clearer in the afternoon or evening? Schedule your study session then. Another method is to study at the same time of day that you will take the test, so that your brain gets used to working on the material at that time and will be ready to focus at test time.

Step 5: Study!

Once you have done all the study preparation, it's time to settle into the actual studying. Sit down, take a few moments to settle your mind so you can focus, and begin to follow your study plan. Don't give in to distractions or let yourself procrastinate. This is your time to prepare so you'll be ready to fearlessly approach the test. Make the most of the time and stay focused.

Of course, you don't want to burn out. If you study too long you may find that you're not retaining the information very well. Take regular study breaks. For example, taking five minutes out of every hour to walk briskly, breathing deeply and swinging your arms, can help your mind stay fresh.

As you get to the end of each chapter or section, it's a good idea to do a quick review. Remind yourself of what you learned and work on any difficult parts. When you feel that you've mastered the material, move on to the next part. At the end of your study session, briefly skim through your notes again.

But while review is helpful, cramming last minute is NOT. If at all possible, work ahead so that you won't need to fit all your study into the last day. Cramming overloads your brain with more information than it can process and retain, and your tired mind may struggle to recall even previously learned information when it is overwhelmed with last-minute study. Also, the urgent nature of cramming and the stress placed on your brain contribute to anxiety. You'll be more likely to go to the test feeling unprepared and having trouble thinking clearly.

So don't cram, and don't stay up late before the test, even just to review your notes at a leisurely pace. Your brain needs rest more than it needs to go over the information again. In fact, plan to finish your studies by noon or early afternoon the day before the test. Give your brain the rest of the day to relax or focus on other things, and get a good night's sleep. Then you will be fresh for the test and better able to recall what you've studied.

Step 6: Take a Practice Test

Many courses offer sample tests, either online or in the study materials. This is an excellent resource to check whether you have mastered the material, as well as to prepare for the test format and environment.

Check the test format ahead of time: the number of questions, the type (multiple choice, free response, etc.), and the time limit. Then create a plan for working through them. For example, if you have 30 minutes to take a 60-question test, your limit is 30 seconds per question. Spend less time on the questions you know well so that you can take more time on the difficult ones.

If you have time to take several practice tests, take the first one open book, with no time limit. Work through the questions at your own pace and make sure you fully understand them. Gradually work up to taking a test under test conditions: sit at a desk with all study materials put away and set a timer. Pace yourself to make sure you finish the test with time to spare and go back to check your answers if you have time.

After each test, check your answers. On the questions you missed, be sure you understand why you missed them. Did you misread the question (tests can use tricky wording)? Did you forget the information? Or was it something you hadn't learned? Go back and study any shaky areas that the practice tests reveal.

Taking these tests not only helps with your grade, but also aids in combating test anxiety. If you're already used to the test conditions, you're less likely to worry about it, and working through tests until you're scoring well gives you a confidence boost. Go through the practice tests until you feel comfortable, and then you can go into the test knowing that you're ready for it.

Test Tips

On test day, you should be confident, knowing that you've prepared well and are ready to answer the questions. But aside from preparation, there are several test day strategies you can employ to maximize your performance.

First, as stated before, get a good night's sleep the night before the test (and for several nights before that, if possible). Go into the test with a fresh, alert mind rather than staying up late to study.

Try not to change too much about your normal routine on the day of the test. It's important to eat a nutritious breakfast, but if you normally don't eat breakfast at all, consider eating just a protein bar. If you're a coffee drinker, go ahead and have your normal coffee. Just make sure you time it so that the caffeine doesn't wear off right in the middle of your test. Avoid sugary beverages, and drink enough water to stay hydrated but not so much that you need a restroom break 10 minutes into the test. If your test isn't first thing in the morning, consider going for a walk or doing a light workout before the test to get your blood flowing.

Allow yourself enough time to get ready, and leave for the test with plenty of time to spare so you won't have the anxiety of scrambling to arrive in time. Another reason to be early is to select a good seat. It's helpful to sit away from doors and windows, which can be distracting. Find a good seat, get out your supplies, and settle your mind before the test begins.

When the test begins, start by going over the instructions carefully, even if you already know what to expect. Make sure you avoid any careless mistakes by following the directions.

Then begin working through the questions, pacing yourself as you've practiced. If you're not sure on an answer, don't spend too much time on it, and don't let it shake your confidence. Either skip it and come back later, or eliminate as many wrong answers as possible and guess among the remaining ones. Don't dwell on these questions as you continue—put them out of your mind and focus on what lies ahead.

Be sure to read all of the answer choices, even if you're sure the first one is the right answer. Sometimes you'll find a better one if you keep reading. But don't second-guess yourself if you do immediately know the answer. Your gut instinct is usually right. Don't let test anxiety rob you of the information you know.

If you have time at the end of the test (and if the test format allows), go back and review your answers. Be cautious about changing any, since your first instinct tends to be correct, but make sure you didn't misread any of the questions or accidentally mark the wrong answer choice. Look over any you skipped and make an educated guess.

At the end, leave the test feeling confident. You've done your best, so don't waste time worrying about your performance or wishing you could change anything. Instead, celebrate the successful completion of this test. And finally, use this test to learn how to deal with anxiety even better next time.

Review Video: Test Anxiety
Visit mometrix.com/academy and enter code: 100340

Important Qualification

Not all anxiety is created equal. If your test anxiety is causing major issues in your life beyond the classroom or testing center, or if you are experiencing troubling physical symptoms related to your anxiety, it may be a sign of a serious physiological or psychological condition. If this sounds like your situation, we strongly encourage you to seek professional help.

Additional Bonus Material

Due to our efforts to try to keep this book to a manageable length, we've created a link that will give you access to all of your additional bonus material:

mometrix.com/bonus948/csc